SPATIAL SQL
A PRACTICAL APPROACH TO MODERN GIS USING SQL

MATTHEW FORREST

LOCATE PRESS

Credits & Copyright

Spatial SQL

A Practical Approach to Modern GIS Using SQL

by Matthew Forrest

Published by Locate Press

COPYRIGHT © 2023 LOCATE PRESS INC.
ISBN: 978-1-7387675-6-4

Direct permission requests to info@locatepress.com
Editors Tyler Mitchell & Keith Mitchell
Interior Design Based on Memoir-LATEXdocument class
Cover Design Matthew Forrest
Design Support Julie Springer
Cover Art Jot Singh & Tom Fisk (Pexels.com)

Publisher Website http://locatepress.com
Book Store Page http://locatepress.com/book/spatial-sql
Book Website https://spatial-sql.com/
Book Data Download https://loc8.cc/sql/data

Version: f6b7643 (2023-12-09)

Contents

1 Introduction   **1**
1.1   Goals for this book 1
1.2   Approach 2
1.3   Skills you will need 2
1.4   What we will cover and outcomes for you 3
1.5   Data and files for exercises 4

1   Getting Started   **7**
   1   Why SQL?   **9**
    1.1   Evolution to modern GIS 9
    1.2   Why learn spatial SQL? 11
    1.3   To use SQL, Python, or both? 13
    1.4   Spatial SQL landscape 14
    1.5   The landscape today 17
    1.6   Expert Voices: Uchenna Osia 24
   2   Setting Up   **27**
    2.1   Setting up PostGIS 27
    2.2   Why Docker? 27
    2.3   Installing PostGIS with Docker 28
    2.4   Installing docker-postgis 31
    2.5   Expert Voices: Getu Abdissa 47
   3   Thinking in SQL   **51**
    3.1   Moving from desktop GIS to SQL 51
    3.2   Importing data 51
    3.3   Database organization and design 51
    3.4   Using PostGIS indexes 59
    3.5   Projections 61
    3.6   Thinking in SQL 63
    3.7   Optimizing our queries and other tips 67
    3.8   Using pseudo-code and "rubber ducking" 71
    3.9   Expert Voices: Giulia Carella, PhD 75
   4   SQL Basics   **77**
    4.1   Importing Data to PostGIS 77
    4.2   ogr2ogr 77
    4.3   SQL Data Types 85
    4.4   Characters 88
    4.5   Numeric 94
    4.6   Dates and Times 96
    4.7   Other data types 100
    4.8   Basic SQL Operators 104
    4.9   Aggregates and GROUP BY 110

2   Learning Spatial SQL   **117**
   1   Advanced SQL Topics for Spatial SQL   **119**
    1.1   CASE/WHEN Conditionals 119
    1.2   Common Table Expressions (CTEs) and Subqueries 121

1.3	CRUD: Create, Read, Update, and Delete	125
1.4	Statistical functions	128
1.5	Windows	132
1.6	Joins	138
1.7	Lateral Joins	148
1.8	Triggers	149
1.9	UDFs	152
1.10	Expert Voices: Fawad Qureshi	156

2 Using the GEOMETRY — **157**

2.1	Understanding the GEOMETRY and GEOGRAPHY	157
2.2	GEOMETRY Types	158
2.3	Size of GEOMETRY data	163
2.4	A note on PostGIS documentation	167
2.5	Working with GEOMETRY data	169
2.6	Constructors	170
2.7	Accessors	175
2.8	Editors	179
2.9	Validators	180
2.10	Inputs	183
2.11	Outputs	184
2.12	Measurements in spatial SQL	198

3 Spatial Relationships — **205**

3.1	Relationship Functions	205
3.2	Ways to use spatial relationship functions	206
3.3	Spatial relationship functions	212
3.4	Distance Relationship Functions	223
3.5	Spatial Joins	226
3.6	Overlay Functions	230
3.7	Cluster Functions	235
3.8	Special Operators	240
3.9	Expert Voices: Justin Chang	243

4 Spatial Analysis — **247**

4.1	Analyses we have already seen	247
4.2	New analyses	258
4.3	Lines to polygons, and polygons to lines	301
4.4	Snap points to grid	303
4.5	Tessellate triangles	303
4.6	Tapered buffers	306

5 Advanced Spatial Analytics — **315**

5.1	Spatial data enrichment or area weighted interpolation	315
5.2	Nearest neighbor in report format	319
5.3	Flat line of sight	321
5.4	3D line of sight	325
5.5	Calculate polygons that share a border	330
5.6	Finding the most isolated feature	338
5.7	Kernel density estimation (KDE)	343
5.8	Isovist	348
5.9	Expert Voices: Danny Sheehan	358

3 Spatial SQL Use Cases — **361**

1 Suitability Analysis — **363**

1.1	Market expansion potential	363

1.2	Similarity search or twin areas	367
1.3	Suitability or composite score	371
1.4	Mergers and acquisitions	383
2	**Working With Raster Data in PostGIS**	**393**
2.1	Raster Ingest	393
2.2	Interpolation	400
2.3	Raster to H3	406
3	**Routing and Networks With pgRouting**	**409**
3.1	Prepare data to use in pgRouting	409
3.2	Create a simple route in pgRouting	416
3.3	Building an origin-destination matrix	427
3.4	Traveling salesman problem	435
3.5	Creating travel time polygons or isochones	444
3.6	Expert Voices: Aaron Fraint	453
4	**Spatial Autocorrelation and Optimization With Python and PySAL**	**455**
4.1	Spatial autocorrelation	456
4.2	Location allocation	475
4.3	Build balanced territories	494
5	**Conclusion**	**505**
5.1	SQL beyond the database	507
5.2	Spatial SQL made easy	509
5.3	Spatial SQL as a central hub	510
5.4	Big data, no problem	511
5.5	Spatial SQL in the field	511
5.6	Spatial SQL in education	512
	Books from Locate Press	**513**

To my two amazing children and my more amazing wife,
I couldn't do anything without you.
And to all the individuals who helped me along the way or
helped answer one of my questions, thank you.

Foreward

Many say that about 80% of our data includes a location aspect. This idea has been important in the geospatial industry for a long time. It shows that knowing where something happens is key. In the past, working with this kind of data was mostly done in special GIS software. But now, things are changing. The world of geography is stepping out of its silo, becoming a regular part of everyone's database.

A big part of this change comes from SQL, the common language of data analysis. SQL helps different technologies and products work together. Adding spatial features to modern data warehouses is making it even more popular.

I remember when Matt Forrest started working with us. His growth from a beginner in SQL to a leader in the field reflects how SQL itself has changed. It used to be a tool for specialists, but now it's a key language in data analysis. This change is important for three reasons:

Making Spatial Analysis Available to More People: With SQL, more people can use spatial data. It's not just for experts anymore. This means more people can understand and use information about locations.

Bringing Geography into Everyday Analysis: As SQL becomes more common, spatial data is no longer unusual. It's part of regular data analysis, making it easier to understand all kinds of data together.

Staying Current with New Technology: Big data platforms like BigQuery, Snowflake, and Databricks are using SQL for spatial data and adding new tech like AI. This keeps Spatial SQL relevant now and in the future.

Looking ahead, as understanding locations becomes more important in different areas, 'Spatial SQL' is the perfect guide. This book invites you to learn and be part of this exciting change.

Javier de la Torre
Founder, CARTO

Preface

Welcome to the book that you have been waiting for, helping to bridge between status quo GIS and the next level of data interaction with enterprise tooling.

To truly push the limits of geospatial technology today, you really need to know how to do some coding and some geospatial data processing. Just knowing one or the other will reduce your opportunities greatly.

Likewise, if you do GIS but do not know SQL (or coding) then you will be limited to using a GUI for everything. That might not sound too bad but errors in GUI-based workflows are incredibly hard to fix when using mouse clicks on the screen. Consulting businesses incur significant losses due to this limitation.

Adopting SQL into your workflow is a simple way of scripting without having to learn a full programming language, making it a good fit for slowly moving toward more advanced spatial data handling.

Matt's experience is both broad and deep with regards to GIS and SQL. Many leading geospatial users and companies adopted databases as part of their overall infrastructure. As open source databases became popular and spatial addons were made available, many system architects wanted to see all types of data move into the database.

Getting data into a database is only the beginning. As Matt shows in this book, working with spatial/-geometry data in a system, like PostGIS, gives you access to more advanced capabilities in a structured way. After getting PostGIS set up, you'll get a well-grounded education in the real power that comes with understanding spatial relationships and the flexibility of applying spatial analysis to tabular, vector, and raster data.

If you have always thought you should be better at using SQL for spatial analysis (and not just for data warehousing), this is the book for you. If you have lamented having so many GIS files sitting around on disks, this book will help you get that loaded and start extracting value. If your SQL skills are already strong but you need to access this new "spatial" stuff, read on.

As always, thank you for supporting our work at Locate Press. Our goal is to help raise awareness and education around open source geospatial topics. Keep in touch if you have a book idea, or want to discuss how to support training using our material.[1]

Tyler Mitchell
Publisher

---

[1] Sign up for news and exclusive discounts: *https://locatepress.com/subscribe*

1. Introduction

The year was 2012, and I was sitting in an office on the border of Soho and Little Italy on Lafayette Street at the then CartoDB offices, looking at some code on a screen I had never seen before:

Listing 1.1: The first SQL query I ever saw

```
1  select
2      *
3  from
4      us_states
```

This was my first introduction to spatial SQL. Up until this point my experience with GIS was all within a desktop environment. I had graduated two years earlier with an undergraduate degree in Geography and had started to use QGIS to do some different spatial analysis and mapping projects. My programming experience was limited to writing a few lines of not-so-great JavaScript and, believe it or not, ActionScript, a scripting language used with Flash (which no longer exists).

Sitting there, watching the speed and ease of data being changed with a few edits to queries was mesmerizing, especially coming from a mostly desktop "point and click" background. Immediately I could see the power of spatial SQL and how it could be a powerful tool for so many types of spatial analysis and data manipulation.

At the same time, I had a ton of questions. How do you load a Shapefile into this thing? What does the *star* mean? How do you save the results? And how is it *so* fast?

From that point I slowly (very slowly at times) started my journey to learn spatial SQL. I didn't learn spatial SQL at any specific time or using any particular methods, but rather through various projects. I kept trying to see if I could accomplish it with SQL and the answer was almost always yes. Big spatial joins, find the three nearest neighbors, find the average median income of block groups in zip codes that have an overlap greater than half the block group area, find the nearest point on a line from another point, aggregate data by state while preserving aggregated data by state and by category in JSON, and the list goes on. As time went on I felt more and more free: if I could think it, I could do it in a few minutes with spatial SQL. I no longer needed to rely on the availability of an analysis in a desktop tool or the performance limits that came along it.

Most of my SQL knowledge was learned by trial and error, help from colleagues, and lots of Google and Stack Overflow searches. While there are a number of books and courses on spatial SQL, oftentimes they focus on the implementation and management of spatial databases rather that the benefits and use cases for using spatial SQL to power spatial analysis.

The goal of this book is to fill that gap, to help you use spatial SQL for geospatial analysis, and get you using it proficiently, as fast as possible. I also want to give you ideas for the wide range of things you can do with spatial SQL. We will cover a lot of ground in the book, but there are nearly endless ways to use spatial SQL.

1.1 Goals for this book

My singular goal for this book is to help you learn spatial SQL for spatial analysis to help you start using it in your daily work. With that in mind, the book will focus on the functional use of spatial SQL for you as an end user rather than the owner or manager of the database. Given that, we will not be focusing on topics like database administration and resource optimization, and will only lightly touch on topics like query optimization and plans.

The first chapters will focus on helping you understand why spatial SQL is important and growing in importance within geospatial careers and education. They will also help you lay the foundational groundwork for thinking in SQL to help you write better queries and translate your current GIS knowledge into a database language.

Next, we will start to learn basic SQL, which will help you learn all the ways you can use it to query, structure, and manipulate non-spatial data. We won't focus on every topic in great detail, but this will give you the knowledge to understand the foundations of SQL and the skills to learn and expand your knowledge on your own as needed.

Then we will start our work with spatial SQL, beginning with the GEOMETRY and GEOGRAPHY data types that make spatial SQL, spatial. We will cover the various functions and building blocks that you need to use within a GIS toolkit: manipulating geometries, measurements, relationships, aggregates, and more. From there we will focus in on a set of use cases for some real world problems to show you how to do common GIS operations like nearest neighbors or spatial joins within SQL, as well as more advanced analysis use cases from clustering to spatial auto-correlation. We will break down each of the different steps to get there to show you the building blocks, so you can start to build a functional knowledge and toolkit so you can start to design and build your own analyses. During the course of the book we will also use PostGIS extensions such as pgRouting for routing analysis using road network data and h3-postgis, an extension to use the H3 spatial index library.[2]

1.2   Approach

All the examples and tools we will use in this book will work on any computer, any operating system, and with or without internet (you will need an internet connection to download the data from the repo and the tools to set up your database, but after that it will work without internet access). As I said earlier, the goal is to help you learn practical analysis skills in using spatial SQL, so with that in mind we will be setting up a PostGIS database, the leading open source spatial extension of the highly popular, also open source, database PostgreSQL.

To run PostGIS we will use Docker to ensure compatibility across operating systems and other installed libraries. We will use several tools to visualize, import, and work with our data. The primary tools will be PGAdmin to query and visualize data and GDAL to import/export data. We will also explore other tools such as KeplerGL and QGIS to explore our results.

1.3   Skills you will need

Even if you have never written a line of code in your life, you can use this book and start to learn spatial SQL. All you need is a willingness to learn, practice, and occasionally make mistakes (mistakes are good, they help you practice and learn along the way). It is written to start from a blank slate, with all the relevant commands and code you will need to run. With that said this book cannot possibly cover all the things you will need to know, but this book will build the foundation for you to continue learning past the pages of this book.

I will also share some tools to help you become proficient in thinking through programming problems such as learning how to debug, using pseudo-code to think through what you want to accomplish and how to do it efficiently in plain text, working through practical exercises, and how to use tools to find

---

[2]See pgRouting: A Practical Guide by Regina Obe and Leo Hsu at *https://locatepress.com/book/pgr*

answers to common problems (and yes this includes Google and Stack Overflow, as everyone uses these tools). Some of our exercises will also have some issues built into them by design (with answers of course) to help you try and think through some common issues and problems to help practice and build proficiency and problem solving in writing spatial SQL.

1.4 What we will cover and outcomes for you

This book will be divided into three core sections:

1. Getting Started: Why SQL and Learning basic and advanced SQL

2. Learning Spatial SQL: The GEOMETRY, Spatial functions, Spatial relationships, and Spatial analysis

3. Use Cases & Using Spatial SQL: Suitability analysis, using raster data, spatial auto-correlation and optimization, advanced spatial analytics, and routing

Our first section is foundational, yet important, for setting up success later on. This section focuses on why spatial SQL is important and all wide range of use cases you can use spatial SQL for. In my experience these are the areas that I have seen many individuals struggle with: setting up a database, moving data into the database, and getting beyond basic queries. Understanding the spatial SQL landscape, actually setting up a database, understanding the different terms and jargon, seeing the advantages to doing things in spatial SQL compared to a desktop GIS, importing data, and thinking SQL-ly are all challenges one faces in the early stages of learning SQL. These topics will help you overcome those common hurdles and build the base for success later on in the book. This section covers using functions, managing and manipulating data including CRUD operations and table management. Then we will cover some advanced SQL topics that are particularly useful for spatial SQL such as joins, common table expressions (CTEs), window functions, using arrays and JSON, and more.

Next, we will start to learn spatial SQL. It is at this point that many other learning resources begin, assuming that you have the knowledge and set up already established. We will only jump into actual spatial SQL after we have built the foundations. All of these foundational elements up to this point will set us up to use our already existing geospatial knowledge to quickly use spatial SQL basics. All the things you know and use today will be easily translated into SQL: managing geometries, buffers, centroids, measurements, spatial relationships, and more. We will also look at advanced topics like clustering, spatial indexes, indexing tables/geometries to improve performance, etc.

Our last section focuses on putting this into practice. You have learned the tools, SQL, and spatial SQL - now comes the most important part which is applying this to your work. We will focus on exercises to do this starting with some simple patterns all the way to advanced topics like isovists and bulk nearest neighbor joins. We will also investigate wider uses for spatial SQL like using pgRouting to analyze network data and H3 spatial indexes to increase performance. We will also showcase different projects where these things have been implemented to help you think about how this can be used in your day-to-day work.

The outcomes you should walk away with from this book are:

1. An understanding of spatial SQL, how it has come to be, and applicability in the GIS and geospatial fields.

2. The ability to create and set up a basic PostGIS instance.

3. Connect to and query data with pgAdmin and QGIS.

4. Skills to think independently in SQL and structure a query.

5. Learning how to import data into a PostGIS database.

6. Knowing how to query and manipulate data in SQL and spatial SQL.

7. Using advanced SQL to structure more complex queries.

8. Understand special topics like spatial analytics and routing in SQL.

9. How to execute a variety of use cases in SQL and be able to explain the steps.

Learning spatial SQL has been one of the most valuable skills that I have learned in my career, and I am passionate about helping others learn it too because I know how much it can help your career but also accelerate the important problems being solved with GIS and geospatial tools today. And with that, let's begin!

1.5   Data and files for exercises

We have several resources for you to access to keep in touch and follow along with the book. Our dedicated book website is `spatial-sql.com`.[3]

Data files for the exercises and examples in this book are available for download from the Locate Press website at `loc8.cc/sql/data`.[4]

Code samples can be browsed and copied from our book's code website at `spatialsqlbook.com`.[5]

Access the Locate Press bookstore page at: `locatepress.com/book/spatial-sql`[6] and send any questions through the contact page at `locatepress.com/contact`.

---

[3]`https://spatial-sql.com/`

[4]`https://loc8.cc/sql/data`

[5]`https://spatialsqlbook.com`

[6]`https://locatepress.com/book/spatial-sql`

Matt has dozens of videos on YouTube teaching on contemporary GIS topics. Subscribe today to follow along and stay up to date.

youtube.com/@MattForrest/

MODERN GIS

SPATIAL SQL

MATT FORREST

FORREST.NYC

SUBSCRIBE

31:50

Potential:
ith DuckDB
go

9:29

GIS vs. Open Source: The ultimate showdown?
1.7K views • 4 months ago

CODING TUT 24:07

Analyze floods using ONLY Python! (aka spatial data science)
5.9K views • 5 months ago

Analyze MILLIONS of
SECONDS (on your co
6.9K views • 6 months ag

15:21

s REVEALED
go

7:12

ChatGPT for GIS | Best Use Cases + Prompts
11K views • 8 months ago

13:07

Modern GIS! (and why it matters to you)
5.5K views • 8 months ago

ZERO

FASTEST Way to Learn and ACTUALLY Get a J
49K views • 10 months ag

7:00

PostGIS,
nd Snowflake...
ago

6:50

Use spatial SQL for GIS TODAY!
2.8K views • 11 months ago

6:06

SQL: The GIS tool you need to NEED to learn NOW!
4.5K views • 1 year ago

GIS and Python: Top C
Learn Geospatial Pyth
12K views • 1 year ago

Part 1

Getting Started

1. Why SQL?

If you are just starting to take your first steps into learning more technical, open-source, or modern GIS, then you likely have addressed the question of what tools or languages to start with. This is a question I receive all the time: "what should I learn and in what order?" While there isn't a right or wrong answer, this chapter will cover the reasons why I believe investing time in spatial SQL is well worth the investment.

1.1 Evolution to modern GIS

To begin, we need to start with an assumption: GIS is changing and moving from a traditional GIS framework to a more modern GIS approach. My definition of modern GIS is as follows:

Modern GIS is the process, systems, and technology used to derive insights from geospatial data. Modern GIS uses open, interoperable, and standards based technology. It can be run locally or in the cloud and can scale to work with different types, velocities, and scales of data.

Compared to traditional GIS, we are now entering a new phase of geospatial technology that is predicated on a more open and scalable paradigm, compared to one that depends on closed/proprietary technology with limited scalability. This chart compares the differences between the two approaches:

	Traditional	**Modern**
Standards	Platform and software-based	Open and standards-based
Cloud Access	Cloud-hosted or on-premises	Cloud-native
Deployment	Local software package up to enterprise software packages	Open-source local use up to full enterprise
Collaboration	Siloed	Interoperable
Scalability	Single-threaded	Serverless
Data	Limited data scale	Scalable, even further in the cloud

This shift is driven by three main changes: two within geospatial and one within the technology space in general:

1. Geospatial data is exponentially increasing in scale and volume.

2. Open source tools are growing in ease of adoption and use.

3. New technology trends and cloud services are changing traditional IT norms.

Geospatial data is increasing in scale and volume

There are numerous reports that show exactly how the geospatial market is expected to grow and expand in the years ahead. The most recent report from MarketsAndMarkets released in 2022 states that the global geospatial analytics market will grow from $59.5 billion in 2022 to $107.8 billion in 2026, with an Compound Annual Growth Rate of 12.6%[7] .

While these numbers indicate massive growth in our industry, the report has some other points that showcase the specific ways the market is growing. First, is the increase in the volume of geospatial data:

"The advent of new technologies, such as cloud services, embedded sensors, and social media, as well as the quick uptake of geospatial technologies by many industries, are making the mapping and analysis of data highly complicated. The introduction of Big Data analytics along with GIS had resulted in increasing growth opportunities for the emerging geospatial analytics vendors, as big data analytics can process large massive amounts of collected data in the quickest amount of time possible, thereby facilitating business intelligence."[8]

Various changes in technology and data collection have only increased the amount of data available to those using GIS. The increase in data generated from mobile devices, more frequent and detailed imagery, increase in data providers, and increase in the size of publicly available data including Open-StreetMap are all contributing factors to this increase in data. This continued growth in available data includes the frequency in which data is updated (or the time-series factor), total number of rows of data, and complexity and size of the geometry attached to the data.

The report also points to the increase of data as one of the key drivers of the Extract Transform Load (ETL) services increasing as a need in geospatial.

"Among the solutions, the data integration and ETL segment is estimated to grow with the highest CAGR during the forecast period... The data obtained can be linked to location data and analyzed with the help of location analytics. ETL helps in extracting geographic data from any source system, transforming it into a format based on users' needs, and loading it in target systems."[9]

As we will see during the course of this book, spatial SQL can be used to manage, transform, aggregate, and analyze data so it can be more easily consumed by end users. The combination of increased data sizes and the critical role that geospatial data is playing in modern analytics points to a crucial need for skills in spatial SQL.

Open source tools are growing in adoption and ease of adoption

In the past decade, open source geospatial tools have increased in popularity and usage, both within and outside geospatial circles. While open source has been integral to the development and advancement of GIS for years, its popularity has increased namely due to technology shifts outside of the geospatial industry.

In years prior, if you wanted to use an open source toolkit (let's use PostGIS for example), you or your organization would be in charge of the maintenance, security, deployments, updates, and overall management of that service. Not only that, you or someone on your team, would have to have the skills to manage that service. For organizations that are concerned about consistency and security, this presents a risk that generally pushed users towards a more commercial or closed-source solution.

Over time however some of these roadblocks have changed, or have been alleviated in some way. Using containerized services like Docker and orchestration services like Kubernetes, the skills and time needed to orchestrate the deployment of an instance of PostGIS have become easier and far more consistent. Additionally, cloud providers have made it far easier to use a PostGIS database in their cloud

---

[7]https://loc8.cc/sql/bloomberg-markets

[8]https://loc8.cc/sql/marketsandmarkets-geospatial

[9]https://loc8.cc/sql/prnewsite-markets

with services dedicated to PostgreSQL with PostGIS while also investing in features like security and data replication, which makes the proposition for using open source in the cloud more attractive.

This quote from Eddie Pickle from Maxar describes how open source geospatial tools also enables more viewpoints and collaboration compared to closed source technology:

"In the proprietary world, software intellectual property (IP) is tightly controlled and only available to the developers the IP owner allows (usually company employees). This creates a pernicious situation where the company has a strictly limited developer roster, and developers cannot work on the software anywhere else—so developers and owners are both isolated and stuck with each other! Open source's inherent ability to improve collaboration in turn stimulates and accelerates innovation. The open level of interaction among developers and organizations means open source software is available to people with different points of view—diverse backgrounds, goals, perspectives, expertise—spurring creativity. It also means the openness of the software creates the conditions for a rich ecosystem for development."[10]

Open source allows you to take and use exactly what you need, nothing more and nothing less. If you need to add or remove components from your architecture you are free to do so. There is no greater practice that proves this exact point like data science. Pandas, a core data science library for reading and analyzing data has a geospatial extension called GeoPandas that seamlessly integrates into Pandas allowing for any data scientist to install and start using this library with ease.

New technology trends and cloud services are changing traditional IT norms

This was alluded to in our first section, but new ways (such as cloud services) to deploy and maintain software packages is changing. Specifically, the ability to parallelize processes and query or process large amounts of data has greatly expanded the scope and speed of analytics both in geospatial analytics and in the broader analytics space. This includes tools like Spark, and other data warehouses such as Google BigQuery, Amazon Web Services (AWS) Redshift, Databricks, and Snowflake. While, apart from Spark, these are proprietary tools, they all use spatial SQL as a foundational language.

The same report describes why cloud adoption will be critical to the growth within the geospatial industry:

"Increased internet connectivity due to advancements in communication technology and increased flexibility due to cloud computing is changing the way companies are delivering software and services to their customers. Geospatial analytics solution providers are also taking advantage of this improved business ecosystem to provide their customers with easy access to geospatial data. With cloud computing, several users can easily access geospatial data and leverage cloud computing resources to perform analysis and mapping."[11]

More and more, geospatial will move to using more open and interoperable tools, and can leverage the cloud to increase scale and access when the time is right. With that said, **what does any of this have to do with me learning spatial SQL?** Let's find out.

1.2 Why learn spatial SQL?

For the changes we discussed earlier, spatial SQL can and likely will play a critical role in the new, modern GIS paradigm. While traditional systems used local files or shared file systems, or even enterprise servers to store data, they often used any number of languages to access that data. Today, SQL has become the *lingua franca* of modern analytics practices, and it appears that geospatial is headed in

---

[10]https://loc8.cc/sql/maxar-osgis

[11]https://loc8.cc/sql/bloomberg-markets

the same direction. Spatial SQL already has a robust set of GIS and geospatial functionality, and as the ecosystem grows, more will be added to fold in other functionality over time.

Before we go any further, I also want to take a moment to define the term **spatial SQL**. Spatial SQL is not a separate language and also does not refer to a single tool or system. In the simplest terms, spatial SQL is a commonly accepted set of functions, naming conventions, and data types that can be used in any number of tools that support SQL.

"Spatial SQL is an interoperable language for working with spatial data enabling geospatial analysis, spatial data science, application development.

It provides GIS and geospatial users the ability to work in the same location as other data in databases and data warehouses, removing the traditional silos between GIS and other areas of an organization.

Spatial SQL supports advanced operations such as spatial modeling and machine learning in the same location that the data resides."

Let's focus on the key points from this definition.

First, and quite possibly most important, is interoperability. The concept that you can use spatial SQL across any number of database and tools is quite important and that means that you can move to a new tool or combine tools as needed, which means you are never locked in to any single solution. While there may be some steps required to migrate, overall your analytical code and structure can be easily replicated between databases.

Next is that it enables different use cases. There are only a few listed here but there are a multitude that spatial SQL can serve. Let's take a look at some problems you can solve with spatial SQL:

- Query and manage spatial datasets
- Manage projections and re-project data
- Store spatial data in multiple formats (WKT, GeoJSON, etc.)
- Analyze and understand many types spatial relationships
- Perform spatial clustering and perform nearest neighbor analysis
- Transform geometries using buffers, Voronoi polygons, and convex/concave hulls
- Calculate distances – straight line and using the curve of the earth
- Query and manage 3D data
- Create triggers to change and update data based on different events such as an INSERT into a specific table
- Connect to APIs and other external services
- Create user-defined functions in other languages such as Python, Javascript, and SQL
- Perform statistical analysis and machine learning using functions and tools like BigQuery ML
- Store and manage unstructured data like JSON or arrays
- Return data in many formats such as GeoJSON or Shapefiles
- Produce and generate map tiles for frontend apps

The next section focuses on removing silos and working in the same location as other data within your organization. For years, the saying **"spatial is special"** could be heard by many within the geospatial industry, and indeed we kept business data and geospatial data separate: in separate databases, servers, software, etc. But the need to treat geospatial data differently than normal data is decreasing rapidly. Most databases support spatial data and functions, and most data warehouses are now fully adopting geospatial support. This means that geospatial data and the expertise of those who know how to use it can now pair with other business users and use cases, in the same place and with the same data.

Imagine the power of being able to quickly combine data from a complex query a colleague wrote, join it to your spatial data, and run spatial analysis - in the same language and in the same tool. The language and tool barriers that have existed for so long are no longer necessary, and SQL is what is driving that change.

Not only that, SQL took the top spot in the IEEE Spectrum's interactive rankings of top programming languages in 2022[12]. This replaced other common languages such as C-based languages, and the ever popular Python. Here is a quote from their article:

"SQL dominated the jobs ranking in IEEE Spectrum's interactive rankings of the top programming languages this year. Normally, the top position is occupied by Python or other mainstays, such as C, C++, Java, and JavaScript, but the sheer number of times employers said they wanted developers with SQL skills, albeit in addition to a more general-purpose language, boosted it to No. 1.

So what's behind SQL's soar to the top? The ever-increasing use of databases, for one. SQL has become the primary query language for accessing and managing data stored in such databases—specifically relational databases, which represent data in table form with rows and columns. Databases serve as the foundation of many enterprise applications and are increasingly found in other places as well, for example taking the place of traditional file systems in smartphones."[13]

And the final component of spatial SQL speaks to its extensibility. More and more, you are starting to see different data warehouses and even databases adding machine learning capabilities. Everything from linear regression, to logistic regression, classification, and even popular models like XGBoost. Most data warehouses like Redshift, BigQuery, Snowflake, and Databricks do this, but even PostgreSQL has an extension called postgresml[14] that adds machine learning capabilities into PostgreSQL, and by extension, PostGIS.

You can do the same with more pure spatial models as well. PostGIS has implementations of the popular clustering methods KMeans and Density-based spatial clustering of applications with noise (DBSCAN). Other spatial functions like Moran's I and Getis-Ord Gi* have been implemented in data warehouses by CARTO in their Analytics Toolbox. You can also perform raster analysis and complex routing queries and analysis using popular tools like pgRouting for PostGIS.

But why would you bother doing this in SQL when all these tools exist in Python? The reason is that the closer you run your analysis to the data, the faster the analysis will run. Sure, for small problems or small volumes of data this can work great, but as you scale up you will inevitably need to find efficiencies to make things run faster. When using Python, that either means adding more compute resources or some type of parallelization. In SQL however, you already have the added bonus of running your models right where the data resides, and on a lower level language (for example PostgreSQL is written in C).

I don't think SQL will ever replace Python, and in the same IEEE/Spectrum report they point to a major reason for the rise in SQL is employers looking for *"SQL+ roles"*, meaning SQL plus something else. Now let's take a quick look at when or how you might use these two popular languages together.

1.3   To use SQL, Python, or both?

Python has had a meteoric rise in the past few years, driven in part by the rise of data science and machine learning. Most of the first data scientists were using either R or Python in their research, and over time Python has increased in popularity since it is ease for others to learn and easy to develop

---

[12]https://spectrum.ieee.org/top-programming-languages-2022

[13]https://spectrum.ieee.org/the-rise-of-sql

[14]https://github.com/postgresml/postgresml

with.

But as the need to use more data started to grow, those same data scientists needed new tools to increase their capacity. Some used larger servers to add more computational resources on the machines running their code. Others started to use GPU accelerated tools to greatly increase their performance.

Yet the method that seems to be winning out is using SQL based technologies, either databases or data warehouses. One reason is that SQL is also an easy language to use, and you can offload much of your data prep into the database or data warehouse. You can also do aggregations and reporting with time series data, so the database can accelerate the time to prepare your data while also making it ready for analysis in Python or other tools in a shorter time. The field of Data Engineering has taken off due to the need for more and cleaner data in a common location, and other technologies like Spark have helped to expand the usage of SQL too.

For me, these are the set of recommendations, not rules, that I use when deciding between the two. There are no right or wrong answers, but this is usually what I follow:

I use Python when I need to:

- Load and explore some data really quickly from a flat file
- Quickly visualize some data
- Translate between data formats (or I use GDAL on the command line)
- Perform exploratory spatial data analysis (always with PySAL)
- Analyze territory design problems
- Perform location allocation problems (although sometimes it is more efficient to create an origin destination matrix in SQL)
- Call APIs programmatically via Python to collect data

I use spatial SQL when I need to:

- Store larger spatial datasets that I access frequently
- Perform joins across tables – spatial or otherwise
- Analyze spatial relationships
- Perform spatial feature engineering (covers almost all use cases)
- Aggregate data spatial or otherwise
- Create tile sets (although Python is still used in the API service)
- Route between lots of points

I flip flop between spatial SQL and Python when I need to:

- Write custom functions to manipulate my data
- Perform geocoding (Python generally has more options)
- Re-project data (spatial SQL has the edge in this case)
- Manipulate geometries
- Make based aggregations like H3 or Quadkey
- Perform spatial clustering
- Machine learning using tools like BigQuery ML or postgresml

We will cover how you can combine spatial SQL with some of these emerging technologies later in the book so that you can bring your expertise into these exciting fields.

1.4   Spatial SQL landscape

During the course of this book, we will primarily be using PostGIS to run spatial SQL. It has the most spatial functions and is generally the standard that most others look to follow when they add spatial

SQL functionality. With that said the amount of tools that have adopted spatial SQL has grown significantly in the past years, so we will first take a look back to see how spatial SQL evolved, and then what the spatial SQL landscape looks like today.

History of spatial SQL

There is not a central source of truth when it comes to the history of spatial SQL. This section is my attempt to document the different developments of spatial databases over time and how spatial SQL came to be today. SQL itself dates back to the 1970s:

"The SQL programming language was developed in the 1970s by IBM researchers Raymond Boyce and Donald Chamberlin. The programming language, known then as SEQUEL, was created following Edgar Frank Codd's paper, 'A Relational Model of Data for Large Shared Data Banks' in 1970." *[15]

SQL as a language was made widely available in 1979 by the company that eventually became Oracle, and they were the driving force behind SQL and databases for many years.

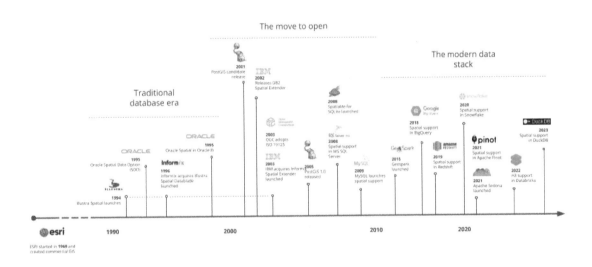

Figure 1.1: Timeline of spatial SQL development

When it comes to the history of spatial SQL, the first few years have many different developments, but in a strange way they all built on top of each other, as shown in Figure 1.1. Apart from Oracle which introduced the Spatial Data Option (SDO) in 1995, there appear to be three other companies that drive the adoption of spatial SQL: Illustra, Informix, and the open source option PostGIS. Strangely enough Illustra was later acquired by Informix, and the key person that founded Illustra was actually Michael Stonebraker, the eventual creator of PostgreSQL.

Things really started to take off around 2003 when the Open Geospatial Consortium adopted the SQL/MM Spatial Standard, which standardized function naming and data types within SQL databases[16].

---

[15]https://www.businessnewsdaily.com/5804-what-is-sql.html

A few others entered the space including Spatialite, a spatial extension of SQLite, Microsoft SQL, and MySQL.

From that point on most of the focus and development in the database space was focused on "big data". While I feel that term is somewhat outdated, the core developments in the database space that were being developed focused on technologies like Spark, data warehouse, Hive, and other parallelized processes for managing and querying large datasets.

This is where you see the next big burst of activity, starting with GeoSpark, which eventually turned into Apache Sedona. Often there is a gap between the original development of the technology and the spatial functionality being added. With PostgreSQL it was 7 years (1994 was the release of PostgreSQL, PostGIS was released in 2001). Spark and GeoSpark were only one year. Then came the migration to data warehouses. Amazon Web Services (AWS) Redshift launched in 2012, geospatial functionality launched in 2019. Google Cloud Platform (GCP) BigQuery launched in 2010, geospatial functionality launched in 2018. Snowflake launched in 2014, geospatial support launched in 2020.

We have yet to see how geospatial will play out in the next big push with SQL, which appears to be within the data engineering space with ETL and ELT tools as well as tools like dbt (data build tool) or within distributed query engines like Trino or PrestoDB (both of which support spatial functions).

- 1994 - Illustra Spatial launches, which as far as I can tell is the first SQL database featuring a spatial data type and spatial functions. Michael Stonebraker was developing what was called POSTGRES (or POST inGRES) at the University of California - Berkeley at the time and Illustra was the effort to commercialize that work.[17]

- 1995 - Shortly after, Oracle launched the Spatial Data Option or SDO in Oracle 4. This was developed in conjunction with a research team at the Canadian Hydrographic Service (CHS).[18]

- 1996 - Illustra was acquired by Informix and was renamed the Informix Spatial Datablade. MapInfo was heavily integrated with the Spatial Datablade.[19]

- 1998 - Oracle releases a new upgraded version of Oracle Spatial in Oracle 8i which added "native internet protocols".[20]

- 2001 - PostGIS launches the first candidate version. PostGIS was born out of the need to add superior support for the geometric type object in PostgreSQL. Refractions Reseach and Paul Ramsey lead much of the efforts around PostGIS from Victoria, British Columbia, Canada.[21]

- 2002 - IBM releases the DB2 Spatial Extender. This provided compatibility with the Esri product suite.
- 2003 - Informix, which was acquired by IBM, releases the Spatial Extender which also provides compatibility with the Esri product suite.
- 2003 - One of the more consequential moments in the history of spatial SQL was when the Open Geospatial Consortium (OGC) adopted the standards for Simple Feature Access, or ISO 19125. This provided the blueprint for spatial data and functions within a SQL database environment.[22]

---

[16]https://www.ogc.org/standards/sfs

[17]https://en.wikipedia.org/wiki/Michael_Stonebraker

[18]https://en.wikipedia.org/wiki/Oracle_Spatial_and_Graph

[19]https://www.bizjournals.com/albany/stories/1997/11/10/daily6.html

[20]https://en.wikipedia.org/wiki/Oracle_Database

[21]http://www.refractions.net/products/postgis/history/

[22]https://www.ogc.org/standards/sfs

- 2005 - PostGIS releases its first stable version in PostGIS 1.0.
- 2008 - Microsoft releases spatial support for Microsoft SQL Server.
- 2008 - SpatiaLite is released as the spatial extension for SQLite which is a much smaller and more compact database than PostgreSQL.
- 2009 - MySQL releases support for geospatial data in version 4.1.
- 2015 - GeoSpark, a geospatial extension of Spark, a "unified analytics engine" used to process massive amounts of data, is started. This integrates common geospatial functions into Spark.
- 2018 - GCP BigQuery releases GIS functions in alpha.
- 2019 - AWS Redshift releases support for geospatial data.[23]
- 2021 - GeoSpark becomes Apache Sedona, and enters support from the Apache ecosystem in incubation mode.[24]
- 2021 - Apache Pinot, a realtime distributed OLAP database, releases support for geospatial data.[25]
- 2021 - Snowflake releases support for geospatial data.[26]
- 2022 - Databricks announces support for H3 spatial indexes.[27]
- 2023 - DuckDB adds support for the *SPATIAL* extension natively[28]

1.5   The landscape today

The landscape of spatial SQL databases, data warehouses, and supportive tools is growing and expanding greatly. More and more tools are adopting spatial SQL than ever before, increasing the opportunity to learn one language and apply it to a multitude of tools. In this section we will review the current set of systems that support spatial SQL as of the writing of this book.

Relational databases

Relational databases are generally the most common type of database used today. These databases are designed to perform transactions with data, meaning that records are stored, created, updated, and deleted. These databases provide powerful tools for geospatial analytics as well, but many organizations will separate their databases to have an analytical database in a different location then the real data being processed in that database.

PostGIS

By and large, PostGIS is the most popular option for spatial SQL. It is completely open source and it extends an already popular database, PostgreSQL. It has the largest number of spatial functions available for a wide range of use cases and supports 2D vector data, 3D/4D vector data, and raster data. PostGIS also has other extensions like pgRouting that allow for routing options, mobilitydb for spatial movement data, postgis_tiger_geocoder for geocoding data in the US, address_standardizer for standardizing address data, pgpointcloud to use point cloud data, and a range of foreign data wrappers to query external databases.

---

[23]https://aws.amazon.com/blogs/aws/using-spatial-data-with-amazon-redshift/

[24]https://github.com/apache/incubator-sedona/releases/tag/sedona-1.0.0-incubating

[25]https://pinot.apache.org/blog/2021/06/13/DevBlog-Geospatial/

[26]https://loc8.cc/sql/snowflake-geoanalytics

[27]https://loc8.cc/sql/databricks-h3

[28]https://duckdb.org/2023/04/28/spatial.html

PostGIS is the database we will be using for most of the activities in this book due to its popularity and breadth of spatial functions. While it is near impossible to track how many installations of PostGIS there are, Docker Hub shows that it has over 100 million pulls as of December 2022 for this installation method alone.[29]

PostGIS will serve almost any general purpose needs for a spatial database, so it is helpful across a wide range of use cases. We will discuss the advantages and disadvantages for the remaining databases in this list as well. There are some logical limits with PostGIS in terms of size of data and query time, but much of that can be managed, except for the largest of spatial data, with different methods and spatial indexes. It is a larger install compared to SpatiaLite and also requires the user to be in charge of deployment, updates, and security, although many cloud managed solutions exist for PostGIS.

SpatiaLite

If you need a very small and lightweight system to manage spatial data, SpatiaLite, the spatial extension for SQLite, is a great choice. It provides spatial functions in a small lightweight package suitable for a range of use cases. Since it is such a small installation this is really useful for individual use cases. SQLite describes why it is advantageous:

"SQLite is a C-language library that implements a small, fast, self-contained, high-reliability, full-featured, SQL database engine. SQLite is the most used database engine in the world. SQLite is built into all mobile phones and most computers and comes bundled inside countless other applications that people use every day."

SQLite is deployed in every Android and iPhone, so it claims to be the most deployed database in the world. SpatiaLite is also used in GDAL, specifically ogr2ogr, to add a spatial SQL component to transform data within a data transformation command. SpatiaLite only lists one use case where it is not suitable:

"Conditions where a SQLite/SpatiaLite solution may not be the best choice... for support for multiple concurrent access, a client-server DBMS, such as PostgreSQL/PostGIS, is required"

This basically means when multiple clients are connecting to a common server.

MySQL

MySQL is a very common database, more comparable to PostgreSQL. The primary differences between PostgreSQL and MySQL are that MySQL is open source but maintained by Oracle (after MySQL was acquired by Oracle, the founder forked it and created a fully open source version called MariaDB) and that PostgreSQL is object-relational whereas MySQL is just relational. This means that PostgreSQL works with more complex data types, but also adds complexity into the queries and operations you can do.

MySQL is a very popular database which is used by Wordpress, Facebook, YouTube, Drupal, Twitter, and more. It doesn't appear that geospatial use cases are as common with MySQL as they are in PostGIS or other spatial databases, but the simple fact that spatial SQL functionality exists in an incredibly popular database means that spatial use cases and data can be leveraged from these database systems.

---

[29]`https://registry.hub.docker.com/r/postgis/postgis/`

Enterprise Spatial Databases

In effect there are four main "enterprise" (meaning commercial only) databases that support spatial data: Oracle Database, Microsoft SQL Server, Informix Spatial DataBlade (owned by IBM), and IMB Db2. These are all proprietary databases, some of which include the earliest spatial databases (Informix and Oracle). Each of these support spatial functionality and functions in addition to their standard core features. While some offer free trials or limited free versions, most of the full functionality will only be accessible if you or your organization has a full license to them. On inspection of their public documentation it does appear that these tools have a wide set of functions for spatial analysis and data management.

Data warehouses

While the concept of a data warehouse has been around for quite some time, in the past few years the adoption of cloud data warehouses has greatly increased, driven in part by the massive increase in available data that organizations are producing. There are two main factors that distinguish data warehouses from databases: the separation of compute resources and storage, and focusing on analytics first.

The separation of compute resources and storage has several implications for the performance and purpose of a data warehouse. The first is that data is being created in more formats, at faster velocity, and in greater volumes. Because of this the concept of a data lake has become increasingly popular. In simple terms a data lake is a place to store lots of data efficiently and commonly takes the form of cloud storage tools like GCP Cloud Storage or AWS Simple Storage Service (S3). This means you can dump and store data in a semi organized manner and then use the data warehouse as the query interface for that data. You may still need to ingest the data into the warehouse, but the data lives in one location and the query engine, or the engine using the compute resources to process and orchestrate the query, live elsewhere.

Why does this matter? This means that you can store the data efficiently, and at a low cost, in a tool optimized for general data storage (sometimes called blob storage) and the data warehouse query engine can use the computing power it needs. The data warehouse also parallelizes the query, or splits the job into smaller parts then assembles the results, which results in far faster query times for specific operations. Some data warehouses also offer serverless options. This means that instead of having compute services running around the clock even when you are not using them, the data warehouse will look at the query and delegate an appropriate amount of compute resources for that specific job. Once the job is complete those resources shut down. It's basically the difference between owning a car versus taking a cab or ride-share.

The other difference is that data warehouses are purpose built for analytics. Databases, while often used for analytics purposes, are built for online transaction processing (OLTP). On the other hand, data warehouses are generally defined as online analytical processing (OLAP) services which means they are designed specifically to manage analytical queries. This means that things like aggregations, joins, *WHERE* queries, and other operations are well suited for these tools. This is not to say that using databases to perform analytics is wrong, but certainly data warehouses can provide more performance when moving to very large volumes of data.

There are many data warehouses available but the most common ones that are used for geospatial analysis currently are AWS Redshift, GCP BigQuery, and Snowflake. All of these tools support the geometry data type natively and have built in spatial functionality as well as the ability to extend that functionality. CARTO has done so with it's Analytics Toolbox which has open-source functions for a number of operations like using spatial indexes like H3 or Quadbin, the former of which we will explore in this book.

Spark based systems

In the realm of big data processing, currently Spark has become a leader in this category. There have been a number of systems that have been used to store and query big data, and for a period of time Apache Hadoop, and its counterpart Apache Hive which provides a SQL interface to Hadoop, where the clear category leaders in big data. Apache Spark, which was released in 2014 by the University of California - Berkeley's AMPLab, has quickly become the category leader for processing large amounts of analytical data.

While comparing Hadoop to Spark is not an apples to apples comparison as there are slight differences between them in terms of focus areas. Spark can outperform Hadoop in terms of processing time anywhere from 10 to 100 times faster[30]. It improves upon the Map Reduce framework used by Hadoop to use a Directed Acyclic Graph or DAG to map out how the tasks should be performed. Spark uses "drivers" which turns the code you write into multiple tasks that can be run across a network of nodes. The "executors" do exactly what the name sounds like: executes the tasks assigned to the nodes. Apart from speed, Spark provides a far easier API to run code and commands and, important to our purposes, a SQL compliant toolkit for querying data known as Spark SQL.

Each of the major clouds support the Spark based tool, Databricks, which provides a complete data analytics platform on top of Spark. The founders of Spark founded Databricks and helped develop this ecosystem while also continuing to develop Spark as an open source project.

As it relates to geospatial analytics, Spark currently does not support geospatial data as a native data type. That said, there are two tools that provide geospatial support on top of Spark. This provides a scalable analytics platform using Spark native programming in addition to Spark SQL, as well as tools for visualizing data and producing map layers.

Apache Sedona

Formerly known as GeoSpark, Apache Sedona is an extension of Apache Spark as well as Apache Flink which effectively extends the Resilient Distributed Dataset (RDD) or the core data structure of Spark, to support the geometry. This description from a post on Medium by Mo Sawat, a maintainer of Apache Sedona, describes this in more detail:

"A SpatialRDD consists of data partitions that are distributed across the Spark cluster. A Spatial RDD can be created by RDD transformation or be loaded from a file that is stored on permanent storage. This layer provides a number of APIs which allow users to read heterogeneous spatial object from various data format.

GeoSpark allows users to issue queries using the out-of-box Spatial SQL API and RDD API. The RDD API provides a set of interfaces written in operational programming languages including Scala, Java, Python and R. The Spatial SQL interfaces offers a declarative language interface to the users so they can enjoy more flexibility when creating their own applications. These SQL API implements the SQL/MM Part 3 standard which is widely used in many existing spatial databases such as PostGIS (on top of PostgreSQL)."

In effect, it provides a geospatial analytics platform on top of Spark using spatial SQL. It also has the ability to run with other languages and use within the context of a Python notebook. The project graduated from incubating to Apache top project in January 2023, so there will likely be more features released as it expands.

---

[30]https://loc8.cc/sql/infoworld-spark

GeoMesa

While *GeoMesa* is not a Spark specific tool, it is worth mentioning here because it now includes a connector to SparkSQL. At its core, GeoMesa is described as:

"...an open source suite of tools that enables large-scale geospatial querying and analytics on distributed computing systems. GeoMesa provides spatio-temporal indexing on top of the Accumulo, HBase, Google Bigtable and Cassandra databases for massive storage of point, line, and polygon data. GeoMesa also provides near real time stream processing of spatio-temporal data by layering spatial semantics on top of Apache Kafka. Through GeoServer, GeoMesa facilitates integration with a wide range of existing mapping clients over standard OGC (Open Geospatial Consortium) APIs and protocols such as WFS and WMS. GeoMesa supports Apache Spark for custom distributed geospatial analytics."

It primarily focuses on the Hadoop ecosystem, but also incorporates many other database connections as well. It also allows for the creation of map tile layers. As for the scope of this book, SparkSQL is the primary location where you will find spatial SQL within GeoMesa, although the primary interface will be with Java or Scala.

GeoMesa certainly could fall under the later section of distributed query engines as it positions well alongside other tools that support a wide range of non-geospatial specific tools for distributed querying. But as the only spatial SQL component, apart from a connection to PostGIS (as of version 3.5.0), this felt more appropriate here for the time being.

Other OLAP Tools

We mentioned the term OLAP in the data warehouses section, and there are many more currently being developed that are gaining popularity such as Apache Druid and Clickhouse which have limited geospatial support and do not support spatial SQL.

DuckDB

DuckDB was originally listed as one of the OLAP tools that did not have geospatial support when I first wrote this chapter, but in the course of writing this book it added geospatial support with it's "SPATIAL" package which provides support for reading, writing, and querying geospatial data and files[31]. DuckDB has a few unique attributes that makes it an increasingly appealing choice for spatial analytics.

First is that it is a no dependency package, meaning that all you need to run it is the DuckDB package installed on your computer. It is an OLAP which means it is made to query and process large amounts of data, but it is unique in the sense that it can do this from your laptop by using your computers built in processing power. It is also a columnar-vector query execution engine which is explained here from the DuckDB website[32]:

"DuckDB contains a columnar-vectorized query execution engine, where queries are still interpreted, but a large batch of values (a "vector") are processed in one operation. This greatly reduces overhead present in traditional systems such as PostgreSQL, MySQL or SQLite which process each row sequentially. Vectorized query execution leads to far better performance in OLAP queries."

It does not require you to import any files either. You can query files on your computer or from cloud storage services like AWS S3 or Google Cloud Storage. You simply call the filename as the table and

---

[31]https://duckdb.org/2023/04/28/spatial.html

[32]https://duckdb.org/why_duckdb

you can start using it. And if you need more power from cloud computing power MotherDuck, a serverless cloud platform that supports DuckDB, can provide that and allow you to intermingle data from your computer and data in the cloud.

Additionally, you can create a database that is contained in a single file which you can then share to any other user who uses DuckDB. You can also access and install DuckDB directly through Python and pass the returned data immediately into a Pandas dataframe. DuckDB has been referred to as the SQLite for analytics, but it's ease of use, portability, and simple installation will, I believe, make it an increasingly popular choice for spatial analytics in the short and long term.

Apache Pinot

The notable exception is *Apache Pinot*. Released in 2019, this OLAP datastore that supports realtime (streaming) analytics from Apache Kafka and other topics as well as stored file data has gained popularity and is currently in use by LinkedIn, Uber, Slack, Stripe, DoorDash, Target, Walmart, Amazon, and Microsoft[33]. I learned about geospatial support for Apache Pinot at Apachecon North America 2022 in a presentation from Yupeng Fu[34] from Uber where they used Pinot to provide real time analytics within the Uber Eats app.

What makes Pinot unique is that it is effectively a database you can query directly with SQL, and in turn spatial SQL. This works with not only static data but also data event streams. In the case of Uber, they used static data (their restaurant partner locations) and real time data (streams of orders) to produce end user analytics. This differs from internal analytics such as reports and dashboards and is analytics for the end user, potentially hundreds of thousands, or millions of users. Pinot is able to scale horizontally to support this volume of requests but also show analytics like the image below in Figure 1.2, on the next page.

The query would look something like this:

Listing 1.1: Spatial queries in Apache Pinot

```
1   SELECT
2       *
3   FROM
4       Orders
5   WHERE
6       ST_Distance(location_st_point_1, ST_Point(-90.5, 14.596, 1)) < 16000
7       AND numberOfItems > 0
8       AND createdOrderTimestamp > 1612997591
```

This would show you recent orders within ten miles of your location where items ordered are greater than 0 and the order created timestamp is greater than a specified time. This opens a whole new range of possibilities for end user applications that embed the ability to learn the same spatial SQL you are using in this way.

Distributed query engines

Another area that is continuing to gain popularity are distributed query engines, the two most prominent are Presto, released in 2013, and Trino, released in 2019. Presto was the original development which took place at Meta (then Facebook) and while Presto is still open source, the original founders created a fork in 2019 which came to be known as Trino.

---

[33]https://pinot.apache.org/who_uses/

[34]https://www.apachecon.com/acna2022/slides/02_Fu_Geospatial_support_pinot.pdf

Figure 1.2: Uber Eats Near Me feature powered by Apache Pinot ("Geospatial support in Apache Pinot" - presentation by Yupeng Fu at Apachecon North America 2022)

These tools also leverage distributed computing processing similar to Spark or Hadoop, known as massively parallel processing. It has workers that coordinate the tasks and split them up to query the data. The main differences are that it can use a multitude of sources to connect to and you only need to know SQL to use it. The SQL you write is processed and turned into different execution steps similar to SparkSQL.

Some example connections you can use (list taken from Trino):

- BigQuery
- Cassandra
- ClickHouse
- Cloud Storage (GCP Cloud Storage, AWS S3) via Hive Connector
- Delta Lake
- Elasticsearch
- Google Sheets
- Hadooop
- Hive
- Kafka
- Local File
- MariaDB
- MongoDB
- MySQL
- Oracle
- Pinot
- PostgreSQL
- Redshift

- SQL Server

What this means is that you can query one or many of these data sources together in unison in a distributed manner, all with SQL. Trino and Presto also support a wide range of spatial SQL queries that are SQL/MM compliant based on the OGC standards which allows you to do all the great things with spatial SQL that you might need. The downside is that they don't support the *GEOMETRY* or *GEOGRAPHY* data type natively so you have to create this from Well-Known Text, Well-Known Binary, or other format for storing the geographic data, which inevitably lengthens the query processing. As this is an evolving space I am interested to see how these systems will be used for larger scale geospatial analysis in the future, especially as it now provides the full power of big data systems all in SQL.

GPU accelerated databases

The last group that I will cover are GPU, or graphical processing units, accelerated databases. Where most databases run on central processing units, or CPUs, databases that use GPUs have a much higher performance boost simply based on the number of cores that can be used to process operations since GPUs are optimized to handle many operations concurrently, like rendering complex graphics in video games. This means that databases that run with GPUs can run more tasks concurrently, sometimes thousands more, which results in much faster operations. This is why GPU processing has become popular for large scale machine learning and deep learning operations.

There are three main GPU accelerated databases that provide geospatial functionality: HEAVY.AI (formerly known as MapD and OmniSci), Kinetica, and Brytlyt. While these solutions are mainly commercially focused, HEAVY.AI and Kinetica have free versions that you can use, but the developer version doesn't allow you to take advantage of the GPU tooling. HEAVY.AI does have open source components that you can also download or contribute to and is the only open source version available of the three.

This wraps our section on all things spatial SQL. In the next chapter we start to get our hands dirty with setting up our spatial SQL set up we will use in the rest of the book, how to think in SQL, and how to migrate (or mix and match) from a GIS desktop set up to spatial SQL.

1.6   Expert Voices: Uchenna Osia

One goal of this book for me was to include other perspectives apart from my own from those using spatial SQL in innovative ways around the globe. To do that, several professional colleagues and connections were gracious enough to share their experiences and knowledge. The first of these comes from Uchenna Osia.

Name: Uchenna Osia **Title**: PhD Student in Geospatial Analytics at North Carolina State University

How/where did you learn spatial SQL?

I learned spatial SQL during the Geospatial Data Management course at NCSU.

Why do you enjoy using spatial SQL?

I enjoy using spatial SQL because it allows me to represent space in a way that is most appropriate within the context of a given problem. It provides clarity in executing my end goal and enables the capture of nuanced relationships formed within data. Spatial SQL offers a structured approach to handling difficult problems, its capabilities make it easier to derive valuable insight that can be used to drive decision-making.

Can you share an interesting way or use case that you are using spatial SQL for today?

Presently, I am designing a spatial database that will model a network of disaster relief organizations operating in North Carolina. I will use spatial SQL to investigate how organizations can adjust their reach to be more equitable in their service and connect those that share aligned missions.

2. Setting Up

Now that we have reviewed the complete spatial SQL landscape and history, it is time to build our spatial SQL set up that we will be using for the rest of this book. As I mentioned in the previous chapter, we will primarily be using a combination of PostGIS as our database and pgAdmin as our method to access and query our data. In this section we will also cover some other tools you can use to access, import, and query data such as ogr2ogr (part of the GDAL package), and QGIS.

2.1 Setting up PostGIS

The first step in the process is to set up PostGIS on your computer. This instance of PostGIS will live only on your computer or, as I will refer to it going forward, locally. You won't be able to use it with a web app or any other computer. So how is this database able to run on your computer without living somewhere else, such as the cloud?

In short, the cloud is more or less just a collection of servers, similar to the one that runs on your computer. It has computing resources like CPU, RAM, and hard disk storage to store data. They have far more of these and on top of the actual hardware they provide specific services, everything ranging from pure compute access with the command line, to databases like PostgreSQL, services for messaging, machine learning and artificial intelligence, and more. Now in effect there is not much difference in installing PostGIS on your local machine compared to a web server or in the cloud, apart from the fact that you can access the database from the internet.

There are many methods to actually install PostgreSQL on your computer. Below are some of the other options which we will not be covering in this book (more on that later). The recommended path for installing PostGIS on Windows is to download the PostGIS for Windows package from the PostGIS website and then install it using the StackBuilder application that comes with the download. For MacOS users, it is recommended that you use the Postgres.app which is a simple download, then run a simple command from the command line to install PostGIS. For Linux users, you will have a few more steps, but this Medium post from Joe T. Santhanavanich provides a great guide in 5 steps[35] (see footnote for URL). I recommend checking the PostGIS website for updated instructions as these may change in the future, but these three paths are the best and most supported methods to install PostGIS if you choose to go this route.

The instructions I will provide will be using the PostGIS Docker image which will work cross-platform, and is easy to set up with minimal command line instructions.

2.2 Why Docker?

In recent years the software deployment method known as containerization has become increasingly popular for a number of reasons, and Docker is the most popular tool used to build and manage various containers. A container is effectively a self-contained, portable, and standardized method of deploying software.

The best way to think about a container is that it is a completely blank slate before we provide it any

---

[35]https://loc8.cc/sql/joets-install-postgresql

instructions. It has no operating system, no information about what it should run, no data, nothing. The `Dockerfile` tells the container what to install, including an operating system. It then tells the container the steps it should run, such as other things to install and commands on the command line. As a user, you don't actually have to do any of this, apart from installing and starting the Docker container itself. Even better, Docker provides a desktop application to view and manage your container(s).

So why use this approach over the approved approaches? First is that the Docker container will run the same code on each and every computer used by the users in this book. Since the container is "contained" in your computer and will follow the same set of installation instructions every time, the experience will be consistent no matter what computer or operating system you are using.

The second is a pretty consistent issue when trying to create repeatable and consistent instructions when installing software: version of other tools running on computers. There is no possible way to know the myriad of issues that could arise from different versions of operating systems or languages that are installed on the computers of every person using this book. The great part about Docker is that there is no need to worry about that since the container will run the same using the same `Dockerfile` for everyone, the steps will be the same.

Third is updating your database to new versions to take advantage of new features that are released. Updating is as simple as installing the new version, creating a dump of data from your existing database, moving the data dump over to the new version, and deleting the old version. The container will persist the data you have in it even if you shut it down or restart it.

2.3 Installing PostGIS with Docker

Download Docker

To set up PostGIS our first step is to download and install Docker. You can simply go to the Docker download page[36] and download the correct version for your computer. Once it downloads, go ahead and install Docker and open it. This will also install the Docker Engine, Docker CLI client, Docker Compose, Docker Content Trust, Kubernetes, and Credential Helper.

Check if Docker is up and running

Next we are going to open our command line terminal. We will be running a few commands from the terminal so if you have not used the terminal before, here are a few tips to get started.

The one universal command that you will want to know is cd, which is short for change directory. In short, you are basically navigating the folder structure of your computer, but instead of using the user interface, you are using the command line to do so. For example let's imagine that you are in a folder called 'Home'. There is a folder within that folder called 'Documents' and within that folder there is a folder called 'SpatialSQL'. To navigate to the Documents folder we can use the command

```
cd Documents
```

And from here we can navigate to the `SpatialSQL` folder using this command:

---

[36]https://docs.docker.com/get-docker/

```
cd SpatialSQL
```

Let's say you want to navigate out to the `Documents` folder:

```
cd ..
```

Or if you want to go from the `SpatialSQL` folder all the way back to Home:

```
cd ../..
```

You can also list the items in the folders using `ls` on Mac or Linux, and `dir` on Windows.

At least for this book you won't need any more knowledge than this, but you can find plenty of tutorials online on more advanced command line prompts as needed.

From here create the folder in the location that you want to store your Docker container and PostGIS data files, and navigate to that folder in the command line. Once you have navigated to that folder, our first step is to make sure Docker is up and running. You can use this command to check and see.

```
docker info
```

You should see an output that looks something like Figure 2.1, on the following page.

Troubleshooting

If you get any error here, make sure to:

- Check to make sure the Docker Desktop has installed correctly.
- Ensure Docker Desktop is open and running on your computer.
- If those fail, delete Docker and re-install.

Installing docker-postgis

In addition to installing PostGIS, we will also add the following PostGIS extensions to help us perform more advanced analysis throughout the book. In a normal PostgreSQL installation, these can be installed via any number of methods such as compiling the code yourself or using an extension manager. The extensions we will be using are:

- `postgis_raster`: An extension that is already bundled within PostGIS that allows you to work with raster data inside the database[37]

- `pgRouting`: An external extension that allows you to import network data such as roads, bike routes, even shipping lanes, and perform common routing analysis with them[38]

- `pg-h3`: An external extension that allows you to work with the H3 global discrete grid system in PostGIS[39]

---

[37] https://postgis.net/docs/RT_FAQ.html#idm34630
[38] https://pgrouting.org/

```
> docker info
Client:
 Context:    default
 Debug Mode: false
 Plugins:
  buildx: Docker Buildx (Docker Inc., v0.9.1)
  compose: Docker Compose (Docker Inc., v2.13.0)
  dev: Docker Dev Environments (Docker Inc., v0.0.5)
  extension: Manages Docker extensions (Docker Inc., v0.2.16)
  sbom: View the packaged-based Software Bill Of Materials (SBOM) for an image (Anchore Inc., 0.6.0)
  scan: Docker Scan (Docker Inc., v0.22.0)

Server:
 Containers: 11
  Running: 7
  Paused: 0
  Stopped: 4
 Images: 11
 Server Version: 20.10.21
 Storage Driver: overlay2
  Backing Filesystem: extfs
  Supports d_type: true
  Native Overlay Diff: true
  userxattr: false
 Logging Driver: json-file
 Cgroup Driver: cgroupfs
 Cgroup Version: 2
 Plugins:
  Volume: local
  Network: bridge host ipvlan macvlan null overlay
  Log: awslogs fluentd gcplogs gelf journald json-file local logentries splunk syslog
 Swarm: inactive
 Runtimes: io.containerd.runtime.v1.linux runc io.containerd.runc.v2
 Default Runtime: runc
 Init Binary: docker-init
 containerd version: 770bd0108c32f3fb5c73ae1264f7e503fe7b2661
 runc version: v1.1.4-0-g5fd4c4d
 init version: de40ad0
 Security Options:
  seccomp
   Profile: default
  cgroupns
 Kernel Version: 5.15.49-linuxkit
 Operating System: Docker Desktop
 OSType: linux
 Architecture: aarch64
```

Figure 2.1: Checking that Docker is installed and running

Now installing each of these extensions on your own would require varying levels of difficulty, ranging from simple with postgis_raster to complex with pgRouting. But fortunately for us there is a Docker container that is set up to handle all of this out of the box. Another wonderful feature of Docker is that there are containers that already exist that are maintained by the community that make it very easy to start with new tools. The container we will use in this case is very similar to the main PostGIS container. It is called docker-postgis[40] which is maintained by Kartoza[41], an IT service company focused on geospatial. In fact, they maintain a number of containers for a variety of geospatial services, so I want to make a special acknowledgment of their efforts here which saves you (and myself) time in using these features.

To set this up is quite simple since we already have Docker up and running on our computer. There

---

[39]https://github.com/zachasme/h3-pg

[40]https://github.com/kartoza/docker-postgis

[41]https://kartoza.com/

are several methods to do this but the method that I prefer is using `docker-compose`' since this greatly decreases the complexity of the commands we need to run and allows us to also benefit from another container to back-up our database. In short, the docker-compose format embeds all your options into a file that then passes those to Docker to build or stand up your container or multiple containers. The `docker-compose` option for `docker-postgis` includes PostGIS with all of the extensions except H3 ready to use and a second container that creates database backups at regular intervals.

2.4   Installing docker-postgis

1. First make sure Docker is up-to-date and running on your computer

You can do this using Docker desktop or by running `docker update` in your command line interface. Note that this may not work if you are using Windows. See this documentation for more details.[42]

2. Our next step will be to download a file from the `docker-postgis` GitHub repo. Note that this file is included in the course files so you do not have to download it yourself, but I will include the instructions here so you can see how to do it on your own. First, go to the Kartoza GitHub repo.[43]

Once you are there, click on the file named `docker-compose.yml` (Figure 2.2), or you can find it directly by going to this link footnote.[44]

Figure 2.2: The docker-compose.yaml in GitHub

3. From here, you can download the file by clicking the download button, as shown in Figure 2.3, on the following page.

This will download the `docker-compose.yml` to your computer. Move the file to a location that you will remember as we will need to navigate to that location in the command line in the coming steps.

---

[42]https://loc8.cc/sql/docker-windows

[43]https://github.com/kartoza/docker-postgis

[44]https://github.com/kartoza/docker-postgis/blob/develop/docker-compose.yml

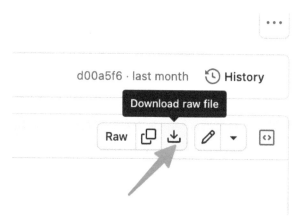

Figure 2.3: Downloading the docker-compose.yaml file

4. Before we run the containers, we have to make a small modification to the `docker-compose.yml` file. Open this file with a text editor of your choosing. This is a YAML, or a markup language file which is also known as Yet Another Markup Language. As of the publishing of this book the relevant code is on line 21 of the YAML file, which looks like this:

```
- POSTGRES_MULTIPLE_EXTENSIONS=postgis,hstore,postgis_topology,postgis_
raster,pgrouting
```

This argument in the file defines the extensions that will be installed in your PostGIS database. The `Dockerfile` for the PostGIS database already installs the extensions we need to use the H3 functions, but we will need to add them here to this line of code. The text we want to add is:

```
,h3,h3_postgis
```

Which when completed will look like this:

```
- POSTGRES_MULTIPLE_EXTENSIONS=postgis,hstore,postgis_topology,postgis_
raster,pgrouting,h3,h3_postgis
```

Ensure that there are commas separating all the values and that there are no spaces. If you downloaded the file from the GitHub repo, you will also need to replace this line on line 10:

```
image: kartoza/postgis:${POSTGRES_MAJOR_VERSION}-${POSTGIS_MAJOR_
VERSION}.${POSTGIS_MINOR_RELEASE}
```

With this, replacing the placeholders for *POSTGRES_MAJOR_VERSION, POSTGIS_MAJOR_VERSION,* and *POSTGIS_MINOR_RELEASE*

```
image: kartoza/postgis:15-3.3
```

We need to do the same on line 31 for our backups Docker container from this:

```
image: kartoza/pg-backup:${POSTGRES_MAJOR_VERSION}-${POSTGIS_MAJOR_
VERSION}.${POSTGIS_MINOR_RELEASE}
```

To this:

```
image: kartoza/pg-backup:15-3.3
```

The final code should look like Figure 2.4.

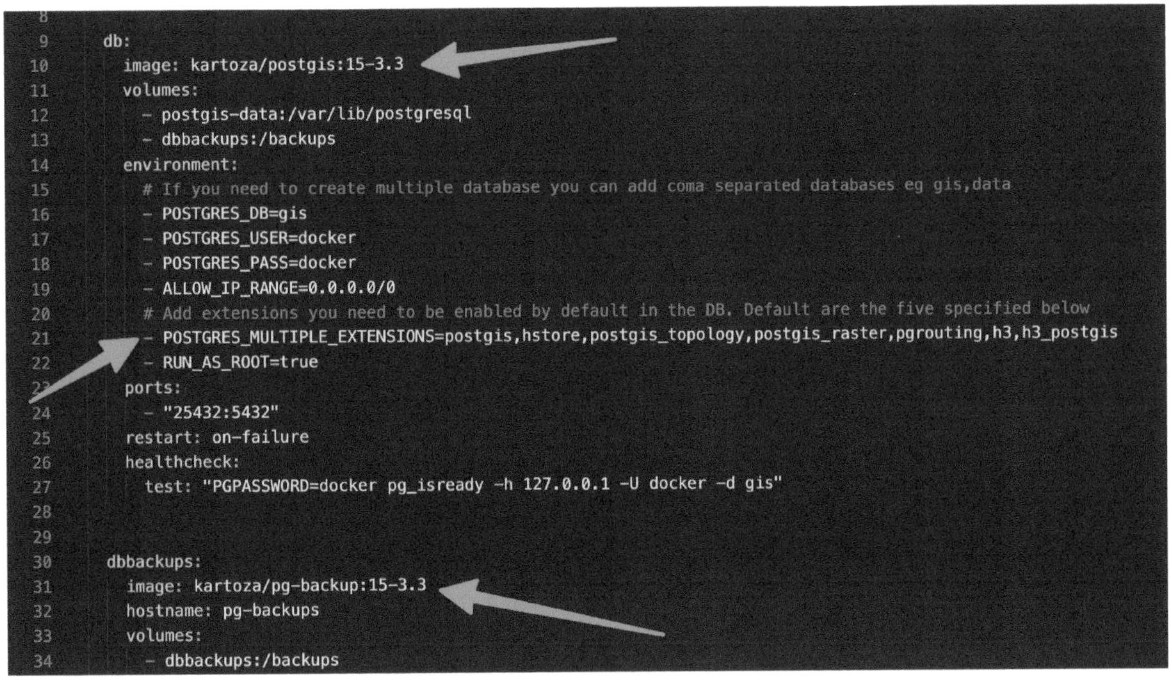

Figure 2.4: The docker-compose.yaml file after modifications

Special note for MacOS users using Apple products with a Apple silicon chip, currently the M1 or M2 chips

If you are using a Mac laptop or computer that was released after 2019, then it is likely that your computer falls into this category. You can find out if you are using an M1 or M2 chip by clicking on the "apple" icon on your computer, then clicking on **About This Mac**. This will open a window that will tell you which chip your computer is using (Figure 2.5, on the following page).

If you do fall into this category then you need to add one more line to the docker-compose.yml file immediately after line 10, or this code:

```
image: kartoza/postgis:15-3.3
```

The code you need to add is as follows:

```
platform: linux/amd64
```

This is because the Apple silicon chips use the ARM architecture, whereas most Docker containers and other computers use the AMD64 architecture. Without going into too much detail these are different

Figure 2.5: Checking if you have a Mac M1 or M2 chip

microchip architectures that are used by various chip manufacturers. Once you have added the code make sure your indent is consistent with the line above it as indentation matters in YAML.

The final file will look like Figure 2.6, on the next page.

5. Now we need to use our terminal to navigate to the location where our `docker-compose.yml` file is located. For illustration purposes, lets imagine that my file is located first within my **Documents** folder, and then inside a folder named **spatial-sql**.

To get to that folder, open your terminal where we will use the commands we just learned. In our example we are in our home folder, or the folder that your terminal opens up to when launched. In our example we are in our `Home` directory. Our first step will be to navigate into our `Documents` folder:

```
cd Documents
```

And then our `spatial-sql` folder:

```
cd spatial-sql
```

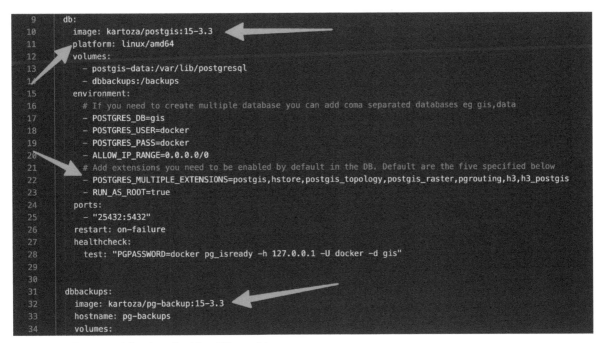

```
 9    db:
10        image: kartoza/postgis:15-3.3
11      platform: linux/amd64
12        volumes:
13          - postgis-data:/var/lib/postgresql
14          - dbbackups:/backups
15        environment:
16          # If you need to create multiple database you can add coma separated databases eg gis,data
17          - POSTGRES_DB=gis
18          - POSTGRES_USER=docker
19          - POSTGRES_PASS=docker
20          - ALLOW_IP_RANGE=0.0.0.0/0
21          # Add extensions you need to be enabled by default in the DB. Default are the five specified below
22          - POSTGRES_MULTIPLE_EXTENSIONS=postgis,hstore,postgis_topology,postgis_raster,pgrouting,h3,h3_postgis
23          - RUN_AS_ROOT=true
24        ports:
25          - "25432:5432"
26        restart: on-failure
27        healthcheck:
28          test: "PGPASSWORD=docker pg_isready -h 127.0.0.1 -U docker -d gis"
29
30
31    dbbackups:
32        image: kartoza/pg-backup:15-3.3
33        hostname: pg-backups
34        volumes:
```

Figure 2.6: Extra modifications for Mac Silicon chips

To confirm you are in the correct location, you can run this command which will list the files in that folder, where you should see the docker-compose.yml file:

```
ls
```

If you see it there then you are ready to move to the next step! If not, there are some shortcuts you can use to find the path of the file and navigate directly to the file:

- **MacOS**: Right click (*Control + Click*) on the docker-compose.yml and you should see a menu pop up. While that menu is open, click and hold the *Option* key and you should see an option named *Copy docker-compose.yml as path name* (Figure 2.7, on the following page). Click on that then paste the result into your terminal, and press *Enter*.

- **Windows**: While holding *Shift*, right click on the docker-compose.yml file, the select *Copy as Path*. Then paste the result into your terminal, and press *Enter*
- **Linux**: When the docker-compose.yml file is highlighted, press *Control + L*. This will make the path editable and then you can copy that text, and then paste the result into your terminal, and press *Enter*.

6. Now we can run the last step of the process which is running the command to start our containers:

```
docker-compose up -d
```

This command will download the Docker containers for the PostGIS database and the PostGIS backups container based on the specifications in the docker-compose.yml file and build/start both containers. The -d flag tells Docker to run it in detached mode, which means that you will not have to keep your terminal open and, once it is set up for the first time, manage your containers via the Docker desktop app.

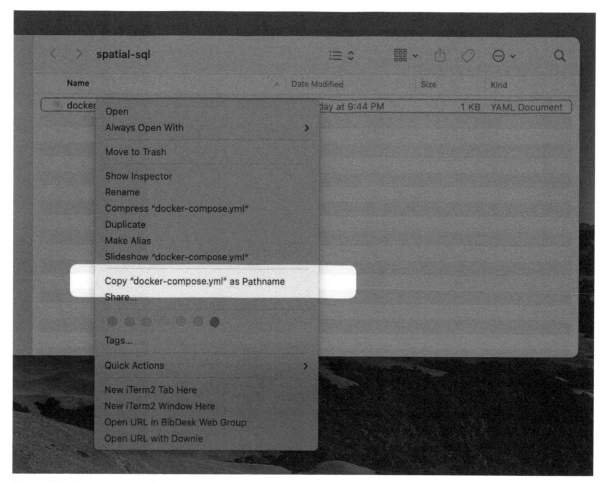

Figure 2.7: Copying the path name

Once you have run the command to start the Docker containers you should see them live in your Docker desktop app (Figure 2.8, on the next page):

From here you can turn your Docker container on and off by pressing the stop button (see the arrow in Figure 2.8, on the facing page).

Troubleshooting

First, you will need to find the logs for your new container using the Docker Desktop app. This will provide you information to what is happening within the container. Your terminal will tell you any issues with the docker run command itself.

Within your terminal

- Error contains "no space left on container"
    - Your Docker does not have enough resources allocated.
    - You can either run this command to remove images that are not in use - `docker system prune` (you shouldn't need to do this if this is your first time using Docker)
    - Open up Docker Desktop and navigate to *Settings (Gear Icon) → Resources → Advanced* and change the the the Virtual Disk Limit or other settings as needed.

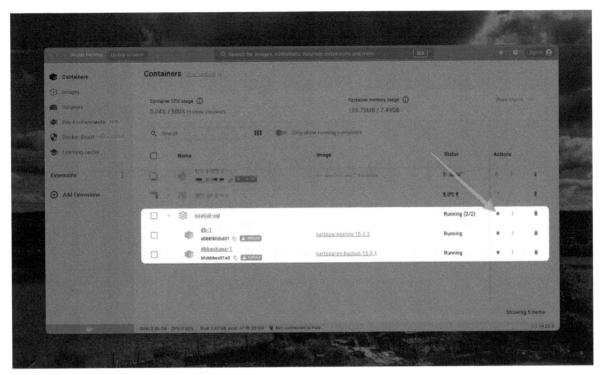

Figure 2.8: Running and stopping your Docker containers

- docker: Error response from daemon: Conflict. The container name "/spatialsql" is already in use by container "RANDOM_ALPHA_NUMERIC_CODE". You have to remove (or rename) that container to be able to reuse that name.
  - You already have a container running that is called "spatialsql". You can either delete that container (if you are doing this for the first time I recommend that) or change your container name.
- WARNING: The requested image's platform (linux/amd64) does not match the detected host platform (linux/arm64/v8) and no specific platform was requested.
  - This will likely happen if you are using a Mac with an M1 chip (or Apple Chip). You can add this flag to the end of the command, right before "postgis/postgis:15-3.3": `--platform linux/amd64`
  - Change the part after the –platform flag to match whatever the name in is this section: The requested image's platform (**linux/amd64**)
- Bind for 0.0.0.0:5432 failed: port is already allocated.
  - You have another tool on your machine or computer using port 5432, likely another PostgreSQL or PostGIS database. Either shut down or remove that database, or change both port values to something new like 5433

Connect PostGIS to QGIS

Now we can connect our new PostGIS database to QGIS. If you have not downloaded QGIS you can do so on the QGIS website[45].

---

[45]https://qgis.org/

We are using QGIS since it is a free and open source project and allows us to quickly and easily view our data from our PostGIS database. The only limitation is that you do have to create what is known as a VIEW or a new TABLE from a query in your PostGIS database, which is why we will also show you how to connect pgAdmin to view data directly from queries. QGIS also has tools to easily import data via QGIS too like Shapefile, GeoJSON, etc.

First, open QGIS and in the *Browser* panel on the left, right-click on the PostGIS label and click *New Connection* (Figure 2.9).

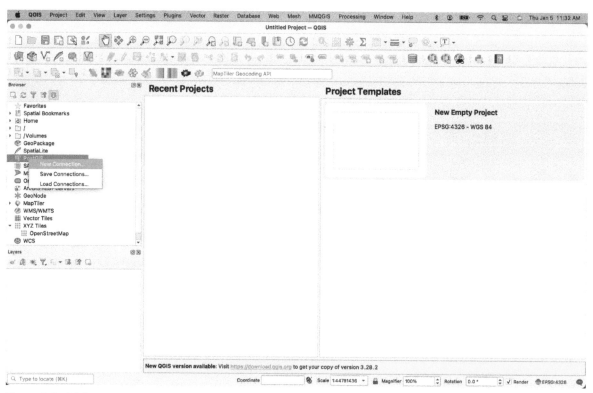

Figure 2.9: Adding a connection in QGIS

Next we need to fill in the details for our connection. You can follow along here if you used the exact commands as above, but if you changed any variables please adjust accordingly (Figure 2.10, on the facing page).

- **Name**: any name you choose for your connection
- **Host**: localhost
- **Port**: 25432
- **Database**: gis
- **Authentication**
    - Click the "Basic" Tab and enter
        * **User**: docker
        * **Password**: docker

From here you can test the connection to make sure everything is working appropriately and if it is you should see the blue success message as shown below (Figure 2.11, on the next page).

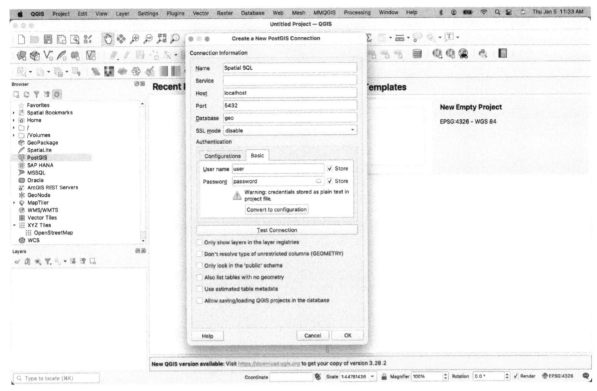

Figure 2.10: Connection parameters in QGIS

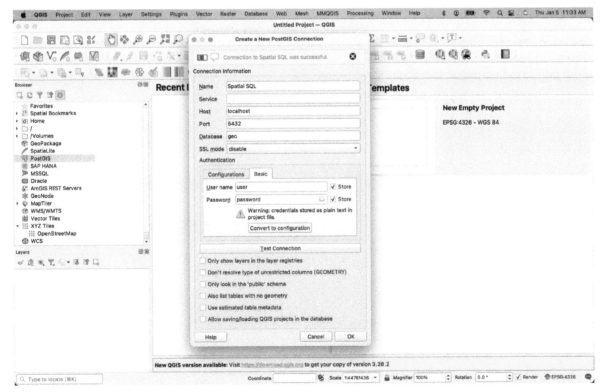

Figure 2.11: Testing the connection

Troubleshooting

- Make sure your PostGIS Docker container is active and running by making sure it is showing in the color green in the *Containers* section of the app. This is the most likely error at this stage.
- Ensure that all the parameters you entered match the ones in the Docker command you used.

Upload your first dataset

Let's upload our first dataset into PostGIS. At this stage we can keep it simple by using QGIS to handle this for us. The dataset we will be using is a Shapefile of United States Counties which can be found in the resources downloads for this book. You can also use any other dataset of US Counties that you want, but ours was downloaded from the US Census Website.

First, download the dataset or open the dataset from the downloaded files from book resources. You will need to unzip the .zip file named cb_2018_us_county_500k.zip. Once it is unzipped, you can either go into that folder and double-click the file named cb_2018_us_county_500k.shp or in **QGIS Layer → Add Vector Layer**. In the dialog, click the three dots in the section labeled Source → Vector Dataset(s) and navigate to the folder to select the file cb_2018_us_county_500k.shp (Figure 2.12).

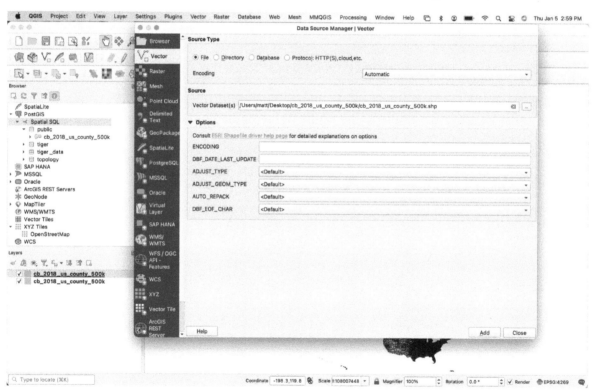

Figure 2.12: Adding the counties data to the map

This will open up the counties layer in QGIS. To add it to PostGIS, in QGIS select the Database item in the menu bar and click on DB Manager where you should see this dialog pop up (Figure 2.13, on the next page):

From here, click on *PostGIS → Spatial SQL* (if that is the name you used for your connection) → *Public*. Once Public is selected, click on *Import Layer/File* (Figure 2.14, on the facing page).

QGIS allows you to import layers that you have already added into QGIS as well as files directly. In

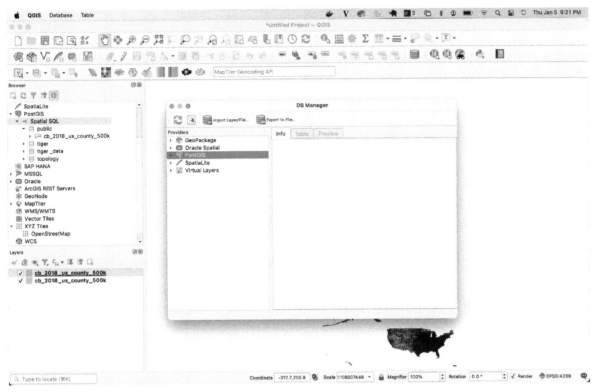

Figure 2.13: Using the QGIS PostGIS data importer

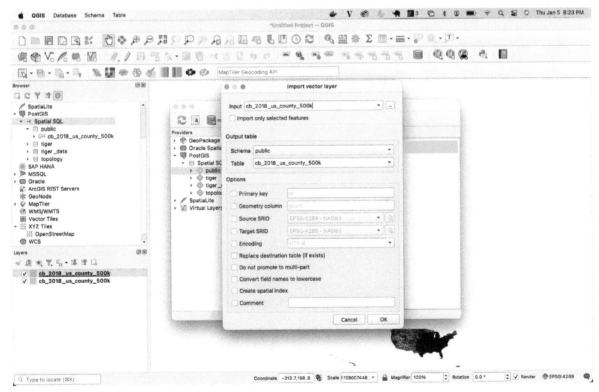

Figure 2.14: Using the QGIS PostGIS data importer

this case, we can just add the layer we already added to the map. You do not need to adjust any of the selections in options unless you want to. One that is helpful here is creating a spatial index, which we will cover later in the book.

Once complete hit **OK** and once complete you should see the following dialogue (Figure 2.15):

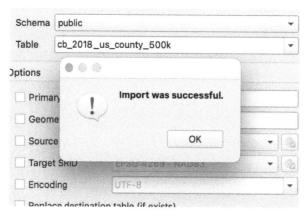

Figure 2.15: A successful import

Running your first query

Now it is time to run your first query in QGIS! In the same *DB Manager* window you can click on the icon that looks like a piece of paper with a wrench (Figure 2.16):

Figure 2.16: Running a query in QGIS

This will open a *Spatial SQL* window for you to write SQL. There are a lot of different features within this window for you to inspect tables and other features. If you click on the table you have created which should be named *cb_2018_us_county_500k* (find it by going to *PostGIS → Spatial SQL → Public → cb_2018_us_county_500k*) you will see several tabs.

- **Info**: This will tell you some general information about the table such as the geometry column and type, projection, field names and data types (which will be important going forward)
- **Table**: shows a preview of a limited set of rows of the table
- **Preview**: shows a preview of the data in a map view

Now, navigate back to the tab that says Query (Spatial SQL) where we will run our first query:

Listing 2.1: Query to select the data for Wisconsin

```
1   select
2       *
```

```
3   from
4       cb_2018_us_county_500k
5   where
6       statefp = '55'
```

Let's break down what this query is doing (note we are not using any spatial SQL, yet)

- SELECT - designates that this is a select statement which means we are going to query data from the database.
- '*' - select all columns in the table.
- FROM - this is telling PostGIS that we are about to designate a table to pull the data from.
- cb_2018_us_county_500k - the table name.
- WHERE - this tells PostGIS that we are about to add a conditional statement to filter our data.
- statefp - this column contains the two digit FIPS (Federal Information Processing System) for each state. This column's data type is a VARCHAR(2), which means it is a string with a length of 2.
- = - operator that tells PostGIS we are looking for values that match what will follow the "=" symbol.
- '55' - This is the FIPS code for Wisconsin. It is contained within single quotes since it is a string. If we did not include the quotes, this would be a number and there would be no results returned.

Go ahead and click on 'Execute'. You should see a dialog that looks like this when complete (Figure 2.17):

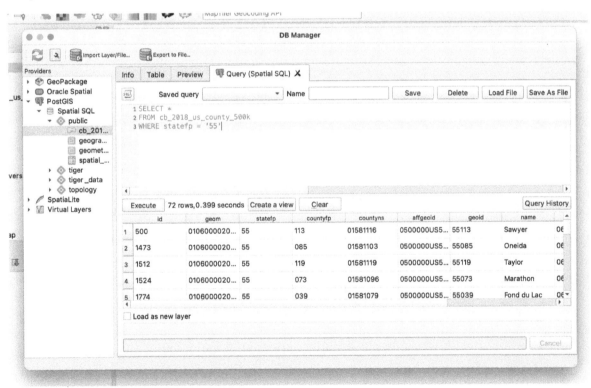

Figure 2.17: Executing a query

We can see that the query returned 72 rows, which is the correct number of counties in Wisconsin. You can see the rows that have been returned from the query as well.

To see the results on the map, we can actually load the layer on the map using the *Load as new layer* toggle at the bottom. You can leave the options the same for our purposes or change them as you see fit. Once it loads you should see the data on the map (Figure 2.18):

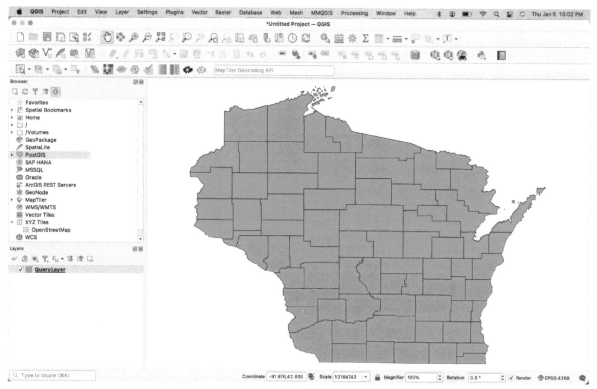

Figure 2.18: Counties in Wisconsin

Before we move forward let's write some basic spatial SQL. First let's turn our counties into centroids. To do so we will use the ST_Centorid function. This is the definition from the documentation in PostGIS:

Synopsis

```
geometry ST_Centroid(geometry g1);

geography ST_Centroid(geography g1, boolean use_spheroid=true);
```

Description

Computes a point which is the geometric center of mass of a geometry.

Let's first focus on this line:

```
geometry ST_Centroid(geometry g1);
```

We can see that it starts with the word *'GEOMETRY'*. This means that the function will return a geometry. Functions return a lot of different data types so it is important to read the docs to know what is going into a function and what is coming out. The next part of the line says **ST_Centroid(geometry g1)** which tells us that the function called ST_Centroid takes one argument, a geometry.

You can also use this with a GEOGRAPHY data type which has an additional option called use_spheroid, we will discuss the difference between GEOMETRY and GEOGRAPHY.

As we go through this book I will try to reference back to the arguments that go into a function and the return values, but I always recommend using the documentation and using it as a resource as you go forward. Being able to read documentation independently is one of the core skills that will help you become independent, not just in spatial SQL, but in any programming venture.

With that said let's write our second SQL query:

Listing 2.2: Turning polygons into centroids

```
1  select
2      id,
3      st_centroid(geom) as geom
4  from
5      cb_2018_us_county_500k
6  where
7      statefp = '55'
```

We separate the id column with a comma, then add this statement after it, which creates a new temporary column in the scope of our query. As stated above this will return a geometry, and we have given it an alias or temporary name using the AS clause, called geom. Note that in almost all cases you will need a unique identifier column in your data. If you can reuse one that you already have that is usually the fastest route but you can always create one if needed.

First, let's query our data with this new function. This should return the results in the tabular format so we can see that we have our id column and our new GEOMETRY column (Figure 2.19).

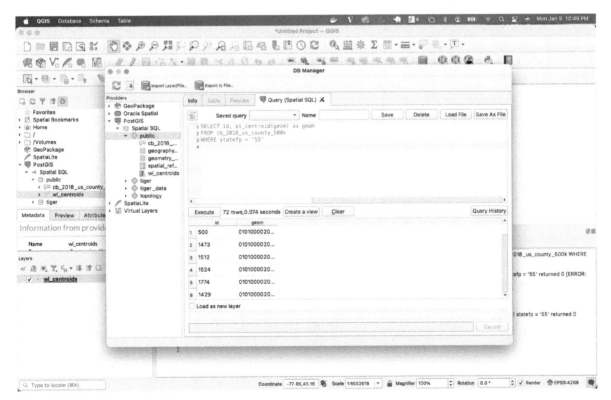

Figure 2.19: Creating centroids

The numbers you are seeing in each row of the *geom* column are the geometry represented in Well Known Binary. This is a common format used to represent geometries but just so you know that the geometry data is there. Let's go ahead and try to add this query to the map (Figure 2.20, on the following page):

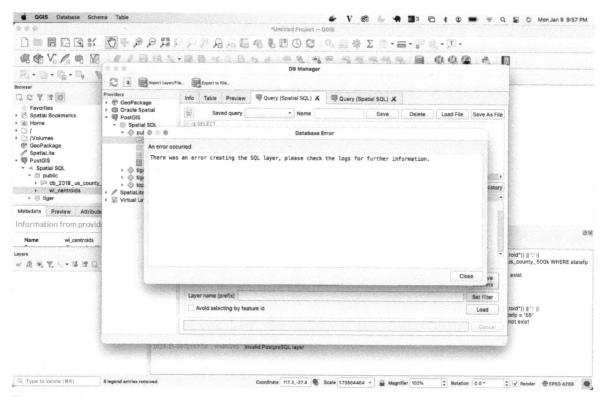

Figure 2.20: An expected error

You will likely see this same error that is showing above (note that this may vary depending on your version of QGIS). While you can visualize this data in other tools through a query only such as pgAdmin, in QGIS it requires you to create something known as a view within your database. A view is sort of a "virtual table" that you can query just like a table, but is based on the results of a query. This means that should the results of a query change, that view would change as well. You can click the button that says "Create a view" to do this (Figure 2.21) and add a new name for your view (Figure 2.22, on the facing page):

Figure 2.21: Creating a view

You could accomplish the same result by running this query:

Listing 2.3: Creating a VIEW for use in QGIS

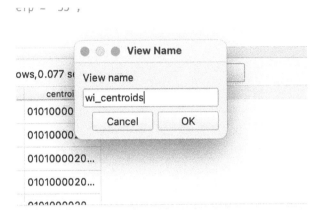

Figure 2.22: Naming a view

```
1  create
2  or replace view wi_centroids AS
3  select
4      id,
5      st_centroid(geom) as geom
6  from
7      cb_2018_us_county_500k
8  where
9      statefp = '55'
```

With that complete, we can now go to the left-hand panel in QGIS to find our newly created view which we can then add to the map (Figure 2.23) resulting in the map seen in 2.24, on the following page.

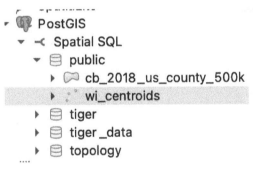

Figure 2.23: Your new view in PostGIS

You have just run your first few spatial SQL queries! While there is a lot to learn, you have cleared one of the first major hurdles by installing a database, loading data, and connecting to a tool to query and view your data.

2.5   Expert Voices: Getu Abdissa

Name: Getu Abdissa **Title**: GIS Specialist, UN Integrated Electoral Support Group (IESG)

How/where did you learn spatial SQL?

I took a course called Mastering Geospatial SQL from Kuba Konczyk (https://kubakonczyk.com/). This was the best personal investment I made as I paid it out of my pocket. It was very tricky to fall for a

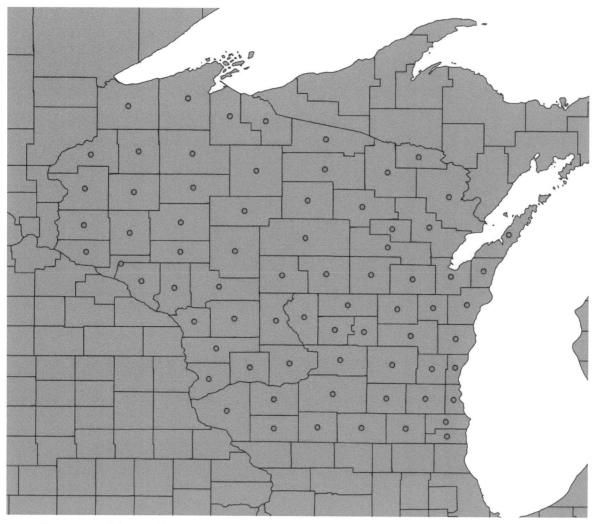

Figure 2.24: Successful centroids

training ad that claims to provide a non-existing course module and has so much value. I was glad to have taken the course as modules helped me take my GIS and SQL skills to a whole new level. I had prior knowledge of basic SQL while working as an intern at United Nations Economic Commission for Africa.

Why do you enjoy using spatial SQL?

Although I am a fan and an ardent user of Excel spreadsheets, they're often annoying. They work slowly, and when you do a lot of entries - they get stuck and it is difficult to control them in teamwork. When working for GeoMark systems I had to deal with XYZ data points having more than the allowed number of rows excel can handle. Managing it in SQL and relational databases are a much better solution. SQL is very powerful and way better than Excel. I enjoy it as It makes my job easier.

Can you share an interesting way or use case that you are using spatial SQL for today?

I have worked on an election project which was promoting a "One-person-one-vote" election in Somalia. My job as a GIS specialist includes identifying and locating suitable voter registration/polling sites in a security-constrained environment. The best use case Spatial SQL is when I used Spatial SQL to answer queries such as which sites are securable (Closer to security infrastructures), Which ones can serve internally displaced populations (IDPs) to ensure inclusiveness. Spatial SQL helped the management in making key decisions as whittling down the number of voter registration sites to optimize security resources while ensuring inclusiveness.

3. Thinking in SQL

3.1 Moving from desktop GIS to SQL

Another major hurdle in moving from a traditional GIS set up is understanding how to transition from a desktop oriented set up with files that are either on your desktop or in an enterprise GIS server. There are a few topics that you need to think about when you are moving to a database set up. This includes:

- File organization to database organization
- Opening files to importing data
- Transforming data in a tool to using views
- Re-projecting data using ST_Transform
- Sharing files or server access to database access
- Event based data to using triggers

While you may or may not use all of these tools in your work and projects, understanding each will ensure you are able to use them should the time come.

3.2 Importing data

The main difference between a database and a desktop GIS system is that with a database or data warehouse you will generally need to import that data into the database to make use of it. In a traditional GIS environment simply opening the file will load the file into the program that you are using.

While there are many file types that exist for both raster and vector data, there is not a single "file format" that exists within a database. Since we are using PostGIS for the purposes of this book, I will limit the examples to PostGIS since it would be too difficult to cover the nuances of every single technology covered in the previous section.

The best way to think about data within a PostGIS database is to conceptualize **files** as **tables**. Tables are tabular data that exist within the database, but also contain some other information about them. If you open QGIS and click on the table *cb_2018_us_county_500k* that we already created in the DB Manager dialogue you will see the information in Figure 3.1, on the next page.

You can see details about what the table type is, the owner, rows, and more. You can also see details related specifically to PostGIS such as the geometry column, geometry type, dimensions, spatial reference system or projection, and an estimated extent or bounding box of the data.

While there is not a direct correlation between tables and files, this is probably the easiest way to think about this when first migrating from a desktop to database set up.

3.3 Database organization and design

While the focus of this book is not on database design and management, there are a few concepts and tips that can help make your databases performant and organized.

Figure 3.1: Database structure in QGIS

Using schemas to manage your data and access

When you look at the view in the DB Manger in QGIS, you will see that there is a tab called *public* (Figure 3.2). This is known as the schema that exists within the database we are using, which was created in the Docker command when we created our database.

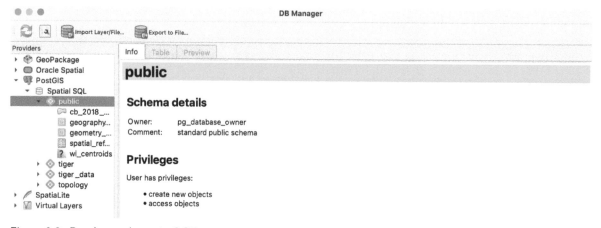

Figure 3.2: Database schema in QGIS

A schema stores lots of information such as triggers, sequences, tables, views, functions, stored procedures, data types, and more. See Figure 3.3, on the next page for the comparable view of our *public* schema in pgAdmin.

What is important for the scope of this book is using schemas effectively to save and separate data. While this may not be the best example, you can use schemas similarly to how you might use folders in a traditional GIS system. Each schema can hold data, grant access to certain users for specific operations, and be managed as needed. In this sense, schemas can provide an effective way to manage and organize your data, especially coming from a desktop system.

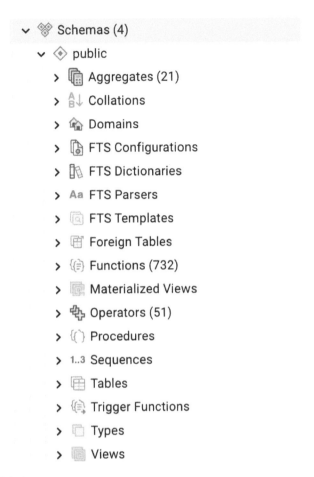

Figure 3.3: Schemas in pgAdmin

Managing your geometries

The other key point is using the GEOMETRY or GEOGRAPHY data in your tables effectively within a database. Geometries and geographies are likely to be the largest data types within your tables. Let's take a look at an example of the data in our database.

Go ahead and run this query in QGIS:

Listing 3.1: Query to find the size of our geometry

```
1    select
2      name,
3
4      -- Use the length() function to find the number of letters, or length of the name
5      length(name),
6
7      -- Use the pg_column_size() function to find the size of the column in bytes
8      pg_column_size(name),
9
10     -- Here we are doing a few things
11     -- 1. Getting the size of the geom column in bytes using ST_MemSize()
12     -- 2. Casting the result of ST_MemSize() to a numeric value since
13     --    ST_MemSize() to format it as a number implicitly
14     -- 3. Use pg_size_pretty() to format the bytes in human readable sizes like kb or mb
15     pg_size_pretty(st_memsize(geom) :: numeric)
```

```
16   from
17     cb_2018_us_county_500k
18
19     -- Using order by to order the results of ST_MemSize()
20     -- from largest to smallest, or descending using desc
21   order by
22     st_memsize(geom) desc
```

You will notice that there are now comments in the query which can be identified since they start with "--".

These comments won't affect the query and are there to better annotate what is happening in the query itself. You should see the data return with results that look like Figure 3.4.

	name	length	pg_column_size	pg_size_pretty
1	Aleutians West	14	15	221 kB
2	Valdez-...	14	15	202 kB
3	Aleutians East	14	15	174 kB
4	Prince of ...	21	22	173 kB
5	Kodiak Island	13	14	144 kB
6	Kenai ...	15	16	142 kB
7	Hoonah-...	13	14	126 kB
8	North Slope	11	12	97 kB
9	Nome	4	5	86 kB

Figure 3.4: Query results in QGIS

Let's take a look at the first three columns:

- **Name**: name of the county
- **Length**: total number of characters in the string
- **pg_column_size**: size in bytes of the column "name"

You will see that the value in *pg_column_size* is always the length + 1. And this matches with the PostgreSQL documentation:

"The storage requirement for a short string (up to 126 bytes) is 1 byte plus the actual string, which includes the space padding in the case of character."[46]

Note that longer strings will have a base of 4 bytes but for this data it will not exceed 126 bytes.

Now, let's take a look at the bytes storage required for the GEOMETRY data type, located in the documentation at the link in the footnotes and shown in Figure 3.5, on the next page.[47]

So we can see that the number of bytes in a polygon data type can be calculated by starting with a 40 byte base, and then 16 bytes for every point. We can try and confirm this with the following query:

Listing 3.2: Calculating the number of points in our polygons

```
1   select
2     name,
3
4     -- Calculate the total number of points in the geometry using ST_NPoints()
```

---

[46]https://www.postgresql.org/docs/current/datatype-character.html

[47]https://www.postgresql.org/docs/current/datatype-geometric.html

Table 8.20. Geometric Types

Name	Storage Size	Description	Representation
`point`	16 bytes	Point on a plane	(x,y)
`line`	32 bytes	Infinite line	{A,B,C}
`lseg`	32 bytes	Finite line segment	((x1,y1),(x2,y2))
`box`	32 bytes	Rectangular box	((x1,y1),(x2,y2))
`path`	16+16n bytes	Closed path (similar to polygon)	((x1,y1),...)
`path`	16+16n bytes	Open path	[(x1,y1),...]
`polygon`	40+16n bytes	Polygon (similar to closed path)	((x1,y1),...)
`circle`	24 bytes	Circle	<(x,y),r> (center point and radius)

Figure 3.5: Data type sizes from the PostgreSQL documentation

```
5    st_npoints(geom) as n_points,
6
7    -- Calculate the size of the geometry using ST_MemSize()
8    st_memsize(geom) as size_bytes,
9
10   -- Using the formula we saw, calculate the size of the geometry as: 40 + ( no. of points * 16)
11   40 + (16 * st_npoints(geom)) as calculated_size
12 from
13   cb_2018_us_county_500k
14 order by
15   st_memsize(geom) desc
```

And results are shown in Figure 3.6, on the following page.

As you can see our calculation is not correct. This is because our "polygons" are actually *MultiPolygons*, with multiple polygons within them. We can add two functions to our query to try and recalculate this for each polygon.

Listing 3.3: This time accounting for multi-polygons

```
1  select
2    name,
3
4    -- Use ST_GeometryType to see our geometry type
5    st_geometrytype(geom) as geom_type,
6    st_memsize(geom) as size_bytes,
7
8    -- Use ST_NumGeometries to see our geometry type
9    st_numgeometries(geom) as num_geoms,
10
11   -- Try and calculate using the formula (no. of geometries * 40) + (no. of points * 16)
12   (st_numgeometries(geom) * 40) + (16 * st_npoints(geom)) as calculated_size
13 from
14   cb_2018_us_county_500k
15 order by
```

	name	n_points	size_bytes	calculated_size
1	Aleutians West	14045	225872	224760
2	Valdez-...	12840	206576	205480
3	Aleutians East	11050	177936	176840
4	Prince of ...	11023	177408	176408
5	Kodiak Island	9144	147008	146344
6	Kenai ...	9045	145376	144760
7	Hoonah-...	7990	128624	127880
8	North Slope	6183	99424	98968
9	Nome	5495	88128	87960

Execute   3233 rows, 0.699 seconds   Create a view   Clear

☐ Load as new layer

Figure 3.6: Number of points in each polygon

```
16    st_memsize(geom) desc
```

And Figure our 3.7 shows the results:

Execute   3233 rows, 0.939 seconds   Create a view   Clear   Query History

	name	geom_type	size_bytes	num_geoms	calculated_size
1	Aleutians West	ST_MultiPoly...	225872	70	227520
2	Valdez-...	ST_MultiPoly...	206576	69	208200
3	Aleutians East	ST_MultiPoly...	177936	69	179560
4	Prince of ...	ST_MultiPoly...	177408	63	178888
5	Kodiak Island	ST_MultiPoly...	147008	42	147984
6	Kenai ...	ST_MultiPoly...	145376	39	146280
7	Hoonah-...	ST_MultiPoly...	128624	47	129720
8	North Slope	ST_MultiPoly...	99424	29	100088
9	Nome	ST_MultiPoly...	88128	11	88360

☐ Load as new layer

Cancel

Figure 3.7: Accounting for multi-polygons

This time our results are too high! So to see why this is the case, you need to know what the base bytes that are being used are actually storing. I pulled this information from a blog post from Dan Baston[48].

---

[48]http://www.danbaston.com/posts/2016/11/28/what-is-the-maximum-size-of-a-postgis-geometry.html

- 4 bytes to tell Postgres how large the PostGIS object is
- 4 bytes to store the SRID and various flags
- 4 bytes to store the geometry type (Point)
- 4 bytes to tell us how many points are in our geometry
- 16 bytes for the coordinates themselves

So how do we calculate the correct value for a multi-polygon?

- First as we can see above we need 32 base bytes for the entire polygon
    - In my understanding you still need the extra 16 bytes for the multi-polygon to contain the individual polygons
- Since we know the base data such as the SRID and number of points, we only now need to store the 16 base bytes for each geometry in the multi polygon
- Finally, we still need 16 bytes for each point as well

So one more time:

Listing 3.4: The final query

```
1  select
2    name,
3    st_geometrytype(geom) as geom_type,
4    st_memsize(geom) as size_bytes,
5    st_numgeometries(geom) as num_geoms,
6
7    -- Try and calculate using the formula 32 + ((no. of geometries * 16) + (no. of points * 16))
8
9    32 + (
10     (st_numgeometries(geom) * 16) + (16 * st_npoints(geom))
11   ) as calculated_size
12 from
13   cb_2018_us_county_500k
14 order by
15   st_memsize(geom) desc
```

And we did it! See Figure 3.8.

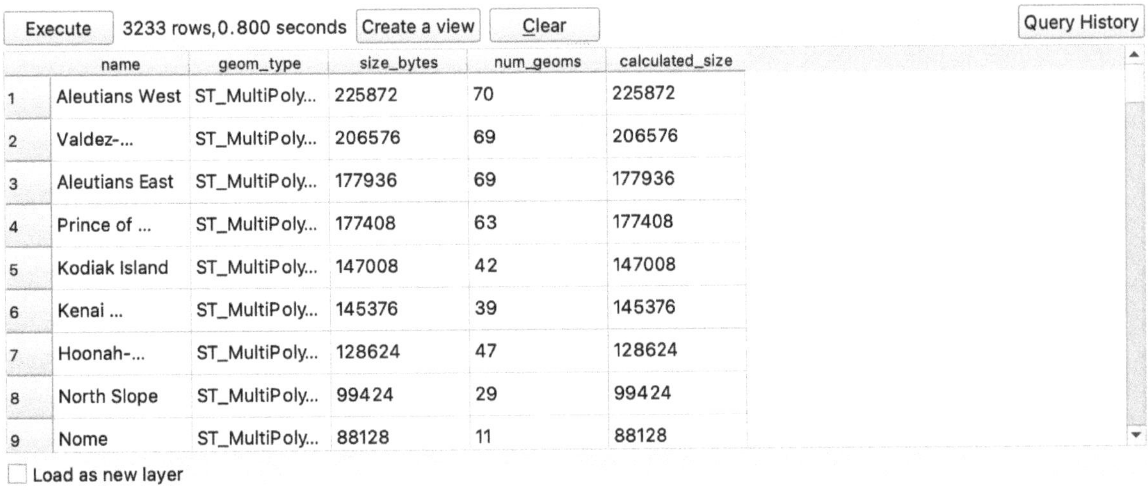

	name	geom_type	size_bytes	num_geoms	calculated_size
1	Aleutians West	ST_MultiPoly...	225872	70	225872
2	Valdez-...	ST_MultiPoly...	206576	69	206576
3	Aleutians East	ST_MultiPoly...	177936	69	177936
4	Prince of ...	ST_MultiPoly...	177408	63	177408
5	Kodiak Island	ST_MultiPoly...	147008	42	147008
6	Kenai ...	ST_MultiPoly...	145376	39	145376
7	Hoonah-...	ST_MultiPoly...	128624	47	128624
8	North Slope	ST_MultiPoly...	99424	29	99424
9	Nome	ST_MultiPoly...	88128	11	88128

Execute   3233 rows, 0.800 seconds   Create a view   Clear   Query History

Load as new layer

Figure 3.8: Final calculation

Why did we spend all this time looking at the data size and number of points in each geometry? Two reasons:

1. Geometries are large, in terms of data storage

2. The more points a geometry has, the more calculations a function has to make on the geometry

As it relates to database organization, my recommendation is to separate your geometries from your tabular data into two separate tables when necessary. While we have not covered the topic of joins yet, PostgreSQL is a great tool for performing joins between two tables, and since we just learned that our geometries are quite large, this will mean that the fewer geometries that are stored, the less space they will take up. Let's walk through two scenarios why you may want to do this.

Scenario 1: Customer lists and postal codes

Imagine that you have two tables, one with postal code geometries and the other with a list of customers. Each row of your customer data contains the following columns:

- First name
- Last name
- Address
- City
- State/Province
- Postal Code
- Customer Joined Date
- Customer ID

And you have a table with geometries of postal codes that include the postal code geometry and the postal code itself. You can easily join these two tables to perform queries as needed such as:

Listing 3.5: Joining tables without a geometry

```
1   select
2       pc.geom,
3       pc.postal_code,
4       count(customers.customer_id)
5   from
6       postal_codes pc
7       join customers using (postal_code)
8   group by
9       pc.postal_code
```

This provides you flexibility to perform any number of analytical queries and only joining to the geometries when you need. You can also update the geometries table should they change without impacting your customers list or any other data that could potentially be impacted.

Scenario 2: Changing or Vintage Data

Imagine you are working for a municipality, and you use two datasets on a regular basis: land/property records and road centerlines. Both datasets have geometric data that is updated yearly or sooner depending on changes to the records, and other tabular data associated with the geometries.

As we saw in the first scenario, you can easily update your tabular data with changes to road names or property owners without impacting the geometry data in your other tables. With that said we also know that our geometries may change on a regular basis with new roads being added or properties being built or even combined. The first advantage is that you can easily update the geometries table by adding and removing, or even modifying the geometry values as needed with the new geometries that are being added to the database.

The other key value is using a common table naming convention to store your data vintages in. This means that you can basically create a table and take a snapshot of your data to be able to look at specific time periods, or a vintage for everything that has changed. You could even do this to store a vintage with just the change only if you wanted to do so. A sample naming schema could look like this:

- **street_centerlines_012023_032023**
- **property_geoms_2023_1**

In our first example, our table has two dates with the MMYYYY formatting. This represents the months the data falls between, in this case January 1, 2023 and March 31, 2023. Our second example has the year, 2023, and the number 1, which stands for the version number for that year.

While you could look for distinct values between two tables, you can easily do so by also adding a date to the geometry to show when it has been updated since we know that other data types in PostgreSQL are smaller than geometries. This would allow you to write queries like this:

Listing 3.6: Selecting by date

```
1  select
2      *
3  from
4      street_centerlines_current
5  where
6      date_added between '01-01-2022'
7      and '06-30-2022'
```

This would return all the roads that have been added between January 2022 and June 2022.

This applies to some use cases but not all, and in the end you need to decide how you want to manage your data, but in cases where data is changing often, or you have non-geospatial data you need to join to a geospatial component, this practice has proven helpful for organizing and separating your data.

3.4 Using PostGIS indexes

This is a topic we will cover later in this book, but indexing in PostGIS is another method that can improve performance by making it easier for the database to better identify a specific feature that it is looking for, especially in the context of spatial relationship queries. It is fairly simple to add an index to your data, but this is another topic to understand when and how to apply it. In short I have two rules for indexing:

- If you are going to use the table to perform spatial relationship analysis such as intersections, overlaps, nearest, etc., use an index
- If you are going to query the data within a bounding box on a regular basis, use an index

There are a few different index options, for example, R-Tree shown in Figure 3.9, on the next page, but we will share some rules of thumb when to use which one later in the book.[49]

Automatic transformations

One great tool in PostgreSQL that can provide some really great functionality, especially for regularly updated data, are triggers. A trigger is basically a tool that, upon a set of conditions being met, runs some code to complete a process. Imagine that you have a table that is being updated with data collected from the field. You can create a trigger that will automatically take some data, say a latitude and longitude, and turn that into a geometry using PostGIS functions to do so. You can create triggers

---

[49]https://www.crunchydata.com/blog/the-many-spatial-indexes-of-postgis

R-tree Hierarchy

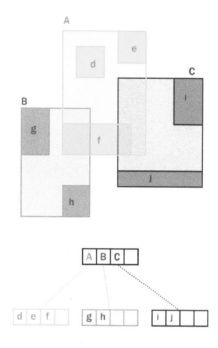

Figure 3.9: R-tree indexing visualized from PostGIS Workshops (postgis.net) - Introduction to PostGIS - 15. Spatial Indexing

for any number of operations in your database, and the functions that are run can be as simple or as complex as you desire.

I recommend that you think of using triggers for annotating your data or adding new columns to your data as you need automatically, instead of creating new columns every time. You can automate a lot of your data annotation and other processes that were more manual in a desktop environment by using SQL.

Exporting data

Just as data has to go into a database, it has to come back out as files for others to download and use as needed. Unless you are providing database access to many users, you will need to export your data to share with those who do not have access to your database.

There are a few different ways to do this but once you have added a layer to your map in QGIS you can right-click on that layer to export the data as the file type of your choice. Similarly, you can use the *ogr2ogr* tools in the Geospatial Data Abstraction Library, or GDAL, to export your data as the format of your choice.

The advantage over a desktop GIS system is that you can simply export the results of a query, rather than creating a new table. Once you have run a query you can just provide that query and export the results.

3.5 Projections

As with all geospatial data, projections are critical to managing and using your geospatial data. While projections are embedded in most geospatial files you might work with in a traditional GIS set up, projections can be used a few different ways in PostGIS:

- Inherited when the data is ingested
- Assigned by the user for geometries created in the database
- Transformed to a new projection using ST_Transform

Each of these will require you to use a spatial reference ID, or SRID with your data. All your spatial references that are installed by default are stored in a table in PostGIS named *spatial_ref_sys*. We can query this table to see specific values:

```
select * from spatial_ref_sys where srid = '4326'
```

Which will return this information (Figure 3.10).

srid [PK] integer	auth_name character varying (256)	auth_srid integer	srtext character varying (2048)
1	4326	EPSG	4326	GEOGCS["WGS 84",DATUM["WGS_1984",SPHEROID["WGS 84",6378137,298.257223563,AUTHORITY["EPSG","7030"]],AUTHORITY["EPSG","6326"]],PRI

Figure 3.10: Spatial reference data in PostGIS

You can also add in projections using the epsg.io website[50]. You can enter the projection you want to add in and then use the code provided to add that projection to PostGIS to your database. Let's imagine we want to add in a new projection for Hennepin County, Minnesota, or EPSG 104726.

You can go to epsg.io/104726[51] to find the projection and other details, as in Figure 3.11, on the next page.

If you scroll down you can then find this section (Figure 3.12, on the following page) which has details of the projection for various languages.

You can then copy the PostGIS code, which is all SQL, to add that projection to your PostGIS database:

Listing 3.7: Add a new projection to PostGIS

```
1   insert into
2       spatial_ref_sys (srid, auth_name, auth_srid, proj4text, srtext)
3   values
4       (
5           104726,
6           'ESRI',
7           104726,
8           '+proj=longlat +a=6378418.941 +rf=298.257222100883 +no_defs +type=crs',
9           'GEOGCS["GCS_NAD_1983_HARN_Adj_MN_Hennepin",DATUM["D_NAD_1983_HARN_Adj_MN_Hennepin",
10          SPHEROID["S_GRS_1980_Adj_MN_Hennepin",6378418.941,298.257222100883,AUTHORITY["ESRI","107726"]],
11          AUTHORITY["ESRI","106726"]],PRIMEM["Greenwich",0,AUTHORITY["EPSG","8901"]],
12          UNIT["degree",0.0174532925199433,AUTHORITY["EPSG","9122"]],AUTHORITY["ESRI","104726"]]'
13      );
```

If you try to run this function, you will see that it is already in your database! You can run this query to create a new view from this data then load it in QGIS:

---

[50] https://epsg.io/

[51] https://epsg.io/104726

ESRI:104726

NAD 1983 HARN Adj. Minnesota Hennepin

Attributes

Covered area powered by MapTiler

Data source: ESRI

Information source: ESRI

Area of use: USA - Minnesota

Description: NAD 1983 HARN Adj. Minnesota Hennepin

Center coordinates
-93.35 46.44

WGS84 bounds:
-97.22 43.49
-89.49 49.38

USA - Minnesota

Figure 3.11: Projection info on epsg.io

Export

OGC WKT

OGC WKT 2

ESRI WKT

PROJ.4

Proj4js

JSON

GeoServer

MapServer

Mapnik

PostGIS   ▸

Definition: SQL (PostGIS)

Open   Copy URL   Copy Text   Download

INSERT into spatial_ref_sys (srid, auth_name, auth_srid, proj4text, srtext) values (104726, 'ESRI', 104726, '+pro

Figure 3.12: 02-setting-up-image__29.png

Listing 3.8: Creating a view with our new projection

```
1  create view mn_104726 as
2  select
3    id,
4    st_transform(geom, 104726)
5  from
6    cb_2018_us_county_500k
7  where
8    statefp = '27'
```

One thing to note is that almost all web based mapping services use the projection EPSG 3857 or WGS84/Pseudo-mercator and for analytical purposes many data warehouses are limited to EPSG 4326 or WGS 84.

Tables and views

Finally, understanding the difference between tables, views, and materialized views are key.

- Tables are stored to the disk in the database, meaning the data is stored within the database.
- Views are views of a table, represented with a query. You can create a complex query and create a view from that with a new name. When you query that view, you are basically querying the results of that query.
- Materialized views are sort of in between. They do the same thing as a view, but store the results in a cache for faster performance, so the results are temporarily written to disk in a cache, or temporary storage.

I recommend using views for slices of data that you want to query or share, and materialized views for the same but for data that will be frequently queried or accessed. This can save you some time and help performance in certain cases. This is a far different concept compared to a desktop GIS infrastructure. The closest thing that I can imagine would be a map file from a desktop service that references a data file (or table) and has some filters or transformations applied to it (the view).

3.6   Thinking in SQL

The other area that can be a big hurdle for many is translating your knowledge of working in a point-and-click GIS environment and taking that thinking to independently structure a SQL query. This was a major leap for me when I was learning SQL. Previously I thought about each step individually: first perform a join to other data, then perform some spatial operation, then do a filter, etc. On top of that, there are a few different areas in SQL that can cause you to run very large or complex queries that can cause things to stall out.

Knowing a few general concepts and some tips that I have used in the past will help set you up for success. These tips are applicable for anyone using spatial SQL and even SQL in general. In this section we will cover a few concepts that will help you understand how a SQL query works under the hood, and how to take a look at where there may be bottlenecks or issues in your query using pgAdmin. We will also talk about using pseudo-code to script out what you want to accomplish in your SQL query and how to translate that into a query that you will write. Finally, we will talk about a few specific things that can cause roadblocks with geospatial data in SQL.

SQL chain of operations

To better understand how to write a SQL query it is important to understand what happens after you run your query and how, in this case PostGIS, handles your query once you send it off for execution.

The SQL order of operations is as follows:

1. `FROM` and `JOIN`s

2. `WHERE`

3. `GROUP BY`

4. `HAVING`

5. `SELECT`

6. `ORDER BY`

7. `LIMIT/OFFSET`

You can basically group these into three stages:

1. **Row Filtering**: This is where the query will figure out what rows to include or exclude based on parameters in your query. This includes `FROM / JOIN`, `WHERE`, `GROUP BY`, `HAVING`.

2. **Column Filtering**: This stage is where the query will pick which columns of data it needs to return and is limited to `SELECT`.

3. **Row Filtering (Part 2)**: This last phase is where the query will shuffle the rows to decide what to keep or not keep. This includes `ORDER BY` and `LIMIT`.

You are likely wondering why you need to know these different steps and how this can apply to how you think about structuring your queries. Here is a simple example that can help you imagine why this matters.

Imagine that we have two tables of data (we will be using this data and importing it in the next chapter):

- A table of 311 Call Requests in New York City from 2021
- A table of postal codes (known as ZIP Codes in the United States) containing the postal code geometry for New York City
- Each table contains a 5 digit value for the postal code (i.e. 10001)

Our job is to create a map of postal codes containing all the incidents where the "complaint_type" is equal to "Illegal Parking". I will share the queries here which we will review in detail later, but the idea is to show how different approaches to writing a query can impact query time and performance.

First, let's install and use pgAdmin so we can run some ad-hoc queries and use the built-in tools to see the performance plans of the query. First, go to pgadmin.org/download/[52] and download the appropriate version for your computer. Once you have it installed, you can navigate to Object → Register → Server. You should see this window pop up where you can enter the same details as we did when establishing the PostGIS connection in QGIS, see Figures 3.13, on the next page and 3.14, on the facing page.

You will only need to enter details into the *General* and *Connection* tabs. Once you add your connection, you will see a lot more information about your database. Since pgAdmin, as the name implies, can be used for any number of administrative tasks, it shows every aspect of the database that is available. For

---

[52]https://www.pgadmin.org/download/

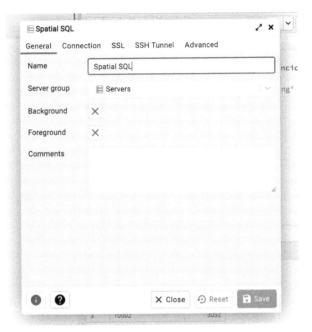

Figure 3.13: Adding a connection in pgAdmin

Figure 3.14: Connection details in pgAdmin

our purposes we will primarily use the information in our database which can be found by navigating to (assuming you used the same names as we have in the book so far):

Spatial SQL → **Databases** → **geo** → **Schemas** → **Public**

Once there you can find two sections, *Tables* and *Views* where your tables and views will be listed respectively (Figure 3.15).

Figure 3.15: Schema structure in pgAdmin

While we have not imported this data yet, we will be importing this data in the next chapter. This query will use several elements we have not yet covered so the query itself will look confusing and I will only annotate it with the high level elements for this exercise.

First, let's join the two tables in one single query:

Listing 3.9: Aggregate by Zip Code

```
1   -- First we select your data from the ZIP codes table
2   -- and aggregate or count the total number of records
3   -- from the NYC 311 data
4   select
5     zips.zipcode,
6     zips.geom,
7     count(nyc_311.*) as count
8
9   -- Then we join the tables on a common ID, in this case the ZIP code
10  from
11    nyc_zips zips
12    join nyc_311 on nyc_311.incident_zip = zips.zipcode
13
14  -- Then we filter using WHERE to the right complaint type
15  -- and group the results by the ZIP code and geometry
```

```
16   where
17     nyc_311.complaint_type = 'Illegal Parking'
18   group by
19     zips.zipcode,
20     zips.geom
```

This query took just under 40 seconds for me to run (I also applied an index to the complaint type column which makes it a bit faster). First, there are a few things we can fix.

3.7   Optimizing our queries and other tips

Since we know that the query will look for the rows to include first using SELECT/JOIN, GROUP BY, WHERE, and HAVING (this one is not in our query) we know that we want to optimize these queries to be as efficient as possible. To see how the query is executing we can actually see this in pgAdmin. Instead of using the **"Play"** button to run our query we can press the small button that looks like a bar chart to run an EXPLAIN ANALYZE query on our query. This basically shows us how the query is executing (Figure 3.16).

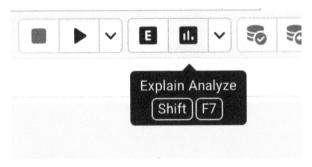

Figure 3.16: Explain analyze in pgAdmin

This will return a graphical view of our query. Now, I don't expect you fully understand the EXPLAIN ANALYZE results but we will refer to them a few times during the course of the book so we can take a look at the query to understand some high level concepts about query improvements. Once you learn a few key concepts, you should be able to optimize most of your queries, and using it, find any major bottlenecks in your code.

With that said let's take a look at the results of our EXPLAIN ANALYZE call, in Figure 3.17.

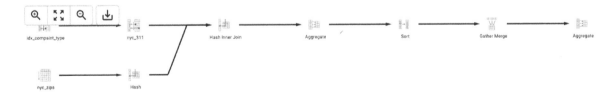

Figure 3.17: Query plan visualized

What you can see here is a visual representation of how our query is being run. Basically the steps are:

1. Our two tables are scanned

2. Then they are joined

3. Our data is aggregated and grouped in the last stages

This is where we can make a few optimizations to improve our query. First, we are counting all the columns in each row in our nyc_311 table which is not necessary. We can count across one column, in this case the "unique id" column. Our new query will look like this"

Listing 3.10: Aggregate by Zip Code

```
 1  select
 2      zips.zipcode,
 3      zips.geom,
 4      count(nyc_311.id) as count
 5  from
 6      nyc_zips zips
 7      join nyc_311 on nyc_311.incident_zip = zips.zipcode
 8  where
 9      nyc_311.complaint_type = 'Illegal Parking'
10  group by
11      zips.zipcode,
12      zips.geom
```

A bit of an improvement, down to 30 seconds total! Next is one major lesson for writing your queries. One strategy is that you should think of your queries as a funnel. You want to get rid of as much data as you can in earlier stages of your query. To do this we can use a Common Table Expression or CTE that essentially acts as a temporary table in the scope of the query.

Since our nyc_311 table has the most records (over 3.2 million roads), let's get rid of as many of those as we can using a CTE:

Listing 3.11: Using a CTE

```
 1  -- In this CTE, which has an alias of "a",
 2  -- we pull the data we need from the nyc_311 data
 3  -- and filter to just the results that match "Illegal Parking"
 4  with a as (
 5    select
 6      id,
 7      incident_zip as zipcode
 8    from
 9      nyc_311
10    where
11      nyc_311.complaint_type = 'Illegal Parking'
12  )
13
14  -- We then join the data from our "temporary table" a to the zipcode data
15  select
16    zips.zipcode,
17    zips.geom,
18    count(a.id) as count
19  from
20    nyc_zips zips
21    join a using (zipcode)
22  group by
23    zips.zipcode,
24    zips.geom
```

This query takes about 39 seconds to run, an increase in time. What did we do wrong? When we check out our analyzed query we can see that we didn't really modify the query execution that much at all (Figure 3.18, on the facing page).

We still have to scan all the 3+ million rows and join to the roughly 100k results that are returned

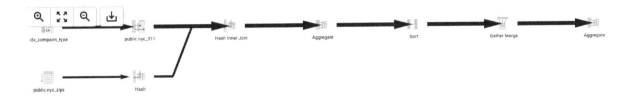

Figure 3.18: Query plan visualized

from the CTE. Let's move more work into the CTE, namely the aggregation of the data using the COUNT function.

Listing 3.12: Moving the aggregation into the CTE

```
1   -- Now we have our entire aggregation in the CTE
2   with a as (
3       select
4           count("unique key") as total,
5           "incident zip" as zipcode
6       from
7           nyc_311
8       where
9           nyc_311."complaint type" = 'Illegal Parking'
10      group by
11          zipcode
12  )
13  select
14      zips.zipcode,
15      zips.geom,
16      a.total
17  from
18      nyc_zips zips
19      join a using (zipcode)
```

Now our query only takes about 21 seconds to complete. When we look at the plan in another tool, called Dalibo, we can see (in Figures 3.19, on the next page and 3.20, on the following page) that the majority of our query cost is tied up in the part of the query that finds all the rows that match the "Illegal Parking" category.[53]

The only things we might be able to do are to create a view of our data and query that view, try some different indexing methods, or cluster our table to group the categories together. Most of these things fall in the category of database administration which is out of the scope of this book. Figure 3.21, on page 71 shows the final results of that query.

What we can apply here is our first lesson about structuring our queries. The more operations that limit the amount of data we are using, much like a funnel, will improve our query performance. Try as much as you can to look at the amount of data you are querying to the first steps in your query or limit to only what you need to get a performance improvement.

The other concepts I like to use when trying to improve or test a query are:

- Use the query EXPLAIN ANALYZE to see where there are roadblocks and if they are persisting throughout the query. pgAdmin has great built in tools but some of the web viewers are also good to help here too. Basically you should be looking out for issues where lots of data is making

---
[53]https://explain.dalibo.com/

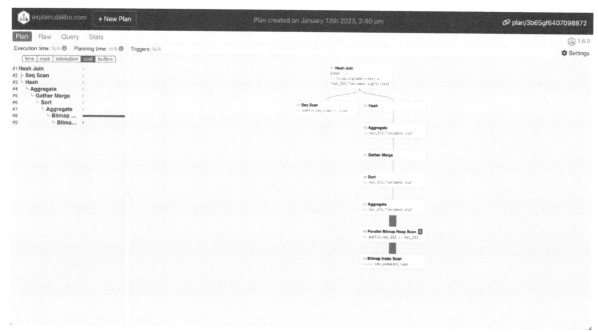

Figure 3.19: Web-based query plan visualized on explain.dalibo.com

Figure 3.20: High cost query step

it down to the later steps of the query.

- Limit the number of columns you need. Try to only SELECT the columns you need and use *
  sparingly. If you do need all the columns, especially in the case of aggregations like our example
  here, only keep the IDs and other columns you need and then join your other columns in a final
  step.
- To test your queries use LIMIT statements to only retrieve some rows of data. If you are doing an
  aggregation like our example here, use the LIMIT in the earlier stages of the query.

We will use these concepts throughout the book, so we will see the in practice later on.

The final tip is related to the GEOMETRY or GEOGRAPHY. As we mentioned earlier moving your geometry
data into its own table is a good idea, but another thing to be aware of is using the GROUP BY statement
with geometries. We did this in the last query and overall this is a bit of a rule breaking. While I did
know that there was only one geometry for zip code, it did add some time to our query. With that said,
if you have a table with multiple geometries that may appear equal, they may in fact not be.

Take a look at Figure 3.22, on the facing page.

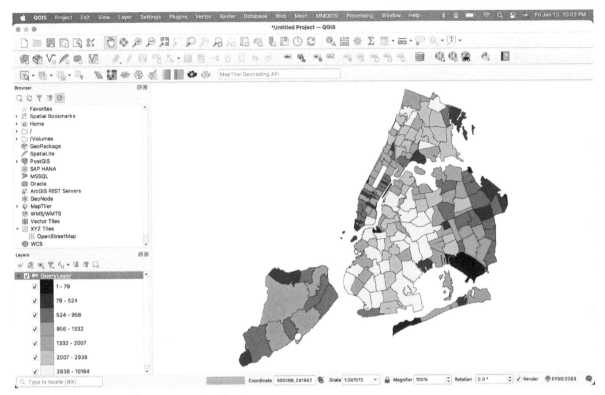

Figure 3.21: Point in polygon count visualized

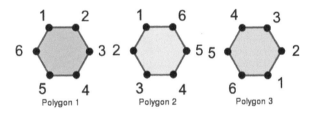

Figure 3.22: The problem with grouping by geometry

This is pulled from a PostGIS workshop on the PostGIS website[54]. What appear to be equal polygons in the image are actually not since the ordering of the points is different in each polygon. Equality is a strict concept in any programming language and spatial SQL is no different. You can read more about the details of this in the workshop link, but for our purposes making sure that you are avoiding grouping by a GEOMETRY is a general good practice. I would also reference this post by Simon Wrigley that has more details on the topic too[55].

3.8   Using pseudo-code and "rubber ducking"

As we go through the course of the book we will use a few challenges that will help to build your skills to become independent in your ability to write spatial SQL. This will take time and practice, but one skill that I have used is using pseudo-code, or the process of writing the code you want to build using human-readable text, and rubber ducking, the process of talking out loud to talk through your code.

---

[54]https://postgis.net/workshops/postgis-intro/equality.html

[55]https://loc8.cc/sql/linkedin-simon-wrigley

The name comes from an excerpt in the book *The Pragmatic Programmer* where a programmer carried around a rubber duck to talk to out loud to try and work through a tough coding problem.

While these strategies may seem a bit strange, using these in early stages to think through the queries you want to write will help you become self proficient in the long run. In this section I'll share some examples of how to do this, but I will also reference back to these concepts in the book as well.

Pseudo-coding

Pseudo-code is essentially the process of writing out how you want an application, function, or in our case query to run. There are no hard and fast rules on how to write pseudo-code and it can be as structured or unstructured as you like. Of all the tutorials I took a look at to reference for this book, strangely enough the one from WikiHow provided the best walkthrough on how I use pseudo-code[56].

My recommended process is three steps:

1. Write down in plain wording the query you want to create

2. Break that sentence apart into pieces and try and order it based on what you know about query structure and the chain of operations

3. Write in the relevant code and convert the pseudo-code to comments

Let's walk through an example.

NYC 311 calls in a specific date range

Let's consider the following pseudo-code statement as step 1 of our process:

"Find all the 311 calls in July that had the complaint of fireworks"

Next, lets structure that as a query. We know a few things:

- We need to query our table nyc_311
- We need to find all the calls in the month of July
- We need to find all the incidents that have fireworks

First let's set up our basic query. We know that we need to filter the data, which requires a WHERE clause, and we have two conditions which will need to use the operator AND:

- SELECT all columns
- from the dataset nyc_311
- WHERE the created date is in the month of July
- AND complaint type is fireworks

You can see I added in the SQL keywords where I could and then used the relevant column names from the data. From here we are left with one challenge: how to find all the dates that are in July. To do this using the date column, we want to identify a function that can help us extract the month from the date. There are two different functions to do this but in this example we will use the DATE_PART function to accomplish what we need. The function takes two arguments: the element you want to extract which can be anything from the century of the date to the timezone, but in our case the month,

---

[56]https://www.wikihow.com/Write-Pseudocode

and the column containing the data[57]. We know that the return value will be the number representing the month, in this case 7

Let's edit our pseudo-code to construct our query:

SELECT all columns

```
select *
```

from the dataset nyc_311

```
from nyc_311
```

WHERE the created_date is in the month of July

```
where DATE_PART('month', created_date) = 7
```

AND "compliant type" is fireworks

```
and "complaint type" = 'Illegal Fireworks'
```

And the result in QGIS is shown in Figure 3.23, on the next page.

This represents a relatively simple example of what we want to accomplish. Of course this represents a perfect world with perfect data, which I am sure you all know is never the case. Let's walk through a real example we will address in the next chapter.

Rubber ducking

Rubber ducking is a way to work through a problem by verbally talking it out. There are plenty of occasions where I have used this process and actually found an answer. More times that I can count, I have tried to Google my way through a problem, trying out any number of random solutions I have found online, only to find that actually talking a problem through has given me much better results. Now let's review the query from our last step:

Listing 3.13: This query will produce an error

```
1   select
2       *
3   from
4       nyc_311
5   where
6       DATE_PART('month', "created date") = 7
7       and "complaint type" = 'Illegal Fireworks'
```

Now what actually happened is that I got an error on my query that told me that the function DATE_PART did not match the arguments I was giving it with the following hint:

HINT: No function matches the given name and argument types. You might need to add explicit type casts.

---

[57] https://loc8.cc/sql/postgresqltutorial-date

Figure 3.23: Illegal fireworks complaints

So, what could be the issue? Take a minute to think about it. I will write out my rubber ducking in the next paragraph to show a real example:

───────────────────

We know that the DATE_TYPE function takes two arguments: first is the date part you want to extract, in this case 'month'. The second is a date or timestamp. Is there an issue with the date created field?

And in fact there is an issue with that field as when we imported our data it came in as a character field not an actual date. When we import this data into our database in the next chapter we will handle this issue, but for now we can simply cast, or transform our data on the fly as so:

Listing 3.14: Casting our data

```
1   select
2       *
3   from
4       nyc_311
5   where
6       date_part('month', "created date" :: date) = 7
7       and "complaint type" = 'Illegal Fireworks'
```

Problem solved. We will use this technique a few times and then provide some prompts to use it as some of the queries will have some issues built into them that you will need to solve (the answers will be provided of course) but these two techniques will help anyone of any skill level start to become fully independent in writing their own spatial SQL queries.

Before we proceed, I want to quickly highlight what you will be able to do by the end of the next chapter.

- You will be able to import a dataset of 3.2 million records into PostGIS
- Easily query it based on its non-spatial data
- Modify the data types and correct any issues on import
- Visualize that data on a map

This is one of those "a-ha" moments that I think is worth reflecting on. For me this is pretty routine having used spatial SQL for years, but if you come from a more traditional GIS set up, just addressing data in the millions can seem like something that was out of the question. With spatial SQL so many doors can open, and I do believe it is important to pause and reflect on the new abilities you will be adding to your toolkit. With that, forward!

3.9 Expert Voices: Giulia Carella, PhD

Name: Giulia Carella, PhD **Title**: Data Scientist

How/where did you learn spatial SQL?

I started using spatial SQL when I joined CARTO as a Data Scientist.

Why do you enjoy using spatial SQL?

As a data scientist working with spatio-temporal data, I enjoy using spatial SQL since it allows processing geospatial data efficiently directly within data warehouses, reducing the need for complex data transfers between different systems.

Can you share an interesting way or use case that you are using spatial SQL for today?

Today, I have been working on creating a composite score to identify areas of high priority for improving network accessibility for senior citizens in the US. The analysis consists of estimating average download/upload speed everywhere in the US, creating the composite score by taking into account the presence of the senior population, the network speed and the level of urbanity of an area, and then leverage an LLM model to interpret the results (Figure 3.24, on the following page).

Figure 3.24: Composite scoring for senior network accessibility

4. SQL Basics

In this section we will start to learn the fundamental building blocks of SQL so we can lay a solid foundation in SQL, or vanilla SQL (since this is a book focused on spatial SQL) before we move into spatial SQL. I believe this is the chapter where you will start to see the true power of SQL and why it is a popular language, not just in the geospatial industry, but also for all aspects of data storage and analysis.

4.1 Importing Data to PostGIS

While many books that teach SQL teach it in the order of SQL operations, I feel it is easier to learn the fundamentals such as data types, functions, and some simple processes like aggregations and WHERE operators. From there we will address more advanced topics in the next chapter. It is important to note that these next two chapters cannot possibly cover all the nuances of SQL. The goal of this chapter is to give you the fundamental elements that we will use in all SQL queries, and that will be of particular importance in spatial SQL.

But before we get there, we need to start importing some data into our PostGIS database!

We already covered the process to import data into PostGIS with QGIS, and this will work great with smaller datasets that are of the size that can easily be viewed/loaded into QGIS. But for larger data we need a few other strategies to do this. There are three methods we will cover in this chapter for vector data: shp2pgsql, ogr2ogr, and the COPY command. These three commands will allow you to expand the scale of data that you can import into your database and with various data formats.

My two favorite methods to use are ogr2ogr and the COPY command. I use ogr2ogr when I have different formats of data like GeoJSON or KMLs. ogr2ogr is also very useful when you want to do some transformations of your data before it lands in PostGIS (using - you guessed it - spatial SQL). I use the COPY command when I have larger datasets, but it only works with CSV files.

4.2 ogr2ogr

If you have not used the GDAL library before, now is as good a time as ever to start. GDAL is one of the most fundamental libraries that exists in the modern GIS ecosystem, and exists in some of the most popular geospatial tools today including Geopandas, QGIS, GeoServer, GRASS GIS, Rasterio, and even parts of PostGIS (for example raster import).[58]

The ogr family of functions were a separate set of tools meant to work with vector data, but were merged into the GDAL project. It originally stood for OpenGIS Simple Features Reference Implementation and, while the original reference has changed, the name stuck[59]. ogr2ogr (often pronounced "Ogre to ogre" which has to be one of my favorite named tools in all of geospatial) is basically a library that allows for the conversion of one vector file type to another. As of the writing of this book, there are currently 79 different vector file formats supported by GDAL.

As it relates to our use case in the scope of spatial SQL, there are two core elements that you can use

---

[58]https://gdal.org/software_using_gdal.html~software-using-gdal

[59]https://gdal.org/faq.html~what-is-this-ogr-stuff

`ogr2ogr` for with spatial SQL: importing data to PostGIS and transforming data within the `ogr2ogr` command with SpatiaLite.

Installing GDAL

Before we do anything, we need to install GDAL on your computer. GDAL can be installed a few ways, but for our needs we will be using the command line version, although you can certainly use Python or other versions too. With that said, the installation instructions vary based on your operating system if you want to install GDAL directly on to your machine. For our needs and to ensure interoperability between operating systems, we will again be using Docker to solve this issue. If you do want to install GDAL on your system directly below are some quick guides to help you do so.

Windows

The GDAL website recommends using Anaconda and Conda Forge to install GDAL. Anaconda is a package management system and platform for Python packages.

First, go to the Anaconda website at anaconda.com[60] and find the "Download" tab[61]. The website should detect your operating system and direct you to download the correct version. When the installation package finishes downloading, go ahead and install it on your computer.

Once it is done installing you can open up the Anaconda program. You can also follow the instructions from the USGS[62] to download and install the Windows binaries directly.

Linux/Ubuntu

In Linux, you can use the Advanced Packaging Tool, or "apt" package manager, to download and install GDAL. Make sure you perform the correct updates of apt prior to installing. Below is the command you can use to install GDAL:

```
sudo apt install libgdal-dev
```

Of course, you can always use the direct website download as well.

MacOS

For MacOS, using the Homebrew package manager. You can install Homebrew using the commands listed on their homepage[63]. Once you have that installed you can use this command:

```
brew install gdal
```

Of course, you can always use the direct website download as well.

Install GDAL using Docker

As stated earlier I recommend using Docker to install GDAL for all the same reasons we discussed when we installed PostGIS. The only downside to this is that you need to add a few extra arguments to the command to run it, but overall using Docker ensures compatibility across all systems. To install GDAL via Docker you can follow these steps:

---

[60]https://www.anaconda.com/

[61]https://www.anaconda.com/products/distribution

[62]https://loc8.cc/sql/nationalmap-gdal-install

[63]https://brew.sh/

First navigate to `https://github.com/OSGeo/gdal/pkgs/container/gdal`[64] and you should see a `docker pull` command with the latest version of the package. To use the same version the commands in this book are using you can use the command below:

```
docker pull ghcr.io/osgeo/gdal:ubuntu-small-3.7.2
```

Or you can open the Docker application and in the search bar in the blue header area, search for the image name, in this case "osgeo/gdal"

/ from one computing environment to another. Learn more

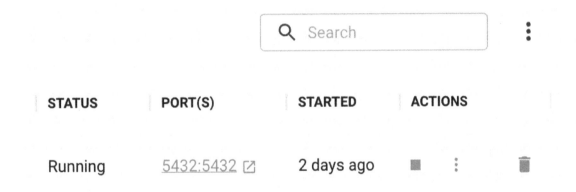

Figure 4.1: Searching for the GDAL image

Once you have found it you can go ahead and hit *"Pull"* to install GDAL. Once it is completed we can run our first command to make sure it has installed correctly.

The command we will be running to start the container looks like this:

```
docker run --rm -v //Users:/Users osgeo/gdal gdalinfo --version
```

Effectively the command we actually want to run is this:

```
gdalinfo -version
```

And the precursor command to access it in docker is this:

```
docker run --rm -v //Users:/Users --network="host" osgeo/gdal
```

---

[64]`https://github.com/OSGeo/gdal/pkgs/container/gdal`

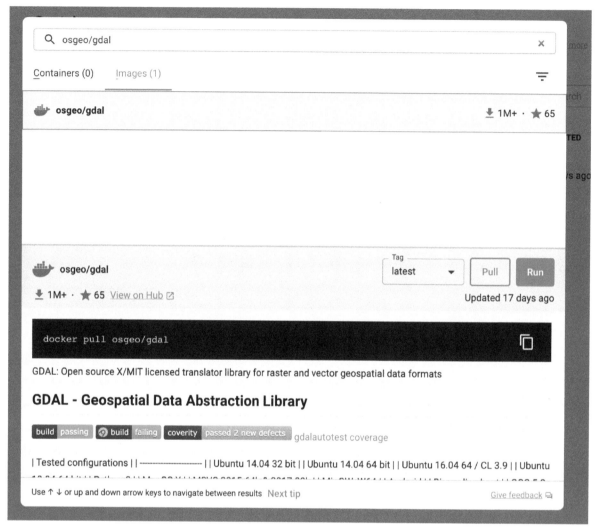

Figure 4.2: Searching for the GDAL image

Breaking this command down so you can understand the pieces:

- `docker run`: Runs the Docker command
- `-rm`: Removes the container when we are done with the command. If we did not remove it we would have a container running for every command we run which is not ideal
- `-v`: Defines the path to the local home volume on our computer for our files.
    - For Mac users this is: `//Users:/Users`
    - For Windows users this is: `C:Users:Users`
    - For Linux users this is: `/home:/home`
- `--network="host"`: Allows the Docker container to communicate with our localhost, in this case the PostGIS database we have running in Docker.
- `osgeo/gdal`: Defines the image we want to run which is of course GDAL
- `gdalinfo --version`: Simple command to tell us which version of GDAL we have installed

You will need to provide an absolute path to your files, so please keep this in mind. For example on my computer this is:

```
/Users/matt/Documents/spatial-sql-book/file.csv
```

While this has some extra steps, Docker provides an easy solution to make sure that any computer can download and access Docker. For this chapter I will include the full functions with the Docker commands but going forward I will only include the specific GDAL command to shorten the code so please keep this in mind as we proceed.

With that let's import one of our first files. We are going to import some data from the New York City Taxi Open Dataset[65].

The NYC Taxi and Limousine Commission (TLC) now publishes their data with only the taxi pickup zone as the location identifier. However, I have a copy of the original data that has data from the first 15 days of June 2016 which has the latitude and longitude pick up and drop off locations. The data has 5,651,686 total rows and is stored in a file type called Parquet.

Parquet is a unique file format that stores tabular data, but in what is known as a columnar storage format. Instead of storing data in rows as many systems do including PostgreSQL, Parquet stores data in columns and has a common index. This allows for more efficient file compression within the data resulting in faster loading and smaller file sizes. As of 2022, there is an effort underway to create the Geoparquet file type which will provide the same advantages but for geometry data.

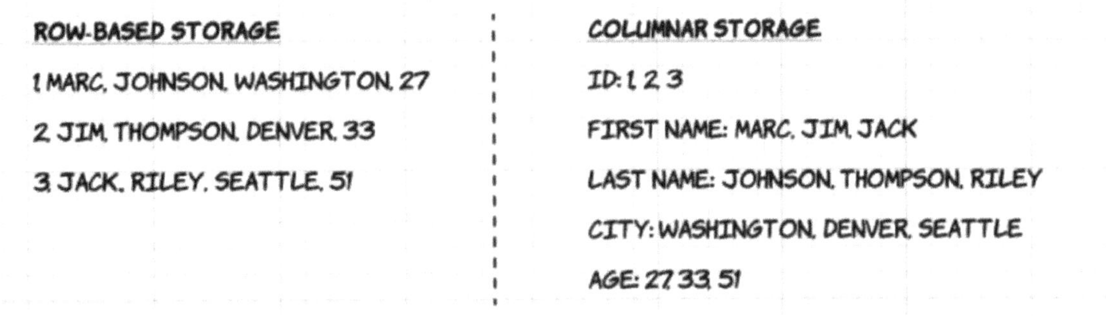

ROW-BASED STORAGE

1 MARC, JOHNSON, WASHINGTON, 27

2 JIM, THOMPSON, DENVER, 33

3 JACK, RILEY, SEATTLE, 51

COLUMNAR STORAGE

ID: 1, 2, 3

FIRST NAME: MARC, JIM, JACK

LAST NAME: JOHNSON, THOMPSON, RILEY

CITY: WASHINGTON, DENVER, SEATTLE

AGE: 27, 33, 51

Figure 4.3: Row based vs. columnar based storage structure

The good news for us is that GDAL already supports Parquet and GeoParquet, so we can import this file with one command right into PostGIS.

These files are available in the book repo for download. To load these files we can use the ogr2ogr command from GDAL that will translate the file from Parquet directly into PostGIS. Below is the command we are going to run, without the Docker commands attached to it.

Listing 4.1: Loading data with ogr2ogr

```
1   ogr2ogr \
2       -f PostgreSQL PG:"host=localhost port=25432 user=docker password=docker \
3       dbname=gis" /Users/matt/Documents/spatial-sql-book/nyc_taxi_yellow_0616-07.parquet \
4       -nln nyc_taxi_yellow_0616 -lco GEOMETRY_NAME=geom
```

And breaking apart the arguments:

---

[65]https://www.nyc.gov/site/tlc/about/tlc-trip-record-data.page

- `ogr2ogr`: invoke the ogr2ogr commands
- `-f PostgreSQL`: -f is the file type flag and PostgreSQL is the file type we are transforming to
- `PG:"host=localhost user=user password=password dbname=geo"`: Details about our database
- `/Users/matt/Documents/spatial-sql-book/fhv_tripdata_2022-07.parquet`: Absolute path to our file (yours will be different)
- `-nln nyc_taxi_forhire_0721`: Flag for "new layer name" or the name of the table we will create
- `-lco GEOMETRY_NAME=geom`: Layer creation option to add the data type GEOMETRY in a column called geom

So bringing it all together with our Docker command:

Listing 4.2: Complete statement with Docker

```
1  docker run --rm -v /Users:/Users --network="host" osgeo/gdal
2  ogr2ogr \
3  -f PostgreSQL PG:"host=localhost user=docker password=docker \
4  dbname=gis port=25432" \
5  /Users/mattforrest/Documents/spatial-sql-data/nyc_yellow_taxi_0601_0615_2016.parquet \
6  -nln nyc_yellow_taxi_0601_0615_2016 -lco GEOMETRY_NAME=geom
```

This will take some of time to run but once it completes you should see your data show up in your PostGIS database. Let's take a look at the data in pgAdmin to see how it all looks.

Import data using the COPY command

The `COPY` command allows you to copy data to and from your PostGIS database, but only works with the CSV file format. This does exactly what it sounds like, it simply copies the data directly from the CSV file into the PostgreSQL database. The data we are going to import in this case is the NYC 311 data[66] that you saw in the previous chapter.

The data is available in the book repo as well, and the data I downloaded were calls from 2021, which contains 3,214,361 rows of data. The only caveat with the `COPY` command is that you have to create a table matching the schema of your CSV file before you can copy the data into it. I created that command for this table which you can see here. We will cover more about this in the coming sections, but effectively this command defines the names of the columns followed by their data type. This means that we are implicitly defining the data type for each column we are pulling into the database based on the data in our CSV. Since we have the data dictionary in the NYC Open Data Portal, we can use that to know what data type is contained within each column.

Listing 4.3: Create table statement for 311 data

```
1   create table nyc_311 (
2      id int primary key,
3      created_date timestamp,
4      closed_date timestamp,
5      agency text,
6      agency_name text,
7      complaint_type text,
8      descriptor text,
9      location_type text,
10     incident_zip text,
11     incident_address text,
12     street_name text,
13     cross_street_1 text,
14     cross_street_2 text,
15     intersection_street_1 text,
```

---

[66]https://loc8.cc/sql/cityofnewyork-311

```
16      intersection_street_2 text,
17      address_type text,
18      city text,
19      landmark text,
20      facility_type text,
21      status text,
22      due_date timestamp,
23      resolution_description text,
24      resolution_action_updated_date timestamp,
25      community_board text,
26      bbl text,
27      borough text,
28      x_coordinate_planar numeric,
29      y_coordinate_planar numeric,
30      open_data_channel_type text,
31      park_facility_name text,
32      park_borough text,
33      vehicle_type text,
34      taxi_company_borough text,
35      taxi_pickup_location text,
36      bridge_highway_name text,
37      bridge_highway_description text,
38      road_ramp text,
39      bridge_highway_segment text,
40      latitude numeric,
41      longitude numeric,
42      location text
43  )
```

Once you run this command we can then COPY the data into our target table. To do so, we need to open a psql shell within pgAdmin. psql is a terminal based command line toolkit to query and access your database. You can install this library yourself but since it already is in pgAdmin we can go ahead and use it there.

To open the psql terminal you can click this button in pgAdmin (Figure 4.4):

Figure 4.4: Opening the PSQL tool in pgAdmin

And you should see this window when it is ready (Figure 4.5, on the following page):

The command we are going to run looks like this:

```
\copy nyc_311 FROM '/Users/matt/Desktop/SQL Book Data/nyc_
311.csv' with delimiter ',' csv header;
```

Breaking down the elements here:

- copy: starts the COPY command
- nyc_311: The target table name as defined in our CREATE TABLE statement

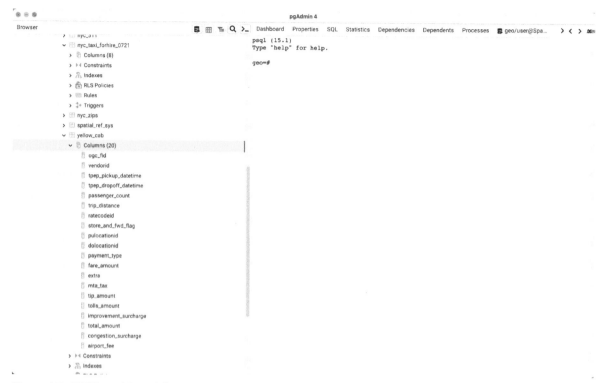

Figure 4.5: PSQL tool in pgAdmin

- '/Users/matt/Desktop/SQL Book Data/nyc_311.csv': Absolute path to our file contained in single quotes
- with delimiter ',': Tells that our CSV data is separated by commas
- csv: Tells that we are importing a CSV
- header: Tells the command to skip the first row which contains our headers

You can go ahead and run this command in the psql terminal in pgAdmin. Once complete you should have all your data imported!

There are a few more files we are going to import using these methods. The commands are listed below:

NYC Building Footprints (Manhattan)

Listing 4.4: NYC Buildings Data

```
1   docker run --rm -v //Users:/Users --network="host" osgeo/gdal \
2   ogr2ogr -f PostgreSQL PG:"host=localhost port=25432 user=docker password=docker dbname=gis" \
3   /Users/matt/Desktop/Desktop/spatial-sql-book/Building_Footprints.geojson \
4    -nln nyc_building_footprints -lco GEOMETRY_NAME=geom
```

2015 NYC Tree Census

Listing 4.5: Tree Census

```
1   docker run --rm -v //Users:/Users --network="host" osgeo/gdal \
2   ogr2ogr -f PostgreSQL PG:"host=localhost port=25432 user=docker password=docker dbname=gis" \
3   /Users/matt/Desktop/Desktop/spatial-sql-book/2015_NYC_Tree_Census.geojson \
4    -nln nyc_2015_tree_census -lco GEOMETRY_NAME=geom
```

NYC Map Pluto (Building Data)

Listing 4.6: Buildings Pluto Data

```
1  docker run --rm -v //Users:/Users --network="host" osgeo/gdal \
2  ogr2ogr -f PostgreSQL PG:"host=localhost port=25432 user=docker password=docker dbname=gis" \
3  /Users/matt/Desktop/Desktop/spatial-sql-book/nyc_mappluto_22v3_shp/MapPLUTO.shp \
4  -nln nyc_mappluto -lco GEOMETRY_NAME=geom \
5  -nlt MULTIPOLYGON -mapFieldType Real=String
```

NYC Zip Codes

Listing 4.7: NYC Zip Codes

```
1  docker run --rm -v //Users:/Users --network="host" osgeo/gdal \
2  ogr2ogr -f PostgreSQL PG:"host=localhost port=25432 user=docker password=docker dbname=gis" \
3  /Users/matt/Desktop/Desktop/spatial-sql-book/ZIP_CODE_040114/ZIP_CODE_040114.shp \
4  -nln nyc_zips -lco GEOMETRY_NAME=geom \
5  -nlt MULTIPOLYGON
```

NYC Bike Routes

Listing 4.8: Bike Routes in NYC

```
1  docker run --rm -v //Users:/Users --network="host" osgeo/gdal \
2  ogr2ogr -f PostgreSQL PG:"host=localhost port=25432 user=docker password=docker dbname=gis" \
3  /Users/matt/Desktop/Desktop/spatial-sql-book/NYC_Bike_Routes.geojson \
4  -nln nyc_bike_routes -lco GEOMETRY_NAME=geom \
```

4.3 SQL Data Types

Now we are ready to take a look at data types and the functions to manipulate those data types in PostgreSQL. Even if you have no experience in programming, you have likely come across data types and functions to change or manipulate data types in your other GIS work or in tools like Excel. For this part of the chapter we will only be using simple SELECT queries that take a subset of rows from our table using the LIMIT argument to show the different data types and functions for transforming them.

Since our goal with this chapter, and the next, are to get you up to speed writing spatial SQL as fast as possible, we will start with the fundamentals and progress in complexity. This will also give you a good understanding of working with GEOMETRY or GEOGRAPHY data when we get there since it is in fact, only another data type in SQL.

One final note. Since we are using PostGIS for our examples it is worth noting that PostgreSQL has its own syntax, or flavor, of SQL. While SQL is highly standardized, there are some variations between each database or data warehouse.

Okay, so let's take a look at the different data types that are available in PostgreSQL:

- **Boolean**: true or false values
- **Characters**: text or string data
- **Numeric**: integers and floats (data with decimal values)
- **Date/Time values**: dates, times, time stamps, etc.
- **UUID**: Universally Unique Identifiers or an alpha numeric code that is completely unique
- **Array**: Data that exists in square brackets, [], that is equivalent to a list in Python
- **JSON**: Data that has key value pairs that exists between curly brackets (ex. {'key': 'value'}) that can contain nested data
- **hstore**: Key value pairs only, but requires an extension
- **Geometry/Geography**: The stuff you are all here to learn about, geometric and geospatial data
- **Network addresses or IP addresses**

A note about NULL

Now while NULL is not a data type per se, it can be in a column of any data type you have in PostgreSQL. NULL is effectively the absence of data. There are some specific ways you can use NULL data and some things you need to be aware of when your data has NULL values or is lacking NULL values.

For example let's consider that you have some data, and it contains a list of first names and last names, however, the values that don't have a name are just blank. Below is a table example of this.

firstname	lastname
Jim	Smith
Nancy	Drew
NULL	NULL

Now let's try and query to find the values where there are no last names. Let's keep in mind that since NULL is the absence of data (even if a cell has just a space or no characters at all this counts as data) we can't use operators like = or != because it is empty, and we cannot compare it to anything. In this case after our WHERE operator we have to add the statement IS NULL to find our NULL values

```
select * from names where firstname is NULL
```

As we can see we still have all our values including the ones where the firstname seems to be empty. This is because the value in that row came in as an empty string or text data without any characters. This is not a NULL value because while there are not characters there the data is still a string.

This is something to be aware of when you are working with your data and you see some odd results. As we go forward keep in mind that any data type can contain NULL values so in addition to all the options available, NULL is also an option.

Boolean

The boolean data type represents a true or false value, and these are the only possible options for a Boolean column. However, there are some different ways you can represent a Boolean column but keep in mind that the column must be a Boolean to use these values.

True	False
true	false
t	f
true	false
y	n
yes	no
1	0

The Boolean type is very simple and there are not any functions that are used to transform or update it. With that said to query or discover the data you will need to use operators, which are effectively functions themselves and are many times used in the WHERE section of your query.

Another thing to know about Boolean values is that many functions have a Boolean as a return value, and many with spatial SQL as well. Let's walk through an example.

Let's query a sample of our data from our NYC 311 data:

Listing 4.9: Querying our NYC 311 data

```
1  select
2      complaint_type,
3      location_type,
4      city
5  from
6      nyc_311
7  limit
8      5
```

complaint_type	location_type	city
Food Poisoning	Restaurant/Bar/Deli/Bakery	BROOKLYN
Noise - Commercial	Store/Commercial	BROOKLYN
Illegal Fireworks	Street/Sidewalk	BROOKLYN
Illegal Fireworks	Street/Sidewalk	BROOKLYN
Noise - Residential	Residential Building/House	BRONX

As you can see here we have three columns and five rows. We used the LIMIT statement to limit our data to 5 rows. Now let's filter our results by the *city* column to results in Brooklyn using a WHERE statement:

Listing 4.10: Using a WHERE statement

```
1  select
2      complaint_type,
3      location_type,
4      city
5  from
6      nyc_311
7  where
8      city = 'Brooklyn'
9  limit
10     5
```

complaint_type	location_type	city
Animal in a Park	Park	Brooklyn
Maintenance or Facility	Park	Brooklyn
Maintenance or Facility	Park	Brooklyn
Maintenance or Facility	Park	Brooklyn
Food Establishment	Restaurant/Bar/Deli/Bakery	Brooklyn

What is happening here is that the WHERE clause is telling the SQL execution engine to only include the results that match true. In different terms, the statement is going row by row and evaluating this equation:

city = 'Brooklyn'

If the value in `city` matches 'Brooklyn', the function (in this case =) evaluates to true, then the row is included. To show this we can add a calculated column on to our query.

Listing 4.11: Seeing this in action

```
1  select
2      complaint_type,
3      location_type,
4      city,
5      city = 'BROOKLYN'
6  from
7      nyc_311
8  limit
9      5
```

complaint_type	location_type	city	?column?
Blocked Driveway	Street/Sidewalk	BROOKLYN	true
Blocked Driveway	Street/Sidewalk	OZONE PARK	false
Illegal Parking	Street/Sidewalk	MIDDLE VILLAGE	false
Noise - Street/Sidewalk	Street/Sidewalk		
PLUMBING	RESIDENTIAL BUILDING	Elmhurst	false

As you can see we now have a column of Boolean values that match our condition. This is important to understand and can help us better understand the WHERE clause and conditionals that go with it. We will go into this in greater detail but effectively every condition after a WHERE clause is a condition that will evaluate to true or false in one way or another.

4.4 Characters

This data type represents any type of text, also known as a string. This includes all characters, numbers (that are inside of a string), and symbols in any language. Strings will (almost) always start and end with single quotes. So in effect this can be any text that you want to store in your database.

There are three different data types you might see within PostgreSQL:

- **VARCHAR(n)**: A string of varying lengths with a limit of length n
- **CHAR(n)** or **CHARACTER(n)**: A string of exactly n length, padded for blanks
- **TEXT** or **VARCHAR**: A string with no fixed length

For the most part you will likely be using TEXT as your primary data type for strings unless you want to enforce a strict limit on the number of characters in a string, in which case you can use VARCHAR(n) or CHAR(n) depending on your need.

Let's take a look at some string data in our database and learn a bit more about the character data type and some functions we can use to work with characters.

First let's run this query in pgAdmin which should return these results (Figure 4.6, on the next page):

Listing 4.12: Concatenation with SQL

```
1  select
2      spc_common,
3      nta_name,
4      health
5  from
```

```
6     nyc_2015_tree_census
7  limit
8     5
```

	spc_common 🔒 character varying	nta_name 🔒 character varying	health 🔒 character varying
1	red maple	Forest Hills	Fair
2	pin oak	Whitestone	Fair
3	honeylocust	East Williamsburg	Good
4	honeylocust	East Williamsburg	Good
5	American linden	Park Slope-Gowanus	Good
6	honeylocust	Lincoln Square	Good
7	honeylocust	Lincoln Square	Good
8	American linden	Clinton	Good
9	honeylocust	Grasmere-Arrochar-Ft. Wadsworth	Good
10	London planetree	Gravesend	Fair

Figure 4.6: Initial query results

Let's review the following functions that we can use to manipulate the text in these results:

- CONCAT
- ||
- LEFT
- RIGHT
- INITCAP
- REPLACE
- REVERSE
- LENGTH
- LOWER
- SPLITPART
- UPPER

CONCAT

In the case you want to concatenate, or join some various text fields together, we can actually do this two different ways. The first is using the || operator between two or more strings. Below is the query that we will run to concatenate the tree common name column to the health column in the NYC trees dataset, with a " - " between:

Listing 4.13: Concatenation with SQL

```
1  select
2      spc_common || ' - ' || health as joined
```

```
3   from
4       nyc_2015_tree_census
5   limit
6       5
```

And you can see our results here.

red maple - Fair
pin oak - Fair
honeylocust - Good
honeylocust - Good
American linden - Good

You can accomplish the same results with the following query:

Listing 4.14: Concatenation with SQL

```
1   select
2       concat(spc_common, ' - ', health)
3   from
4       nyc_2015_tree_census
5   limit
6       5
```

Before we proceed I want to call out one important point about using and reading documentation. Both PostgreSQL and PostGIS have excellent documentation, but at first glance the documentation, or docs for short, can be hard to read if you have never spent much time using or reading docs. They can be very helpful once you are able to navigate them and in the end, they can save you a ton of time from random Googling and reading StackOverflow articles. With that let's take a look at the documentation for the two functions we used today which you can find at the link in the footnotes[67].

First let's look at the docs for the || function (Figure 4.7):

Function	Return Type	Description	Example	Result
string || string	text	String concatenation	'Post' || 'greSQL'	PostgreSQL

Figure 4.7: Concatination shorthand documentation in PostgreSQL

Let's take a look at each section here:

- **Function**: This shows the function, in this case the || and then the two positional arguments (positional meaning the order they need to go in), in this case two strings.
- **Return Type**: This is the type or value that the function returns, in this case a string
- **Description**: What the string does
- **Example**: This is one example of the function in this case 'Post' || 'greSQL'
- **Result**: Result of the function, in this case 'PostgreSQL'

In this one part of the table we can learn everything we need to know about the function. Docs can have their own language and structure, so you need to know what to look for and in what order. Other docs might have more examples or arguments, but PostgreSQL is pretty to the point. PostGIS on the other hand has a bit more in detail which we will see later on.

Taking a look at the other function that we used (Figure 4.8, on the next page):

---

[67]https://www.postgresql.org/docs/9.1/functions-string.html

concat(str "any" [, str "any" [, ...]])	text	Concatenate all arguments. NULL arguments are ignored.	concat('abcde', 2, NULL, 22)	abcde222

Figure 4.8: Concatination documentation in PostgreSQL

As you can see here the function structure is a bit different, as well as the example and description. We can see in the example, concat('abcde', 2, 'NULL, 22)', that there are other values here too strings, two integers (2 and 22), and a NULL value.

We can also take a look at the function definition: concat(str "any" [, str "any" [, ...]]). Certainly this looks a lot different from the other definition. What this shows us is that the argument can be a string or "any" which means any data type. We see this repeat and then the three dots ..., which means that you can pass as many arguments as you choose to this function.

If we take a look at our original function we can see that there is also another function using the "||" function (Figure 4.9):

Function	Return Type	Description	Example	Result
string || string	text	String concatenation	'Post' || 'greSQL'	PostgreSQL
string || non-string or non-string || string	text	String concatenation with one non-string input	'Value: ' || 42	Value: 42

Figure 4.9: Concatination shorthand documentation in PostgreSQL

As well as this message (Figure 4.10):

Note: Before PostgreSQL 8.3, these functions would silently accept values of several non-string data types as well, due to the presence of implicit coercions from those data types to text. Those coercions have been removed because they frequently caused surprising behaviors. However, the string concatenation operator (||) still accepts non-string input, so long as at least one input is of a string type, as shown in Table 9-6. For other cases, insert an explicit coercion to text if you need to duplicate the previous behavior.

Figure 4.10: Concatination shorthand callout

We can see that || can accept any number of arguments as long as at least one is a string. So what is the difference between these functions? Well not much really. But we can see here that by checking the docs and reading everything we have all the information we need. Let's proceed with looking at some other functions.

LEFT, RIGHT

These two functions allow you to trim your string to a specific number of characters from either the left or the right position on the string. You can use this query to see that in action:

Listing 4.15: String functions

```
1  select
2      spc_common,
3      left(spc_common, 5) as left,
4      right(spc_common, 3) as right
5  from
6      nyc_2015_tree_census
7  limit
8      5
```

red maple	red m	ple
pin oak	pin o	oak
honeylocust	honey	ust
honeylocust	honey	ust
American linden	Ameri	den

This can be useful if you need to retrieve the first few characters of a string such as the first two characters of a US Census code which represents the state code.

INITCAP, LOWER, UPPER

These functions change the capitalization and case of the text. INITCAP capitalizes the first letter of each string. UPPER changes the entire string to uppercase, and LOWER changes each to lower case.

Listing 4.16: Text case functions

```
1  select
2      spc_common,
3      initcap(spc_common) as titlecase,
4      upper(spc_common) as uppercase,
5      lower(spc_common) as lowercase
6  from
7      nyc_2015_tree_census
8  limit
9      5
```

red maple	Red Maple	RED MAPLE	red maple
pin oak	Pin Oak	PIN OAK	pin oak
honeylocust	Honeylocust	HONEYLOCUST	honeylocust
honeylocust	Honeylocust	HONEYLOCUST	honeylocust
American linden	American Linden	AMERICAN LINDEN	american linden

REPLACE

REPLACE is a function that takes three arguments: the source, the text to replace, and what to replace it with. Let's go ahead and try this out with our sample data:

Listing 4.17: Replace function

```
1  select
2      spc_common,
3      replace(spc_common, 'locust', ' locust') as new_text
4  from
5      nyc_2015_tree_census
6  limit
7      5
```

red maple	red maple
pin oak	pin oak
honeylocust	honey locust

honeylocust	honey locust
American linden	American linden

As you can see we can change the 'honeylocust' value to 'honey locust' using this function.

REVERSE

You might be able to guess, but this function reverses our string:

Listing 4.18: Reverse function

```
1  select
2      spc_common,
3      reverse(spc_common) as backwards
4  from
5      nyc_2015_tree_census
6  limit
7      5
```

red maple	elpam der
pin oak	kao nip
honeylocust	tsucolyenoh
honeylocust	tsucolyenoh
American linden	nednil naciremA

LENGTH

This function measures the length of a string:

Listing 4.19: Length of text with SQL

```
1  select
2      spc_common,
3      length(spc_common) as how_long
4  from
5      nyc_2015_tree_census
6  limit
7      5
```

red maple	9
pin oak	7
honeylocust	11
honeylocust	11
American linden	15

SPLITPART

SPLITPART takes three arguments: the source data, a delimiter to split by like a comma or space (but this can be any character), and which part of take from the split using an integer. Let's say we want to get the tree type from the columns, we can do that with this query:

Listing 4.20: Use of the SPLITPART function

```
1  select
2      spc_common,
3      split_part(spc_common, ' ', 2) as tree_group
4  from
5      nyc_2015_tree_census
6  limit
7      5
```

red maple	maple
pin oak	oak
honeylocust	
honeylocust	
American linden	linden

Since the 'honeylocust' is only one word we can actually combine two functions to do this:

Listing 4.21: Using SPLITPART with REPLACE

```
1   select
2       spc_common,
3       split_part(
4               replace(spc_common, 'locust', ' locust'),
5               ' ',
6               2
7       ) as tree_group
8   from
9       nyc_2015_tree_census
10  limit
11      5
```

red maple	maple
pin oak	oak
honeylocust	locust
honeylocust	locust
American linden	linden

There are many other string functions which you can find in the PostgreSQL documentation, but these are the functions that I have used with spatial SQL.

4.5 Numeric

Numeric data contains any data that contains a number. Generally you can use the NUMERIC data type which will accommodate any type of numeric value you may need. That said there are a variety of numeric data types that you may encounter at some point. Below is a table showing the different options and constraints from the PostgreSQL 15 Documentation:

Name	Storage Size	Description	Range
smallint	2 bytes	small-range integer	-32768 to +32767
integer	4 bytes	typical choice for integer	-2147483648 to +2147483647
bigint	8 bytes	large-range integer	-9223372036854775808 to +9223372036854775807
decimal	variable	user-specified precision, exact	up to 131072 digits before the decimal point; up to 16383 digits after the decimal point
numeric	variable	user-specified precision, exact	up to 131072 digits before the decimal point; up to 16383 digits after the decimal point
real	4 bytes	variable-precision, inexact	6 decimal digits precision
double precision	8 bytes	variable-precision, inexact	15 decimal digits precision
smallserial	2 bytes	small autoincrementing integer	1 to 32767
serial	4 bytes	autoincrementing integer	1 to 2147483647
bigserial	8 bytes	large autoincrementing integer	1 to 9223372036854775807

The functions with numeric data allow you to perform different mathematical operations. First, you can use any combination of mathematical operators with numeric data. This includes:

- **Addition**: +
- **Division**: /
- **Subtraction**: -
- **Multiplication**: *
- **Modulo** (remainder from division): %

Here is a quick example from our Taxis data set:

Listing 4.22: Query using numeric data

```
1   select
2       total_amount,
3       tip_amount,
4       tip_amount /(total_amount - tip_amount) as tip_percent
5   from
6       nyc_yellow_taxi_0601_0615_2016
7   where
8       tip_amount > 0
9       and trip_distance > 2
10  limit
11      5
```

11.16	1.86	0.19999999999999998
10.3	1.5	0.17045454545454544
10.3	1	0.1075268817204301
10.8	1.5	0.16129032258064516
10.8	1.5	0.16129032258064516

As you can see we can calculate the tip percentage by dividing the tip amount by the base amount, or the total minus the tip.

There are a few other handy functions to use as well:

- **ceil (numeric)**: Rounds up a decimal to the nearest integer
- **floor (numeric)**: Rounds down a decimal to the nearest integer
- **round (numeric)**: Rounds to the nearest integer up or down
- **round (v numeric, s integer)**: Same function but will round v to s decimal places. Ex. round (42.451534, 2) → 42.5
- **log (numeric)**: Base 10 logarithm
- **sqrt (numeric)**: Square root
- **random ( )**: Generates a random number between 0 and 1

My tips and advice are to use the NUMERIC data type, unless you are positive you need or want a specific data type. While there are plenty of other numeric functions, these are the functions that I have used the most.

4.6 Dates and Times

Dates and times can be one of the more complex data types namely because of the multiple ways you can format data and the number of formats your data may come in as. In actuality there are only four data types for date and times:

- **date**: A date with no time of day
- **time**: A time of day with no date (with or without timezone)
- **timestamp**: A day and time (with or without timezone)
- **interval**: Time interval

To manage and deal with times and dates there are really two groups of functions. The first are functions to turn strings into dates and times, the other set has to deal with performing calculations, finding current times, and more.

While dates and times can be a big topic that we can't completely cover here, below are a few topics that I think are most important to understand, at least how to accomplish them, in SQL:

1. How to turn text data into dates and times

2. Extract parts of dates or timestamps like the month or hour of the day

3. Format dates and times as strings

4. Use math on dates to find durations or add time on to a date

5. Format timestamps and times with time zones

First, let's take a quick look at the functions to translate strings into dates and times, and vice versa, borrowed directly from the PostgreSQL 15 docs:

Function Signature	Output Format
to_date (text, text) → date to_date('05 Dec 2000', 'DD Mon YYYY') → 2000-12-05	Converts string to date according to the given format. 2000-12-05
to_char (interval, text) → text to_char(interval '15h 2m 12s', 'HH24:MI:SS') → 15:02:12	Converts interval to string according to the given format. 15:02:12
to_timestamp (text, text) → timestamp with time zone to_timestamp('05 Dec 2000', 'DD Mon YYYY') → 2000-12-05 00:00:00-05	Converts string to time stamp according to the given format. (See also to_timestamp(double precision) in Table 9.33.) 2000-12-05 00:00:00-05
to_char (timestamp, text) → text to_char (timestamp with time zone, text) → text Converts time stamp to string according to the given format. to_char(timestamp '2002-04-20 17:31:12.66', 'HH12:MI:SS') → 05:31:12	Converts time stamp to string according to the given format. 05:31:12

As you can see there are a few different functions for moving data from strings to date/times. But the second argument is the one to pay attention to here. Let's take a look at this example:

```
to_date('05 Dec 2000', 'DD Mon YYYY') → 2000-12-05
```

We can see that there is text here that shows *'DD Mon YYYY'*, which is what we call a date formatter. There are a lot of date formatting options, so I will refer you to the full list in the PostgreSQL docs in the footnotes[68].

Let's test this out on our taxi data to show a few different things you can do. Below is a query that has the start and end timestamp of some taxi trips:

Listing 4.23: Query with timestamps

```
1   select
2       pickup_datetime,
3       dropoff_datetime
4   from
5       nyc_yellow_taxi_0601_0615_2016
6   where
7       tip_amount > 0
8       and trip_distance > 2
9   limit
10      5
```

2016-06-09 21:33:04+00	2016-06-09 21:40:08+00
2016-06-13 06:06:21+00	2016-06-13 06:11:27+00

---

[68]https://loc8.cc/sql/postgresql-datetime

2016-06-07 23:51:08+00	2016-06-07 23:57:39+00
2016-06-03 05:53:43+00	2016-06-03 06:00:14+00
2016-06-04 04:05:27+00	2016-06-04 04:11:47+00

We can see we have the '+00' at the end of the timestamp which is the timezone, which is Greenwich Mean time, not Eastern Standard time. Let's first turn our data into strings using the same format as above.

Listing 4.24: Formatting timestamps to dates

```
1  select
2      to_char(pickup_datetime, 'DD Mon YYYY') as start_date,
3      to_char(dropoff_datetime, 'DD Mon YYYY') as end_date
4  from
5      nyc_yellow_taxi_0601_0615_2016
6  where
7      tip_amount > 0
8      and trip_distance > 2
9  limit
10     5
```

09 Jun 2016	09 Jun 2016
13 Jun 2016	13 Jun 2016
07 Jun 2016	07 Jun 2016
03 Jun 2016	03 Jun 2016
04 Jun 2016	04 Jun 2016

Let's adjust the formatting a bit:

Listing 4.25: More date formatting

```
1  select
2      to_char(pickup_datetime, 'D Month YYYY') as start_date,
3      to_char(dropoff_datetime, 'D Month YYYY') as end_date
4  from
5      nyc_yellow_taxi_0601_0615_2016
6  where
7      tip_amount > 0
8      and trip_distance > 2
9  limit
10     5
```

5 June 2016	5 June 2016
2 June 2016	2 June 2016
3 June 2016	3 June 2016
6 June 2016	6 June 2016
7 June 2016	7 June 2016

And even more:

Listing 4.26: One more time!

```
1  select
```

```
2        to_char(pickup_datetime, 'Day, Month FMDDth, YYYY') as start_date,
3        to_char(dropoff_datetime, 'Day, Month FMDDth, YYYY ') as end_date
4    from
5        nyc_yellow_taxi_0601_0615_2016
6    where
7        tip_amount > 0
8        and trip_distance > 2
9    limit
10       5
```

Thursday	June 9th	2016	Thursday	June 9th	2016
Monday	June 13th	2016	Monday	June 13th	2016
Tuesday	June 7th	2016	Tuesday	June 7th	2016
Friday	June 3rd	2016	Friday	June 3rd	2016
Saturday	June 4th	2016	Saturday	June 4th	2016

Now there are many ways you can format the text of your dates, and you can do the inverse formatting using the functions above to turn strings into dates should your DATE data not import correctly.

The other types of functions for dates and times provide a lot of different functionality such as extracting parts such as a month or hour from a date/timestamp, reading the current time or date, working with intervals, and more. You can see the full set of functions at the link in the footnote[69].

The operations I perform the most are performing calculations on dates/timestamps and extracting parts of dates and timestamps. Let's look at some examples. First let's find the duration between the start and end times for our trips.

Listing 4.27: Calculate time between two dates

```
1    select
2        dropoff_datetime - pickup_datetime as duration
3    from
4        nyc_yellow_taxi_0601_0615_2016
5    where
6        tip_amount > 0
7        and trip_distance > 2
8    limit
9        5
```

00:07:04
00:05:06
00:06:31
00:06:31
00:06:20

Now, let's see if we can find the hour of the day and the day of the week from the start time of each timestamp.

Listing 4.28: Find the numeric day of the week

```
1    select
2        extract(
```

---

[69]https://www.postgresql.org/docs/current/functions-datetime.html

```
 3            dow
 4          from
 5              pickup_datetime
 6       ) as day_of_week,
 7       extract(
 8          hour
 9          from
10              pickup_datetime
11       ) as hour_of_day
12  from
13       nyc_yellow_taxi_0601_0615_2016
14  where
15       tip_amount > 0
16       and trip_distance > 2
17  limit
18       5
```

4	21
1	6
2	23
5	5
6	4

We can see here that we have the day of the week using numbers from 0 to 6, 0 being Sunday and 6 being Saturday, and the hour of the day from 0 to 23.

We will be revisiting dates several times during this book but for now this is a good starting point.

4.7   Other data types

UUID

Universal Unique Identifier or UUID is a unique identifier that is a 32 character length, alpha-numeric string. These are unique across space and time, and while this may seem difficult to believe since UUIDs are used across many tools and languages. Even if you generated one UUID per second, it would take roughly a billion years to create a duplicate[70].

This data type is pretty simple since there is one function to create a unique ID which is gen_random_uuid() which returns a UUID.

Array

If you are familiar with lists in Python or arrays in Javascript, then an ARRAY should be familiar. If not, then an array is a group of data contained within square brackets. Data can be ordered or unordered, but data is accessed by using an index to grab a specific item, and in PostgreSQL there are a number of functions to access, edit, and query arrays[71]. For example imagine you have an array in a row of data that looks like this:

```
['United States', 'Canada', 'Nigeria', 'Spain']
```

---

[70]https://towardsdatascience.com/are-uuids-really-unique-57eb80fc2a87

[71]https://www.postgresql.org/docs/current/functions-array.html

If you wanted to extract Nigeria from the list you could use a query that looks like this:

```
select countries[3] from data
```

PostgreSQL uses a base index of 1 compared to 0 which is used by other programming languages so keep this in mind. Arrays can be helpful for data that you want to keep that may have multiple or different values, such as tags, categories or other data.

JSON

JSON, or Javascript Object Notation, is another popular and flexible data structure which is similar to a dictionary in Python. JSON can store nested data and can vary in structure. Let's take a look at an example. In this query we are using a common table expression, or CTE, which in effect creates a temporary table that exists only in the scope of our query. You will see these many times as we progress through the book, and we will cover them in detail in the next chapter, but for now we are basically creating a temporary table with one column and one row of data that contains the JSON we are writing.

Listing 4.29: Creating a table with JSON data

```
1   with json_table as (
2       select
3           JSON(
4               '{"first": "Matt",
5               "last": "Forrest",
6               "age": 35}'
7           ) as data
8   )
9
10  select
11      data
12  from
13      json_table
```

```
'{"first": "Matt", "last": "Forrest", "age": 35}'
```

As expected, we get back the exact data we put into our CTE query above. Say we want to access the value in the 'last' key, we can use this query.

Listing 4.30: Extracting values from JSON

```
1   with json_table as (
2       select
3           JSON(
4               '{"first": "Matt",
5               "last": "Forrest",
6               "age": 35}'
7           ) as data
8   )
9   select
10      data -> 'last'
11  from
12      json_table
```

Which will return the value in the last name field. Let's add a more complex JSON value:

Listing 4.31: Querying more complex JSON

```
1   with json_table as (
2       select
3           JSON(
4               '{
5                   "first": "Matt",
6                   "last": "Forrest",
7                   "age": 35,
8                   "cities": ["Minneapolis", "Madison", "New York City"],
9                   "skills": {"SQL": true, "Python": true, "Java": false}
10              }'
11          ) as data
12  )
13  select
14      data
15  from
16      json_table
```

```
{
    "first": "Matt",
    "last": "Forrest",
    "age": 35,
    "cities": ["Minneapolis", "Madison", "New York City"],
    "skills": {
        "SQL": true,
        "Python": true,
        "Java": false
    }
}
```

As you can see we can store values of any data type, and even arrays and other JSON, in this case nested JSON. This is why JSON is a really flexible data structure. Let's say we want to query and find the 2nd city in the 'cities' value and then find the value of 'SQL' in 'skills':

Listing 4.32: Extract data from complex JSON

```
1   with json_table as (
2       select
3           JSON(
4               '{
5                   "first": "Matt",
6                   "last": "Forrest",
7                   "age": 35,
8                   "cities": ["Minneapolis", "Madison", "New York City"],
9                   "skills": {"SQL": true, "Python": true, "Java": false}
10              }'
11          ) as data
12  )
13  select
14      data -> 'cities' -> 1 as city,
15      data -> 'skills' -> 'SQL' as sql_skills
16  from
17      json_table
```

```
'"Madison"','true'
```

As you can see we got both the results we wanted, but the data types are still JSON values. We can avoid this by changing the accessor operator from -> to -»:

You can find the full set of JSON functions in the documentation link in this footnote[72]. Overall, JSON gives you a very flexible data structure to work with and is worth understanding. The most interesting use case I have seen for JSON data is with data from OpenStreetMap. Since the tags and data for any feature can vary, JSON provides a great data structure to store that data.

The other data types of note in PostgreSQL include:

- **Geometric Data**: This differs a bit from the geometry data as this data can represent any geometric data that is not tied to a spatial plane. But some of the operators can be used within PostGIS.
- **hstore**: A key/value pair data structure similar to a tuple in Python (ex. (key, value))
- **Network Address**: Things like IP addresses or MAC address
- **XML**: A data type for storing XML data
- **Text** Search Data: Data type and functions for storing data for text searches

We won't be covering these data types in this book, but they exist and showcase the breadth of data PostgreSQL can support and data that can live alongside your geospatial data.

Casting Data

Imagine you want to change your data between data types. Maybe you want to change a number to a string or vice versa. You can do this with casting, and there are two methods to do so. First let's change a number, the zip code in our NYC Zip Codes data:

Listing 4.33: Casting with function

```
1  select
2      cast(zipcode as numeric)
3  from
4      nyc_zips
5  limit
6      3
```

11436
11213
10002

As you can see we can use the CAST function and pass our column name and the type we want to cast to with. We can also use a shorthand version of this using the :: operator.

Listing 4.34: Casting with double colon

```
1  select
2      zipcode :: numeric
3  from
4      nyc_zips
5  limit
6      3
```

This achieves the same result. The double colon method is older and unique to PostgreSQL, so it will not work in other databases.

---

[72]https://www.postgresql.org/docs/current/functions-json.html

4.8   Basic SQL Operators

By now, you have seen some different SQL operators we will cover in this section. In short, SQL operators allow you to filter your data in various ways to retrieve the data that you want. In our SELECT clause alone we just take the table or columns of data as they exist in the table currently. With operators, we can create a more clear set of directions to grab just the data we are interested in. Let's jump in and walk through some operators.

WHERE

The WHERE operator is one of the most essential operators in SQL. It allows you to define a condition that will filter your table based on the conditions in the clause. There are several operators you can use with the WHERE clause, as well as the AND or OR conditionals that allow you to string several conditionals together. The best way to think about the WHERE clause is that it will return the rows that equate to "true" based on the conditions you provide. This will be important later on as we start to use spatial SQL operators in the WHERE clause.

The operators you can use with the WHERE clause are:

Operator	Description
=	Equal
>	Greater than
<	Less than
>=	Greater than or equal
<=	Less than or equal
<> or !=	Not equal
AND	Logical operator AND
OR	Logical operator OR
IN	Return true if a value matches any value in a list
BETWEEN	Return true if a value is between a range of values
LIKE and ILIKE	Return true if a value matches a pattern
IS NULL	Return true if a value is NULL
NOT	Negate the result of other operators

Let's walk through a few different examples.

Equals, Greater/Lesser Than, Not Equal

These are the most fundamental conditionals that you can use in a query. First we can look at our trees dataset and see which trees are in fair condition by following the pattern of:

```
WHERE column_name operator condition
```

Listing 4.35: Using WHERE

```
1   select
2       *
3   from
```

```
4       nyc_2015_tree_census
5   where
6       health = 'Fair'
```

We can do the same with the greater/lesser than or greater/lesser than or equal to operators. Let's find all the trees that are stumps that have a diameter greater than 0 (note that we can achieve the same thing by finding the trees that have the status of 'Stump':

Listing 4.36: Using the greater than operator

```
1   select
2       *
3   from
4       nyc_2015_tree_census
5   where
6       stump_diam > 0
```

It seems that we have hit an error! Don't worry you will see plenty of errors when you write SQL so while this may be the first, it won't be the last. This also is our first challenge, where you will have a change to think about the issue and see what might be the problem. So first let's take a look at our error code:

```
ERROR:  operator does not exist: character varying > integer
LINE 3: where stump_diam > 0
HINT:  No operator matches the given name and argument types. You might need to add explicit type casts.
SQL state: 42883
Character: 62
```

Take a moment to think about it, and we will walk through the problem after the page break.

Let's walk through the error line by line.

```
ERROR:  operator does not exist: character varying > integer
LINE 3: where stump_diam > 0
```

First we can see that the operator does not exist, in this case that our greater than sign cannot equate the relation between 'character varying' and 'integer'. And we can see which line this is taking place on.

We also get a hint from PostgreSQL too.

```
HINT:  No operator matches the given name and argument types. You might need to add explicit type casts.
```

So we can see from our two clues that there seems to be a data issue. Since we know 0 is an integer, reflected by the position of the two data types in the error statement, let's take a look at the data type of stump_diam (Figure 4.11, on the following page):

And there we go. We can see that even though the data in stump_diam should be a numeric type, it has in fact imported as a text column. We can fix this later but for now let's just recast that column to a numeric value and re-run our query:

Listing 4.37: Casting to fix our error

```
1   select
```

Figure 4.11: Casting the stump diameter column results

```
2      *
3   from
4       nyc_2015_tree_census
5   where
6       stump_diam :: numeric > 0
```

Voila! The only other comment on these operators is that you can use them for multiple data types, including dates, and even text.

Listing 4.38: Using operators with text

```
1   select
2       spc_common
3   from
4       nyc_2015_tree_census
5   where
6       spc_common > 'Maple'
```

AND/OR

The AND and OR logical operators allow you string together multiple arguments in your data. You can use one or many together, and you can use AND and OR together as well. Let's look at some quick examples using these operators:

Listing 4.39: Combining conditionals

```
1   select
2       *
3   from
4       nyc_311
5   where
6       complaint_type = 'Illegal Fireworks'
7       and city = 'BROOKLYN'
8   limit
9       25
```

And now using and OR operator. This will include any rows that meet either condition.

Listing 4.40: Using OR

```
1  select
2      *
3  from
4      nyc_311
5  where
6      complaint_type = 'Illegal Fireworks'
7      or agency = 'NYPD'
8  limit
9      25
```

IN

Let's imagine that you want to filter to more than one value on the same column. For two values you can just have two conditionals and join them together with an AND. But what about three, or five, or more?

This is where IN comes into play. You can have more than one value on the same column, and you can use the AND/OR conditionals to string two or more IN operators together. The structure looks like this:

WHERE column_name IN (value1, value2, ...)

The IN operator accepts any value separated by commas. It can also accept an array of values or values returned from a subquery (which we will cover in the next chapter). Let's take a look at a few examples:

Listing 4.41: IN Example 1

```
1  select
2      *
3  from
4      nyc_311
5  where
6      complaint_type IN ('Illegal Fireworks', 'Noise - Residential')
7  limit
8      25
```

Listing 4.42: IN Example 2

```
1  select
2      *
3  from
4      nyc_311
5  where
6      complaint_type IN ('Illegal Fireworks', 'Noise - Residential')
7      and descriptor IN ('Loud Music/Party', 'Banging/Pounding')
8  limit
9      25
```

NOT

If you want to find values that are not in a specific group of values, you can use the appropriately named NOT operator. Here is an example using the most recent query we ran:

Listing 4.43: Using NOT

```
1  select
2      *
3  from
```

```
4      nyc_311
5   where
6      complaint_type IN ('Illegal Fireworks', 'Noise - Residential')
7      and descriptor NOT IN ('Loud Music/Party', 'Banging/Pounding')
8   limit
9      25
```

You can use NOT with the next few operators we are covering here too.

BETWEEN

Another appropriately named operator is BETWEEN which allows you to select values that fall between two other values. BETWEEN is inclusive of the values you add into the statement, so it is synonymous to greater than or equal to the lowest value, and lower than or equal to the lowest value. Let's take a look at how we can use BETWEEN with dates. Note that you can use BETWEEN with numeric and string data as well (i.e. find all the states between California and Texas in alphabetical order).

Here we can see all the yellow taxi trips that were started on June 10th, 2016 between 3:00pm and 3:05pm.

Listing 4.44: Using BETWEEN

```
1   select
2      *
3   from
4      nyc_yellow_taxi_0601_0615_2016
5   where
6      pickup_datetime between '2016-06-10 15:00:00'
7      and '2016-06-10 15:05:00'
```

LIKE/ILIKE

LIKE and ILIKE are two different methods of searching string or text data using pattern matching. The only difference between LIKE and ILIKE is that ILIKE is case insensitive (meaning it will ignore the case of the letters) and is unique to PostgreSQL. These operators use the following methods to perform pattern matching in your data:

- The percent sign (%) will match any sequence of zero or more characters
- The underscore sign (_) will match any single character

So what does this look like in practice? First let's find all the trees in the NYC Tree Census that have the name "maple" somewhere in them, and this will be another coding challenge. First, consider the following scenarios to see which pattern matching will return which values (note that we are just using a query to define arbitrary text - or any other value you want - which is something SQL can also do, and common to see in documentation):

Listing 4.45: Testing the LIKE operator

```
1   -- All return true since it matches the exact word
2
3   select
4      'maple' like '%maple', --true
5      'maple' like 'maple%', --true
6      'maple' like '%maple%' --true
7
8   -- The first returns false since the phrase does not end in the word "maple"
9   select
10     'maple syrup' like '%maple', --false
```

```
11      'maple syrup' like 'maple%', --true
12      'maple syrup' like '%maple%' --true
13
14   -- The second returns false since the phrase does not begin with the word "maple"
15
16   select
17      'red maple' like '%maple', --true
18      'red maple' like 'maple%', --false
19      'red maple' like '%maple%' --true
```

Given that we know there are likely to be maple trees that end with maple, only contain the word maple, and maybe start with maple, which would be the correct operator to select here? Answer after the page break:

If you guessed this query you would be correct:

Listing 4.46: Using double wildcards to find any match

```
1   select
2       spc_common
3   from
4       nyc_2015_tree_census
5   where
6       spc_common like '%maple%'
```

Why is this? Because the % operator finds matches of **0 or more** matching characters which means that the word could start, end, or contain the word maple in it. The underscore operator is much more explicit:

Listing 4.47: Examples of length matching

```
1   SELECT
2       'maple' like 'm___', --false
3       'maple' like 'm____', --true
4       'maple' like 'm_____' --false
```

And if you are not sure of the character capitalization, feel free to use ILIKE as well.

IS NULL

If you want to find the values that are or are not NULL you can use the IS NULL operator. This can help in queries to include or exclude, or update rows that contain no data. Simply add this after a where clause such as:

Listing 4.48: Using NULL in WHERE conditions

```
1   select
2       *
3   from
4       nyc_yellow_taxi_0601_0615_2016
5   where
6       pickup_longitude IS NULL
```

DISTINCT

Now as you saw in the query where we found the names of all the trees that have maple in them, we got a full list of every single row that contained the name maple. Instead, if we wanted to get the name of all the trees that had maple in the name but only one time, we can use the `DISTINCT` keyword in our query to select a single instance of each result in a column. The `DISTINCT` will also be subject to all the other aspects of the query, such as `WHERE` clauses. We can add `DISTINCT` in our query to see the new results

Listing 4.49: Using the DISTINCT keyword

```
1  select
2      distinct spc_common
3  from
4      nyc_2015_tree_census
5  where
6      spc_common like '%maple%'
7  limit
8      5
```

spc_common
Amur maple
black maple
crimson king maple
hedge maple
Japanese maple

These are the first five results but we will only have 1 instance of each tree species.

4.9   Aggregates and GROUP BY

Up until this point we have simply been selecting rows of data from our tables. Let's say that we want to ask a question such as how many maple trees are in each neighborhood in New York City? To do this we can use aggregations and the GROUP BY conditional argument. This allows us to define an aggregation such as a COUNT or a SUM and then group the results by other data in our table. Let's take a look at an aggregation in action based on the scenario above, and then discuss the different available aggregation options.

Listing 4.50: Using COUNT and GROUP BY

```
1  select
2      nta_name,
3      count(ogc_fid)
4  from
5      nyc_2015_tree_census
6  where
7      spc_common like '%maple%'
8  group by
9      nta_name
10 limit
11     5
```

Breaking down our query:

- **select nta_name**: First, we pick the column "nta_name" which contains the neighborhood names in them
- **count(ogc_fid)**: Then we use the COUNT function which will count the number of instances in each group
- **from nyc_2015_tree_census**: Selecting data from our tree census table

- **where spc_common like '%maple%':** Find all the trees that have the name "maple" in them
- **group by nta_name:** Here we use our new operator GROUP BY to group our results by the "nta_name"
- **limit 5:** This will limit to the first 5 grouped results, not the first 5 rows of the source table.

And we can see our results here:

nta_name	count
Allerton-Pelham Gardens	801
Annadale-Huguenot-Prince"s Bay-Eltingville	2935
Arden Heights	1729
Astoria	318
Auburndale	1016

You can also combine your GROUP BY statements to have more than one column. Let's run the same query but this time grouping by neighborhood and then the "problem" column to see if there are any columns with the trees:

Listing 4.51: Grouping with multiple columns

```
1  select
2      nta_name,
3      problems,
4      count(ogc_fid)
5  from
6      nyc_2015_tree_census
7  where
8      spc_common like '%maple%'
9  group by
10     nta_name,
11     problems
12 limit
13     5
```

nta_name	problems	count	
Allerton-Pelham Gardens	BranchLights	167	
Allerton-Pelham Gardens	BranchOther	6	
Allerton-Pelham Gardens	None	400	
Allerton-Pelham Gardens	RootOther	6	
Allerton-Pelham Gardens	RootOther, BranchLights		8

We can see that the first column in our GROUP BY statement, neighborhood, is the first group and then the problem column is second.

For me personally, this is where I started to see the power of SQL. The ability to very quickly explore and modify queries to see your data in new ways show the power of SQL. Of course, there are many more reasons, but this is one of the first places that got me to stop and say, "whoa". With that, let's take a quick look at some different aggregation options:

String Aggregates

- **ARRAY_AGG:** Aggregate string results in an array

- **JSON_AGG**: Aggregate string results in a JSON object
- **STRING_AGG**: Aggregate string results in string with a defined delimiter

Here is a quick example:

Listing 4.52: Using the ARRAY_AGG aggregate function

```
1   select
2       nta_name,
3       array_agg(distinct curb_loc),
4       count(ogc_fid)
5   from
6       nyc_2015_tree_census
7   where
8       spc_common like '%maple%'
9   group by
10      nta_name
11  limit
12      3
```

Notice that I used the DISTINCT operator inside the ARRAY_AGG function since if I did not, I would get every instance of the values in the array, so for our first row, 801 individual values.

Numeric Aggregates

- AVG: Take the average (mean) of numeric values
- **COUNT**: Count of columns that match the conditions in your query
- **MAX**: Finds the maximum value in your numeric values
- **MIN**: Finds the minimum value in your numeric values
- SUM: : Finds the sum of your numeric values

Numeric aggregates operate on numeric columns to find different numeric summaries. There are more statistical aggregation methods that require some other tools which we will cover in the next chapter. For now, let's find the average stump diameter grouped by neighborhood:

Listing 4.53: Using the AVG aggregate

```
1   select
2       nta_name,
3       avg(stump_diam :: numeric)
4   from
5       nyc_2015_tree_census
6   where
7       stump_diam :: numeric > 0
8   group by
9       nta_name
10  limit
11      3
```

nta_name	avg
Allerton-Pelham Gardens	17.7638888888888889
Annadale-Huguenot-Prince"s Bay-Eltingville	12.9958677685950413
Arden Heights	10.7619047619047619

Note that there is no SQL function for median, although there are some methods to compute this using other functions[73]. We will showcase that specific function in the next chapter.

---

[73]https://ubiq.co/database-blog/calculate-median-postgresql/

FILTER

Now if you want to aggregate your data with a condition, in PostgreSQL you can use the FILTER operator to aggregate based on a WHERE condition. This is unique to PostgreSQL and there are other methods to do this in different databases. For example if we wanted to find the average distance of all taxi trips where the tip was greater than $5 between 3:00pm and 3:05pm on June 12th, and group it by passenger count, we can run this query:

Listing 4.54: Using FILTER with an aggregate

```
1  select
2      passenger_count,
3      avg(tip_amount) filter (
4          where
5              tip_amount > 5
6      )
7  from
8      nyc_yellow_taxi_0601_0615_2016
9  where
10     pickup_datetime between '2016-06-10 15:00:00'
11     and '2016-06-10 15:05:00'
12 group by
13     passenger_count
```

In the FILTER function we can add any type of argument we can write into a WHERE operator.

HAVING

What if you want to write a query like this, where you use the WHERE operator but on the results of an aggregated column:

Listing 4.55: You cannot use aggregate functions in WHERE conditions

```
1  select
2      passenger_count,
3      avg(tip_amount) filter (
4          where
5              tip_amount > 5
6      ),
7      count(ogc_fid)
8  from
9      nyc_yellow_taxi_0601_0615_2016
10 where
11     pickup_datetime between '2016-06-10 15:00:00'
12     and '2016-06-10 15:05:00'
13     and count(ogc_fid) > 50
14 group by
15     passenger_count
```

You will be getting this error back:

```
ERROR:  aggregate functions are not allowed in WHERE
LINE 7: and count(ogc_fid) > 50
```

Instead of using WHERE we can use HAVING to achieve the same effect but with aggregate values:

Listing 4.56: Using HAVING in WHERE conditions

```
1  select
2      passenger_count,
```

```
 3        avg(tip_amount) filter (
 4            where
 5                tip_amount > 5
 6        ),
 7        count(ogc_fid)
 8  from
 9        nyc_yellow_taxi_0601_0615_2016
10  where
11        pickup_datetime between '2016-06-10 15:00:00'
12        and '2016-06-10 15:05:00'
13  group by
14        passenger_count
15  having
16        count(ogc_fid) > 50
```

And this will render these values:

passenger_count	avg	count
1	10.594285714285714	1118
2	8.8124	219
3	9.055	82
5	7.63125	82

ORDER BY

In these queries we can see that the data is not organized any specific way. We can change that by using ORDER BY, which uses this simple syntax:

```
ORDER BY column_name (ASC for ascending or DESC for descending)
```

Ascending order is the default setting for ORDER BY, and it works for all data types. First we can see what the largest five tips were in our taxi dataset in the same time window we have been using:

Listing 4.57: Ordering your data

```
 1  select
 2        passenger_count,
 3        tip_amount
 4  from
 5        nyc_yellow_taxi_0601_0615_2016
 6  where
 7        pickup_datetime between '2016-06-10 15:00:00'
 8        and '2016-06-10 15:05:00'
 9  order by
10        tip_amount desc
11  limit
12        5
```

passenger_count	tip_amount
1	60
1	32.8
3	27.35
1	22.57

. . . continued on next page

passenger_count	tip_amount
1	21.58

And now let's take a look at this with our tree census dataset again, ordering our data by the COUNT.

Listing 4.58: Ordering with an aggregate

```
1   select
2       nta_name,
3       count(ogc_fid)
4   from
5       nyc_2015_tree_census
6   where
7       spc_common like '%maple%'
8   group by
9       nta_name
10  order by
11      count(ogc_fid) desc
12  limit
13      5
```

nta_name	count
Annadale-Huguenot-Prince"s Bay-Eltingville	2935
Great Kills	2815
Rossville-Woodrow	2503
Glen Oaks-Floral Park-New Hyde Park	2088
Bayside-Bayside Hills	1988

Keep in mind that you can also order by multiple values.

LIMIT/OFFSET

You have already seen LIMIT plenty of times which limits the number of rows that a query returns. You can also add an operator called *OFFSET*, which allows you to offset the number of rows by a specific amount. In this case we can find the New York neighborhoods with the 6th through 10th most maple trees in them:

Listing 4.59: LIMIT with OFFSET

```
1   select
2       nta_name,
3       count(ogc_fid)
4   from
5       nyc_2015_tree_census
6   where
7       spc_common like '%maple%'
8   group by
9       nta_name
10  order by
11      count(ogc_fid) desc
12  limit
13      5 offset 5
```

nta_name	count
New Springville-Bloomfield-Travis	1945
Arden Heights	1729
Charleston-Richmond Valley-Tottenville	1548
Douglas Manor-Douglaston-Little Neck	1503
Murray Hill	1479

With that we now have our most basic SQL operations covered! In the next chapter we will take a look at advanced SQL topics to round out our SQL training.

Part 2

Learning Spatial SQL

1. Advanced SQL Topics for Spatial SQL

In this chapter we will take a deeper dive into some of the more complex parts of SQL. These new elements will allow you to do write more complex queries while also making you SQL easier, more legible and often times more performant. So, let's jump in!

1.1 CASE/WHEN Conditionals

The first is the CASE / WHEN conditional that acts like if/else statements would in other languages. This allows us to work with any type of data to effectively process data into a new column of data using conditions that we define. The basic structure of the CASE / WHEN statement looks like this:

Listing 1.1: CASE WHEN structure

```
1  case
2      when condition_1 then result_1
3      when condition_2 then result_2 [WHEN ...] [ELSE else_result]
4  end
```

Effectively you can define a condition that you would define in a WHERE conditional, but without the WHERE. If that condition is met, then the data returned will be the result. You can string as many of these together as you want. Finally, you end the statement with an ELSE which will be returned if the condition is not met. For example let's say we have some weather data and there is a column with the temperature in Celsius in it. If we wanted to create a column that described the temperature in text we could write this CASE / WHEN statement:

Listing 1.2: Conditional temperature labels

```
1  case
2      when temp > 35 then 'Super Hot !'
3      when temp between 30
4      and 35 then 'Hot'
5      when temp between 25
6      and 30 then 'Pretty Warm'
7      when temp between 20
8      and 25 then 'Warm'
9      when temp between 15
10     and 20 then 'Cool / Warm'
11     when temp between 10
12     and 15 then 'Cool'
13     when temp between 5
14     and 10 then 'Chilly'
15     when temp between 0
16     and 5 then 'Cold'
17     when temp between -5
18     and 0 then 'Pretty Cold'
19     when temp between -10
20     and -5 then 'Very Cold'
21     when temp between -15
22     and -10 then 'Brrrrr'
23     when temp > -15 then 'Frigid !'
24     else null
25 end
```

Let's take a look at a real example with our tree census dataset:

Listing 1.3: Using conditionals to label all maple trees

```
1   select
2       spc_common,
3       case
4           when spc_common like '%maple%' then 'Maple'
5           else 'Not a Maple'
6       end as is_maple
7   from
8       nyc_2015_tree_census
9   limit
10      10
```

This will create a new temporary column in our data that will return a column that will say 'Maple' or 'Not Maple' depending on if our data meets our condition.

spc_common	is_maple
red maple	Maple
pin oak	Not a Maple
honeylocust	Not a Maple
honeylocust	Not a Maple
American linden	Not a Maple

Now as a coding challenge, see if you can create a CASE / WHEN statement that will classify the tip percentage as Good (between 15 and 20%), Great (between 20 and 25%), Amazing (25 to 30%), and Awesome (Over 30%). For other results you can call those Not Great and limit it to the first 10 rows.

To do this we will need to calculate the tip percentage by dividing the tip amount by the total amount, and then classifying that amount in our case when statement:

Listing 1.4: Categorizing tips

```
1   select
2       fare_amount,
3       tip_amount,
4       case
5           when tip_amount / fare_amount between .15
6           and .2 then 'Good'
7           when tip_amount / fare_amount between .2
8           and .25 then 'Great'
9           when tip_amount / fare_amount between .25
10          and .3 then 'Amazing'
11          when tip_amount / fare_amount > .3 then 'Awesome'
12          else 'Not Great'
13      end as tip_class
14  from
15      nyc_yellow_taxi_0601_0615_2016
16  limit
17      10
```

fare_amount	tip_amount	tip_class
23.5	5.06	Great
23.5	5.06	Great
23.5	5.06	Great
23.5	7.46	Awesome
23.5	7.45	Awesome
23.5	0.01	Not Great

As you can see instead of adding another category for "Not Great" we can just use the last part of the statement to classify all other results since all other results should be covered here.

In other SQL tools outside of PostgreSQL you will also have to use CASE / WHEN in your aggregations instead of FILTER since it is not supported outside of PostgreSQL. Take a look at this example:

Listing 1.5: Conditional counts

```
1  select
2      nta_name,
3      sum(
4          case
5              when spc_common like '%maple%' then 1
6              else 0
7          end
8      ) just_maples,
9      count(ogc_fid) as all_trees
10 from
11     nyc_2015_tree_census
12 group by
13     nta_name
14 limit
15     5
```

nta_name	just_maples	all_trees
Allerton-Pelham Gardens	801	3843
Annadale-Huguenot-Prince"s Bay-Eltingville	2935	12969
Arden Heights	1729	6999
Astoria	318	4393
Auburndale	1016	5332

As you can see we can take the sum of the return results from the conditional values, which will return 1 if the tree is a maple or 0 if it is not a maple.

1.2 Common Table Expressions (CTEs) and Subqueries

You have seen CTEs earlier in this book but subqueries are a new concept. I won't get too deep into subqueries vs. CTEs as there are several different and specific reasons why a subquery may be more advantageous over a CTE, but in many cases a CTE is more legible, is reusable, and acts like a table within the context of your query[74]. This is not a hard rule, but in general I prefer CTEs over subqueries. Let's first dive into subqueries and see where they can be useful and then talk more about CTEs.

---

[74]https://loc8.cc/sql/towardsdatascience-sql-subquery

Subqueries

A subquery looks more like a query contained within the query you are writing. Most commonly they are used within a WHERE clause to grab data from another table, but they can be used as a column of data or within a FROM operator as well. We will actually see this later in the chapter when we use a lateral join which is particularly useful for some specific spatial analysis.

For now let's take a look at examples of sub-queries in the WHERE clause. First let's take a look at the count of maple trees in zip codes with populations greater than 100,000 people. We have a column for zipcodes in our in our Tree Census data and a dataset of our NYC ZIP codes which has a population column. Let's practice our pseudo coding here to write out what we want to accomplish:

Count all the maple trees in each zip code with a population over 100,000

And let's format this in a more SQL friendly structure:

```
select the count of trees and zip code
where the name is like maple
from the trees dataset
where the zip code population is greater than 100,000
```

Looking at this you can see that we may need some way to join the data from the tree census table to the ZIP code table, and that is the logical way to think about this, and it is actually a great use for a subquery:

- The subquery would be used in a WHERE clause
- Return value can be something used in a WHERE conditional, such as a single value to find values equal to it, or a set of values for an IN conditional

In this case we can write a query that looks like this:

Listing 1.6: Using subqueries

```
1   select
2       zipcode,
3       count(ogc_fid)
4   from
5       nyc_2015_tree_census
6   where
7       spc_common like '%maple%'
8       and zipcode in (
9           select
10              zipcode
11          from
12              nyc_zips
13          where
14              population > 100000
15      )
16  group by
17      zipcode
```

zipcode	count
11226	276
11368	272

...continued on next page

zipcode	count
11373	578

As you can see our subquery returns three zip codes which have populations over 100,000. Now in this case we cannot add the population column to the query. If we wanted to do that we would need to do a join. Another way we can look at the query from above is like this.

Listing 1.7: Comparable query using IN

```
1  select
2      zipcode,
3      count(ogc_fid)
4  from
5      nyc_2015_tree_census
6  where
7      spc_common like '%maple%'
8      and zipcode in ('11226', '11368', '11373')
9  group by
10     zipcode
```

The subquery can also look like this if you want to return one value if we want to find how many trees are in the zip code with the lowest population:

Listing 1.8: Subquery with conditional

```
1  select
2      zipcode,
3      count(ogc_fid)
4  from
5      nyc_2015_tree_census
6  where
7      zipcode = (
8          select
9              zipcode
10         from
11             nyc_zips
12         order by
13             population asc
14         limit
15             1
16     )
17 group by
18     zipcode
```

zipcode	count
10048	12

Sub-queries can get a lot more complicated, but the CTE can accomplish many of the same things in a more legible way.

CTEs

The best way to think about a CTE is that it is the same as any other query, but the results that are returned act just like a table in the context of that query. The CTE structure looks like this:

```
with table_alias as (select * from another_table)
```

Let's take a look at an example:

Listing 1.9: Sample CTE

```
1   with lanes as (
2       select
3           ogc_fid,
4           lanecount
5       from
6           nyc_bike_routes
7       order by
8           lanecount desc
9       limit
10          3
11  )
12  select
13      *
14  from
15      lanes
```

ogc_fid	lanecount
609	3
2061	3
2062	3

As you can see above we defined a query in our subquery, and when we query that CTE table, we get the results from that table. What is great about this is that we can use the CTE as any normal table within our query. We can also create more than one CTE within a query:

Listing 1.10: CTEs with UNIONs

```
1   with lanes as (
2       select
3           ogc_fid,
4           lanecount
5       from
6           nyc_bike_routes
7       order by
8           lanecount desc
9       limit
10          3
11  ), lanes_2 as (
12      select
13          ogc_fid,
14          lanecount
15      from
16          nyc_bike_routes
17      order by
18          lanecount desc
19      limit
20          3 offset 12
21  )
22  select
23      *
24  from
25      lanes
26
27  -- the UNION operator allows us to bring
28  -- two tables with matching columns together
29
30  union
```

```
31  select
32      *
33  from
34      lanes_2
```

ogc_fid	lanecount
2062	3
3456	3
3459	3
3454	3
2061	3
609	3

We will be using CTEs **a lot** going forward so you will see these plenty of times in this book, but there are a few rules to keep in mind when using them:

- When you are using CTEs make sure to only return the rows that you need and try and filter as much data out as you can in each step to make the query more performant
- If you plan on reading the results of a CTE more than one time or on a regular basis, consider using a VIEW or creating a new table
- Using a CTE won't make operations more performant, so you will always need to consider query performance, but they generally increase query legibility

1.3 CRUD: Create, Read, Update, and Delete

Now once your tables are in your database you may want to make some changes to your data, or remove it all together. That is where the CRUD operations come in: create, read, update, and delete. Now we have actually already been doing the read step, which is just using the SELECT statement in SQL, so there is no need to go into that further. Let's take a look at each of the other operations in more detail.

The good part about this is that all the foundational elements you have learned already apply here so we will show a few of those in action but won't go into too much detail.

Create

In SQL there are a few ways to create new data:

- Import data into your database (we have done this already)
- Use a CREATE TABLE table_name AS statement (we have also done this)
- CREATE TABLE directly within the database

First we can create a new table or view using this syntax:

Listing 1.11: Sample create table statement

```
1  create table new_table as
2  select
3      *
4  from
5      another_table
6  where
7      some_column = 'some value'
```

This statement creates a brand new table with only the columns and rows returned from that query. You can also write the `CREATE TABLE AS` statement, adding "REPLACE" like below to replace the table if it is already created:

```
create or replace table new_table as
```

Alternatively if you want to do this in the database itself you can do this with the standard `CREATE TABLE` statement:

Listing 1.12: CREATE TABLE statement structure

```
1   create table test (city text, country text, size_rank numeric)
```

This will create a new, empty table in our database. We can add data into the database using this statement:

Listing 1.13: INSERT statement for previous code block

```
1   insert into
2       test (city, country, size_rank)
3   values
4       ('Tokyo', 'Japan', 1),
5       ('Delhi', 'India', 2),
6       ('Shanghai', 'China', 3),
7       ('ãSo Paulo', 'Brazil', 4),
8       ('Mexico City', 'Mexico', 5)
```

You can control the columns you want to insert the data into but the names will need to match those in the table. Then each row of data you want to insert along with the values will insert. You can also use columns like `CURRENT_TIMESTAMP` to add the current date or time, as well as other values.

Update

Once you have created your data there are several ways to update or modify your tables. These statements all use the `ALTER TABLE` statement. From here you can modify rows, columns, and more with all the same tools you can use in your standard SQL syntax. Fair warning that when you use these statements they are **permanent** and unless you have a database backup (we do in our case) or other tool set up, you cannot undo or recover these changes.

First let's add a new column to our test table:

Listing 1.14: ALTER TABLE statement

```
1   alter table
2       test
3   add
4       column population numeric
```

And when we query our new table we can see the new column has been added:

city	country	size_rank	population
Tokyo	Japan	1	
Delhi	India	2	
Shanghai	China	3	

. . . continued on next page

city	country	size_rank	population
São Paulo	Brazil	4	
Mexico City	Mexico	5	

We can also rename a column:

Listing 1.15: Rename a column

```
1  alter table
2      test rename column population to city_pop
```

Change the data type:

Listing 1.16: Change a column data type

```
1  alter table
2      test
3  alter column
4      city_pop type int
```

What is great about this is that you can also selectively run these queries using the other tools we have already learned. Say we want to change the name Mexico City to the Spanish name we can do this:

Listing 1.17: Update a specific value using WHERE

```
1  update
2      test
3  set
4      city = 'Ciudad de éMxico'
5  where
6      city = 'Mexico City'
```

Finally, let's rename our table as well:

Listing 1.18: Rename a table

```
1  alter table
2      test rename to world_cities
```

Delete

Now if we want to delete or drop part of all of a table or column we can use these functions.

To drop a column outright:

Listing 1.19: Drop a column

```
1  alter table
2      world_cities drop column city_pop
```

To drop a row or set of rows based on a condition:

Listing 1.20: Delete a row using WHERE

```
1  delete from
2      world_cities
3  where
4      city = 'Tokyo'
```

And to delete the table outright:

Listing 1.21: Drop a table completely

```
1  drop table world_cities
```

As it relates to spatial SQL, I tend to use the `CREATE TABLE AS` or `CREATE VIEW AS` statements all the time to save results of a query, as well as creating new columns and populating them with new data.

1.4 Statistical functions

Earlier we saw some basic statistical functions such as `SUM` and `AVG`, but PostgreSQL provides many more functions to perform statistical analysis including:

- Correlations
- Standard deviations
- Variances
- Mode
- Discrete and Continuous Percentiles
- Rankings

Let's test out some of these functions with our New York City MAPPLUTO dataset, or property assessment data, first taking a look at the correlation between lot area and the lot assessed value:

Listing 1.22: Correlation between two values

```
1  select
2      corr(assesstot :: numeric, lotarea :: numeric)
3  from
4      nyc_mappluto
```

```
0.5561503500548179
```

As we can see there is a very slight positive correlation between these two variables. Next, let's find the standard deviation and variance between lot areas in Brooklyn.

Listing 1.23: Standard deviation

```
1  select
2      stddev_samp(lotarea :: numeric)
3  from
4      nyc_mappluto
5  where
6      borough = 'BK'
```

```
430938.03381969
```

And then the variance:

Listing 1.24: Sample variation

```
1  select
2      var_samp(lotarea :: numeric)
3  from
4      nyc_mappluto
5  where
6      borough = 'BK'
```

> 185707588992.37929885

Let's also find the mode of lot areas in Brooklyn as well. The MODE function does not take any arguments, and we can choose the column we want which is located in parentheses as an ORDER BY statement. WITHIN GROUP is similar to the FILTER operator we used with aggregated data, but focusing on filtering groups of data.

Listing 1.25: MODE in SQL

```
1  select
2      mode() within group (
3          order by
4              lotarea :: numeric desc
5      )
6  from
7      nyc_mappluto
8  where
9      borough = 'BK'
```

> 2000

In the next view we can analyze data as percentiles and rankings. Let's take a small sample of data from our taxis dataset and find the percentiles for the tips in that data.

Listing 1.26: Using PERCENT_RANK

```
1   select
2       ogc_fid,
3       tip_amount,
4       percent_rank() over(
5           order by
6               tip_amount asc
7       )
8   from
9       nyc_yellow_taxi_0601_0615_2016
10  where
11      pickup_datetime between '2016-06-10 15:00:00'
12      and '2016-06-10 15:00:05'
13      and tip_amount > 0
```

Here we are finding the trips that started within 5 seconds of 3:00 PM on June 10th, 2016. The PERCENT_RANK function uses a window syntax using the OVER operator which we will learn more about in this chapter. Basically, it is telling the query to perform the query within the context of that specific set, or window, of data and how to evaluate that data. In this case that is the tip_amount ordered from smallest to largest. If we take a look at the last values in our data we can see this:

ogc_fid	tip_amount	percent_rank
1402435	0.94	0
3356070	1	0.045454545454545456
4618244	1	0.045454545454545456
1552227	1	0.045454545454545456
2147551	1	0.045454545454545456

... continued on next page

ogc_fid	tip_amount	percent_rank
756994	1	0.045454545454545456
3897062	1.05	0.2727272727272727
3449877	1.28	0.3181818181818182
92072	1.5	0.36363636363636365
1200217	1.55	0.4090909090909091
924313	1.85	0.45454545454545453
1597764	1.95	0.5
168058	2	0.5454545454545454
5466226	2.95	0.5909090909090909
884868	3.26	0.6363636363636364
3284030	4.16	0.6818181818181818
1430706	4.36	0.7272727272727273
2140264	5	0.7727272727272727
4472630	5.56	0.8181818181818182
865468	6.99	0.8636363636363636
2353249	7	0.9090909090909091
1484844	14.55	0.9545454545454546
3875087	27.35	1

This shows us the percentile of each tip in this dataset. We can also rank these results too:

Listing 1.27: Using RANK

```
1   select
2       ogc_fid,
3       tip_amount,
4       rank() over(
5           order by
6               tip_amount asc
7       )
8   from
9       nyc_yellow_taxi_0601_0615_2016
10  where
11      pickup_datetime between '2016-06-10 15:00:00'
12      and '2016-06-10 15:00:05'
13      and tip_amount > 0
```

This will return a ranking which accounts for repeated values:

ogc_fid	tip_amount	rank
1402435	0.94	1
2147551	1	2
4618244	1	3
756994	1	4
1552227	1	5
3356070	1	6
3897062	1.05	7

...continued on next page

ogc_fid	tip_amount	rank
3449877	1.28	8

If we want to exclude gaps in our rankings we can use DENSE_RANK

Listing 1.28: Using DENSE_RANK for same values

```
1   select
2       ogc_fid,
3       tip_amount,
4       dense_rank() over(
5           order by
6               tip_amount asc
7       )
8   from
9       nyc_yellow_taxi_0601_0615_2016
10  where
11      pickup_datetime between '2016-06-10 15:00:00'
12      and '2016-06-10 15:00:05'
13      and tip_amount > 0
```

ogc_fid	tip_amount	dense_rank
1402435	0.94	1
2147551	1	2
4618244	1	2
756994	1	2
1552227	1	2
3356070	1	2
3897062	1.05	3
3449877	1.28	4

We can also find percentile values within our dataset too using PERCENTILE_DISC:

Listing 1.29: Calculating percentile

```
1   select
2       percentile_disc(0.25) within group (
3           order by
4               tip_amount
5       ) as per_25,
6       percentile_disc(0.5) within group (
7           order by
8               tip_amount
9       ) as per_50,
10      percentile_disc(0.75) within group (
11          order by
12              tip_amount
13      ) as per_75
14  from
15      nyc_yellow_taxi_0601_0615_2016
16  where
17      pickup_datetime between '2016-06-10 15:00:00'
18      and '2016-06-10 15:00:05'
19      and tip_amount > 0
```

per_25	per_50	per_75
1	1.95	5

You can also find interpolated values with PERCENTILE_CONT, meaning that if the value at the 50th percentile fell between 9 and 10, this would return 9.5 rather than one of the values that is actually in the data:

per_25	per_50	per_75
1.025	1.95	4.68

1.5 Windows

I mentioned Window functions in the previous section, and while they can be difficult to initially understand, they have a lot of interesting utility for really complex calculations. The PostgreSQL docs do a great job of explaining what a Window function can do:

A window function performs a calculation across a set of table rows that are somehow related to the current row. This is comparable to the type of calculation that can be done with an aggregate function. But unlike regular aggregate functions, use of a window function does not cause rows to become grouped into a single output row — the rows retain their separate identities. Behind the scenes, the window function is able to access more than just the current row of the query result.

So what can you do with a Window function? Here are a few examples

- Rolling averages such as a 30 day or 30 row average (think of GPS points or weather data)
- Averages across groups of data
- Running totals
- Rankings (as we saw above)
- In spatial SQL, calculate clusters using KMeans or DBSCAN

Window functions are actually a great fit to work with our NYC Taxi data, so let's test this out on that dataset. Now the simplest type of window functions work on data with consistent intervals or non-aggregated data. In this case, we can use a CTE to show what this can look like with the total amount. In this case we will find the total fares for each day of our data, then find a rolling 3 day average of that data:

Listing 1.30: A WINDOW function

```
1   with taxis as (
2       select
3           sum(total_amount) as total,
4           pickup_datetime :: date as date
5       from
6           nyc_yellow_taxi_0601_0615_2016
7       group by
8           pickup_datetime :: date
9       order by
10          pickup_datetime :: date asc
11  )
12  select
13      date,
14      total,
15      avg(total) over (
16          order by
17              date rows between 2 preceding
```

```
18              and current row
19      )
20  from
21      taxis
```

As you can see, in our query we are using the window function to find an average OVER the current row and the preceding two rows which makes up our 3 day average, and we are ordering our window by the date.

There is also an argument called PARTITION BY which we can use. In this case let's run the same query but also add in the passenger count and create a running total:

Listing 1.31: WINDOW with PARTITION

```
1   with taxis as (
2       select
3           sum(total_amount) as total,
4           passenger_count,
5           pickup_datetime :: date as date
6       from
7           nyc_yellow_taxi_0601_0615_2016
8       group by
9           pickup_datetime :: date,
10          passenger_count
11      order by
12          pickup_datetime :: date asc,
13          passenger_count desc
14  )
15  select
16      date,
17      total,
18      passenger_count,
19      sum(total) over (
20          partition by passenger_count
21          order by
22              date rows between 2 preceding
23              and current row
24      )
25  from
26      taxis
```

date	total	passenger_count	sum
2016-06-01	4454471.090003965	1	4454471.090003965
2016-06-02	4836297.680004317	1	9290768.770008283
2016-06-03	4706419.480004478	1	13997188.250012761
2016-06-04	4287671.180004338	1	18284859.4300171

Next, let's find a rolling 6-hour average every hour of the tip percentage on June 15th, 2016. Let's plan this out using pseudocode.

Select the average tip percentage (tip divided by total amount) **Over a 6 hour window** Where the date is June 15th 2016 Grouped by the hour of the day

The only new piece here is this section in bold. So let's write the parts of the query that we know right now:

Listing 1.32: Hourly average tip

```
1   select
2       avg(tip_amount / total_amount),
3       extract(
4           hour
5           from
6               pickup_datetime
7       ) as hour_of_day
8   from
9       nyc_yellow_taxi_0601_0615_2016
10  where
11      pickup_datetime :: date = '2016-06-15'
12
13      -- since we can't divide by 0 we will remove all amounts
14      -- that equal 0
15
16      and total_amount > 0
17  group by
18      extract(
19          hour
20          from
21              pickup_datetime
22      )
23  order by
24      extract(
25          hour
26          from
27              pickup_datetime
28      ) asc
```

avg	hour_of_day
0.10381201153091137	0
0.09603191451808368	1
0.09137175846790613	2
0.08759743269474266	3
0.06674264082545112	4
0.09629157470475837	5

So the only thing we need to add in is our window function. Our window functions will roughly follow this signature:

```
FUNCTION(arguments) OVER (PARTITION BY group_name ORDER BY value)
```

To accomplish this we want to use another CTE to group our tip percentages by day and hour. Let's take a look at the query and talk through what it is doing:

Listing 1.33: Using a CTE this time

```
1   with taxis as (
2       select
3           avg(tip_amount / total_amount) as tip_percentage,
4           date_trunc('hour', pickup_datetime) as day_hour
5       from
6           nyc_yellow_taxi_0601_0615_2016
7       where
8           total_amount > 5
9       group by
```

```
10              date_trunc('hour', pickup_datetime)
11      )
12   select
13       day_hour,
14       tip_percentage,
15       avg(tip_percentage) over (
16           order by
17               day_hour asc rows between 5 preceding
18               and current row
19       ) as moving_average
20   from
21       taxis
```

First let's look at line 4 in the CTE. This is a great example of "if there is something you need to do there is probably a SQL function for it". In this case, we want to truncate our pickup timestamp to the nearest hour. We can use the DATE_TRUNC function to do this.

With that added into our query we can select the newly created day_hour column and the tip_percentage and add in our window function. Since we are not grouping the window function we do not need to use the partition by clause. Another great feature of pgAdmin is the ability to quickly make some simple chart visualizations. We can see the results of our average and moving average on a chart (Figure 1.1):

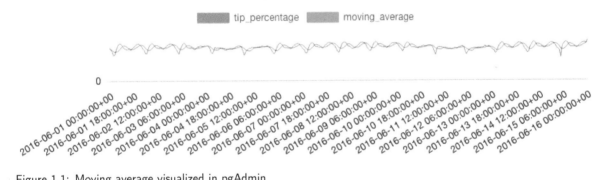

Figure 1.1: Moving average visualized in pgAdmin

Up until this point all our window functions have used the window of number of rows to look back over a period of time, which is not necessary in all window queries. For example below we can simply query a running sum of the total fares by day and partition, or group by, the passenger count.

Listing 1.34: Rolling total

```
1   with taxis as (
2       select
3           sum(total_amount) as total,
4           passenger_count,
5           pickup_datetime :: date as date
6       from
7           nyc_yellow_taxi_0601_0615_2016
8       group by
9           pickup_datetime :: date,
10          passenger_count
11      order by
12          pickup_datetime :: date asc,
13          passenger_count desc
14  )
15  select
16      date,
17      total,
```

```
18      passenger_count,
19      sum(total) over (
20          partition by passenger_count
21          order by
22              date
23      )
24  from
25      taxis
```

date	total	passenger_count	sum
2016-06-01	4454471.090003965	1	4454471.090003965
2016-06-02	4836297.680004317	1	9290768.770008283
2016-06-03	4706419.480004478	1	13997188.250012761
2016-06-04	4287671.180004338	1	18284859.4300171

There are several other window functions that are available, and you can see the complete set using the link in the footnote here[75]. There are three more functions that I have used most often when writing window functions. The first is ROW_NUMBER.

In the case that you need to number a row you can use the ROW_NUMBER window function. This returns a row number starting at 1 for each row in the partition. For example:

Listing 1.35: Adding numbered rows

```
1  select
2      row_number() over() as row_no,
3      ogc_fid
4  from
5      nyc_yellow_taxi_0601_0615_2016
6  limit
7      5
```

Will return 5 rows numbered 1 to 5:

row_no	ogc_fid
1	5243761
2	5243762
3	5243763
4	5243764
5	5243765

We can also use partition here to number the rows based on a grouped value such as:

Listing 1.36: Adding rows with partitions

```
1  select
2      row_number() over(partition by pickup_datetime) as row_no,
3      ogc_fid,
4      pickup_datetime
5  from
6      nyc_yellow_taxi_0601_0615_2016
7  limit
8      5 offset 100000 -- using offset since the first part of the datasets has all passenger counts as 0
```

---

[75]https://www.postgresql.org/docs/current/functions-window.html

row_no	ogc_fid	pickup_datetime
1	2585758	2016-06-01 10:21:38+00
1	2464066	2016-06-01 10:21:39+00
2	3613887	2016-06-01 10:21:39+00
3	4121002	2016-06-01 10:21:39+00
1	3871312	2016-06-01 10:21:40+00

Another useful set of functions are LAG and LEAD. These functions take two arguments, the column and the number of rows you cant to lag or lead by. In this case we will use lag to look at the daily total change in total amount of fares grouped by the number of passengers.

Listing 1.37: Day to day change with LAG

```
1  with taxis as (
2      select
3          sum(total_amount) as total,
4          passenger_count,
5          pickup_datetime :: date as date
6      from
7          nyc_yellow_taxi_0601_0615_2016
8      group by
9          pickup_datetime :: date,
10         passenger_count
11     order by
12         pickup_datetime :: date asc,
13         passenger_count desc
14 )
15 select
16     date,
17     total,
18     passenger_count,
19     total - lag(total, 1) over (
20         partition by passenger_count
21         order by
22             date
23     )
24 from
25     taxis
```

date	total	passenger_count	?column?
2016-06-01	4454471.090004012	1	
2016-06-02	4836297.68000439	1	381826.59000037797
2016-06-03	4706419.48000454	1	-129878.19999985024
2016-06-04	4287671.1800044235	1	-418748.3000001162
2016-06-05	3939447.030003368	1	-348224.15000105556
2016-06-06	4376279.250003793	1	436832.22000042535

Using LEAD we could find the same values in the other direction for the total of the current row minus the total from the next day in the future.

1.6 Joins

Up until now we have only been working with queries on one table. Some of the real utility of SQL comes when you start to join tables. Joins can seem like a complex topic, especially if you have only worked on joining data in a GIS toolkit, but when planned out correctly and with a set of a few simple rules, joins will help you quickly make your analysis far more useful and fast, in fact joins will become an easy task.

Joins in SQL allow you to join two or more datasets based on one or more conditions. You can join the data with multiple different methods, including only matching columns, matching columns from one table and all other columns from another table, all matches and non matches, or join every column to every other column.

For me, the best way to think about a join was always visually. Below is a quick illustration of the different types of joins (Figure 1.2):

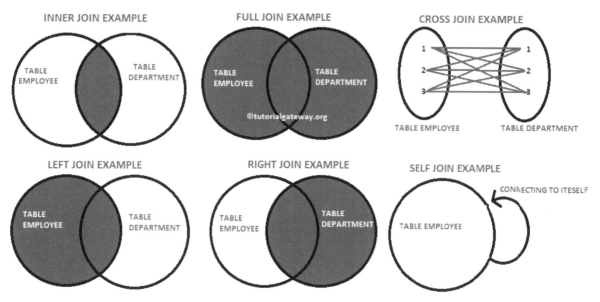

Figure 1.2: SQL join types visualized from tutorialgateway.org

We will be using two tables, our tree census and our zip code dataset to practice a few joins. We can then structure the same illustration with our tables and the joins that we will be doing.

With that there are a few tips and tricks I like to use when setting up a join:

- As much as possible, use inner joins, represented by the keyword JOIN
- Instead of switching between LEFT and RIGHT joins, just use one and move the table order
- In most cases you will want to use an INNER join rather than an OUTER join, which you don't need to designate the INNER keyword.
- CROSS JOIN can be used in very specific use cases as we will see later

With that let's do a very simple join between our two tables:

Listing 1.38: Our first join

```
1  select
2      nyc_311.complaint_type,
3      nyc_311.incident_zip,
4      nyc_zips.population
```

```
5  from
6      nyc_311
7      join nyc_zips on nyc_311.incident_zip = nyc_zips.zipcode
8  limit
9      5
```

There are a few things to notice here. First is that before every column we are using the table name, followed by a period, followed by the column name. Since we are using two tables we need to designate which tables each column is coming from.

Next is the join syntax itself:

```
from nyc_311 join nyc_zips on nyc_311.incident_zip = nyc_zips.zipcode
```

First we designate our left table in the `FROM` clause. Followed by the right table, which has `JOIN` listed before it. We can then use the `ON` keyword to tell the query how to join our two tables based on a condition. That condition will equate to true between two columns. In most cases this will be an equation that uses = since that will join based on a specific value.

Keep in mind just like any other SQL query you can also use a `WHERE` conditional as needed in addition to the join. So if we wanted to join only a specific type of 311 call we could do so with the `WHERE` clause, the `JOIN` is only representative of the key which we want to join on.

So when we run our join, you can find the results here:

complaint_type	population
Food Poisoning	69255
Noise - Commercial	69255
Illegal Fireworks	80857
Illegal Fireworks	80857
Noise - Residential	56670

We can test the same query by adding a `WHERE` clause:

Listing 1.39: Conditional joins

```
1  select
2      nyc_311.complaint_type,
3      nyc_311.incident_zip,
4      nyc_zips.population
5  from
6      nyc_311
7      join nyc_zips on nyc_311.incident_zip = nyc_zips.zipcode
8  where
9      nyc_zips.population > 80000
10 limit
11     5
```

complaint_type	incident_zip	population
Illegal Fireworks	11230	80857
Illegal Fireworks	11230	80857

...continued on next page

complaint_type	incident_zip	population
Illegal Parking	11220	97257
Noise - Residential	11377	90852
Noise - Residential	11355	82809

As stated earlier, we have to reference the table names prior to the columns we want to reference. Now when you have longer table names this adds a ton of typing. The good news is that we can actually use a table name alias by adding a table name of one character (must start with a character not a number) or more to the tables, then use those as the table name alias. For example, we can rewrite our query above to:

Listing 1.40: JOINs with table aliases

```
1  select
2      a.complaint_type,
3      a.incident_zip,
4      b.population
5  from
6      nyc_311 a
7      join nyc_zips b on a.incident_zip = b.zipcode
8  where
9      b.population > 80000
10 limit
11     5
```

I usually use one letter in alphabetical order or a shorthand name for my tables where I will recognize what each shorthand name is referencing

LEFT and RIGHT Joins

The LEFT and RIGHT joins will perform the same operation as the (*INNER*) JOIN above, but will also include non-matching values. To illustrate this, we can write a subquery that grabs 30 rows from our zip codes table.

```
with b as (select population, zipcode from nyc_zips limit 30)
```

Listing 1.41: LEFT JOIN

```
1  with b as (select population, zipcode from nyc_zips limit 30)
2
3  select
4      a.complaint_type,
5      a.incident_zip,
6      b.population
7  from
8      nyc_311 a
9      left join b on a.incident_zip = b.zipcode
10 limit
11     5
```

complaint_type	incident_zip	population
Food Poisoning	11209	

. . . continued on next page

complaint_type	incident_zip	population
Noise - Commercial	11209	
Illegal Fireworks	11230	80857
Illegal Fireworks	11230	80857
Noise - Residential	10460	

As you can see here the rows that don't match from the left table, in this case our 311 table, are still shown but there are null values in the rows from the zip code table. The RIGHT join will accomplish the exact opposite of this.

Listing 1.42: RIGHT JOIN

```
1   with a as (
2       select
3           complaint_type,
4           incident_zip
5       from
6           nyc_311
7       limit
8           30
9   )
10  select
11      a.complaint_type,
12      a.incident_zip,
13      b.population
14  from
15      a
16      right join nyc_zips b on a.incident_zip = b.zipcode
17  limit
18      5
```

complaint_type	incident_zip	population
		18681
		62426
Request Large Bulky Item Collection	10002	81305
		35473
		5850

FULL OUTER Joins

A FULL OUTER join will join all possible rows, matches and non-matches. Very few times have I actually had to use a FULL OUTER join, but we can take a look at it here just in case it comes up for you.

Listing 1.43: FULL OUTER JOIN

```
1   with a as (
2       select
3           complaint_type,
4           incident_zip
5       from
6           nyc_311
7       limit
8           30
9   ), b as (
10      select
```

```
11          population,
12          zipcode
13      from
14          nyc_zips
15      limit
16          30
17  )
18  select
19      a.complaint_type,
20      a.incident_zip,
21      b.population
22  from
23      a full
24      outer join b on a.incident_zip = b.zipcode
25  limit
26      100
```

I won't show the full results here but you should see three categories of results:

- Results that match from the left table (311 data in CTE)
- Results that match from the left table (zip code data in CTE)
- Results that match both tables

CROSS Joins

Cross joins are joins between two tables that compute each row in the left table to every other row in the right table. In effect, if you have a table of 10 rows and another table of 10 rows, your resulting join will have 100 rows. While this may not seem useful, I have actually used a cross join many times for creating origin destination matrices or distance tables. Since you are joining every single row, you don't actually need a join condition. There are two ways to accomplish this, and we will show both using a simple subquery with 2 rows in each table.

In the first method we can explicitly call out the CROSS JOIN

Listing 1.44: CROSS JOIN

```
1   with a as (
2       select
3           neighborhood
4       from
5           nyc_neighborhoods
6       limit
7           2
8   ), b as (
9       select
10          population,
11          zipcode
12      from
13          nyc_zips
14      limit
15          2
16  )
17  select
18      a.neighborhood,
19      b.population
20  from
21      a
22      cross join b
```

And in the next we can just separate the tables using a comma for a more shorthand method.

Listing 1.45: CROSS JOIN shorthand method

```
1   with a as (
2       select
3           neighborhood
4       from
5           nyc_neighborhoods
6       limit
7           2
8   ), b as (
9       select
10          population,
11          zipcode
12      from
13          nyc_zips
14      limit
15          2
16  )
17  select
18      a.neighborhood,
19      b.population
20  from
21      a,
22      b
```

In most cases you will want to compute something between the two tables. Here we can divide the value of the population of the zip code and the shape area of the neighborhood boundary. While this has no analytical value, you can see some use cases for a cross join:

Listing 1.46: Cross join calculations

```
1   with a as (
2       select
3           neighborhood
4       from
5           nyc_neighborhoods
6       limit
7           2
8   ), b as (
9       select
10          population,
11          zipcode
12      from
13          nyc_zips
14      limit
15          2
16  )
17  select
18      a.neighborhood,
19      b.population,
20      b.population / 1000 as calculation
21  from
22      a,
23      b
```

ntaname	shape_area	population	calculation
St. Albans	77412747.7931	18681	0.00024131684422220038
St. Albans	77412747.7931	62426	0.0008064046527174714
Van Cortlandt Village	25666124.5948	18681	0.0007278465407194666
Van Cortlandt Village	25666124.5948	62426	0.0024322331861759768

Aggregations and Joins

While joins are great you can also perform aggregations alongside joins and this is where things start to get really powerful. Of course you can perform basic calculations such as math as well as other functions between tables with a join, but aggregations allow you to aggregate a longer table and join it to other data. This will come up later in spatial joins as well.

For a quick example let's look at how many buildings fall within each zip code:

Listing 1.47: Counting buildings in zip codes

```
1   with a as (
2       select
3           ogc_fid,
4           zipcode :: text
5       from
6           nyc_mappluto
7   )
8   select
9       count(a.ogc_fid),
10      b.zipcode
11  from
12      nyc_zips b
13      join a using(zipcode)
14  group by
15      b.zipcode
16  order by
17      count(a.ogc_fid) desc
```

count	zipcode
21000	10314
19436	10312
19389	11234
17021	10306
14682	11236

As you can see we also used a new keyword, USING, to join our data. If your column names that you want to join on are the same name and same data type (I had to cast the *zipcode* column from the buildings data to achieve this) then you can simply designate that single shared column name inside the USING join parameter.

Multiple Joins and Other Issues

Now you can join more than one table, but there are some caveats here that you want to be careful of. Let's take a quick scenario using our aggregation from above with adding another aggregation to our query with two other datasets:

Listing 1.48: Warning: for example purposes only

```
1   with a as (
2       select
3           ogc_fid,
4           zipcode :: text
```

```
5        from
6            nyc_mappluto
7        order by
8            ogc_fid desc
9        limit
10           5000
11   ), c as (
12       select
13           ogc_fid,
14           zipcode
15       from
16           nyc_2015_tree_census
17       order by
18           ogc_fid desc
19       limit
20           5000
21   )
22   select
23       count(a.ogc_fid) as buildings,
24       count(c.ogc_fid) as trees,
25       b.zipcode
26   from
27       nyc_zips b
28       join a using(zipcode)
29       join c using(zipcode)
30   group by
31       b.zipcode
32   order by
33       count(a.ogc_fid) desc
```

Full warning, I do not recommend running this query without limits it will take a very long time to complete, and I will explain why below. Let's take a look at the results:

buildings	trees	zipcode
43605	43605	10312
31320	31320	10309
16618	16618	10307
36	36	10304

As you can see both our counts are actually the same. We can check and see if that is accurate by running each join separately. First for our buildings layer:

Listing 1.49: Testing our multi-join

```
1    with a as (
2        select
3            ogc_fid,
4            zipcode :: text
5        from
6            nyc_mappluto
7        order by
8            ogc_fid desc
9        limit
10           5000
11   ), c as (
12       select
13           ogc_fid,
14           zipcode
15       from
16           nyc_2015_tree_census
```

```
17        order by
18            ogc_fid desc
19        limit
20            5000
21    )
22    select
23        count(a.ogc_fid) as buildings,
24        -- count(c.ogc_fid) as trees,
25        b.zipcode
26    from
27        nyc_zips b
28        join a using(zipcode)
29        -- join c
30        -- using(zipcode)
31    group by
32        b.zipcode
33    order by
34        count(a.ogc_fid) desc
```

buildings	zipcode
3480	10309
1187	10307
323	10312
3	10304

Then for our trees:

Listing 1.50: Now with the other table

```
1    with a as (
2        select
3            ogc_fid,
4            zipcode :: text
5        from
6            nyc_mappluto
7        order by
8            ogc_fid desc
9        limit
10           5000
11   ), c as (
12       select
13           ogc_fid,
14           zipcode
15       from
16           nyc_2015_tree_census
17       order by
18           ogc_fid desc
19       limit
20           5000
21   )
22   select
23       -- count(a.ogc_fid) as buildings,
24       count(c.ogc_fid) as trees,
25       b.zipcode
26   from
27       nyc_zips b
28       -- join a using(zipcode)
29       join c using(zipcode)
30   group by
31       b.zipcode
```

```
32        -- order by count(a.ogc_fid) desc
33   order by
34       count(c.ogc_fid) desc
```

trees	zipcode
211	11375
190	11230
177	11105
168	10457
146	11370

So we can see that neither of the two have the same amount in our first query. So instead we can single out one specific zip code, 10312, and see what the results for that one zip code look like. You can add this as a WHERE clause to your queries from above but we can skip ahead to the results, first for buildings:

buildings	zipcode
323	10312

Then for trees:

trees	zipcode
135	10312

If you haven't guessed it yet, our first return value for the zip code 10312 was 43,605, which is the result of multiplying 135 by 323. So then why did our query do this? In short, each table join will return a single, intermediate table, also known as a derived table. The multiple joins will read each step sequentially, so in the case above when we reference our second join to the first table, we are inadvertently returning a Cartesian join, or cross join, because one table may match 50 rows in the first join, while the second could match 1000, for example.

If you take a look at the visual analysis of the query you can see that the aggregation only happens at the final part of the query, so that is why the rows are in effect multiplied. Here you can see the visualized query plan in 1.3).

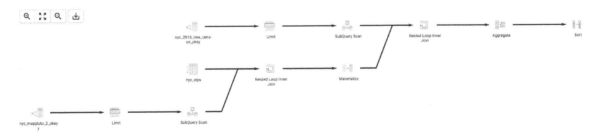

Figure 1.3: Query plan visualization

So to accomplish this query we can simply use CTEs to aggregate our data twice then join it in one final query. We can then get rid of the temporary CTEs and write our full query:

Listing 1.51: Double join with CTEs

```
1   with a as (
2       select
3           count(ogc_fid) as buildings,
4           zipcode :: text
5       from
6           nyc_mappluto
7       group by
8           zipcode
9   ),
10  b as (
11      select
12          count(ogc_fid) as trees,
13          zipcode
14      from
15          nyc_2015_tree_census
16      group by
17          zipcode
18  )
19  select
20      a.buildings,
21      b.trees,
22      c.zipcode
23  from
24      nyc_zips c
25      join a using(zipcode)
26      join b using(zipcode)
27  order by
28      b.trees desc
```

buildings	trees	zipcode
19436	22186	10312
21000	16905	10314
17021	13030	10306
10572	12650	10309
19389	11253	11234

So this gives us the correct counts and runs quite quickly given the total amount of data we are analyzing. We are joining a table of 683,788 rows in our trees table and 856,997 rows in our buildings table.

1.7   Lateral Joins

Now there is one other specific type of join that requires a section of its own because of its applicability for advanced analysis with spatial SQL. What makes a LATERAL JOIN special is that the join:

- Follows the FROM statement as a separate subquery
- Can access data (i.e. columns) from the left table, or the table preceding the LATERAL JOIN

We will cover why this has some very special applications for spatial data later in the book but for now let's show what this can look like in practice. To show what this looks like we will actually use a CROSS JOIN that will take every combination of records, even though we are just returning one result. Using this syntax we can divide the count of the total number of trees in each neighborhood divided by the shape_area column which is the size of the neighborhoods in square yards.

Listing 1.52: LATERAL JOINs

```
1  select
2      a.neighborhood,
3      trees.trees_per_sq_meter
4  from
5      nyc_neighborhoods a
6      cross join lateral (
7          select
8              count(ogc_fid) / a.area :: numeric as trees_per_sq_meter
9          from
10             nyc_2015_tree_census
11         where
12             a.neighborhood = neighborhood
13     ) trees
14 order by
15     trees.trees_per_sq_meter desc
```

ntaname	trees_per_sq_yrd
Upper East Side-Carnegie Hill	0.00023288887617650641
Central Harlem South	0.00018488732748556470
Brooklyn Heights-Cobble Hill	0.00017696398193253380
Upper West Side	0.00017105904160212209
Fordham South	0.00016801727715830502

As we can see Upper East Side-Carnegie Hil has the most tree density.

What is great about the LATERAL JOIN is that you can calculate across many rows within the lateral join and use aggregates like we did above.

1.8 Triggers

TRIGGER functions allow you to write a SQL action that will "trigger" based on one of four event types on your table: INSERT, UPDATE, DELETE, or TRUNCATE. Within the TRIGGER we will be using a new language variation of SQL known as PL/pgSQL[76] or SQL Procedural Language. This allows you to do more scripting like operations similar to Python, in fact you can actually use Python as a scripting language with PostgreSQL as well using PL/Python[77].

To do this we can use a temporary table that we used in our CRUD operations earlier. If you already have that table you can delete it and start from scratch or make a second table with another table name.

Let's create our table again with a new column named:

Listing 1.53: Creating a test table for triggers

```
1  create table cities (
2      city text,
3      country text,
4      size_rank numeric,
5      time_zone text,
6      time_zone_abbrev text
7  )
```

---

[76]https://www.postgresql.org/docs/current/plpgsql.html

[77]https://www.postgresql.org/docs/current/plpython.html

Next we will create our trigger that will look up the city's time zone using the city name. The first step is to create a new function (which we will cover in more detail in the next section). For now we can use this function and run it in pgAdmin:

Listing 1.54: Creating our trigger function

```
1   create
2   or replace function set_timezones() returns trigger language plpgsql as $$ begin
3   update
4       cities
5   set
6       time_zone = a.name,
7       time_zone_abbrev = a.abbrev
8   from
9       pg_timezone_names a
10  where
11      a.name like '%' || replace(city, ' ', ' _ ') || '%';
12
13  return new;
14
15  end;
16
17  $$
```

A few notes:

- We are looking up the timezone against a built-in table in PostgreSQL named (pg_timezone_names) which you can query in pgAdmin
- The section '% || city || %' wraps our column from the cities table, the city name, in the "%" to do the wildcard search
- We can see if that column value is null using the IF statement
    - Later we end the IF statement and return the new row, then finally END the function procedure

Next we can create our TRIGGER:

Listing 1.55: Creating a trigger call

```
1   create trigger update_city_tz
2   after
3   insert
4       on cities for each row execute procedure set_timezones();
```

So if we did everything correctly we can run our insert statement and then our trigger should take action once this statement is run.

Listing 1.56: Inserting into cities

```
1   insert into
2       cities (city, country, size_rank)
3   values
4       ('Tokyo', 'Japan', 1),
5       ('Delhi', 'India', 2),
6       ('Shanghai', 'China', 3),
7       ('ãSo Paulo', 'Brazil', 4),
8       ('Mexico City', 'Mexico', 5)
```

And now let's query our cities table:

city	country	size_rank	time_zone	time_zone_abbrev
Delhi	India	2		
São Paulo	Brazil	4		
Mexico City	Mexico	5		
Shanghai	China	3	Asia/Shanghai	CST
Tokyo	Japan	1	Asia/Tokyo	JST

So it looks like only Shanghai and Tokyo updated. What might be the issue? Here is another coding challenge for you. Take a look and think why the data is not updating. A few hints to think about:

- Is everything in our function written correctly?
- Is the trigger working?
- Does the equality function capture all the potential matches of data?
- Is there an issue with the spelling of the cities?

Check out the answer below the break.

Okay so let's think backwards and think where the issue might be:

- Our rows inserted correctly
- We know the trigger ran since the data was updated after an insert like we specified
- We know the function matched the cities correctly for two cities

The likely remaining issue is the equality operator between our two tables. In that case maybe we can take a look at the timezones table:

```
select * from pg_timezone_names
```

And here is one row from that table:

name	abbrev	utc_offset	is_dst
Africa/Sao_Tome	GMT	00:00:00	false

So for cities with a space in their name we can see that it uses an underscore.

So we can update our function to use the REPLACE function, and then run the process over again.

Listing 1.57: Rewriting the trigger function

```
1   create
2   or replace function set_timezones() returns trigger language plpgsql as $$ begin
3   update
4       cities
5   set
6       time_zone = data.name,
7       time_zone_abbrev = data.abbrev
8   from
9       (
10          select
11              name,
12              abbrev
```

```
13        from
14             pg_timezone_names
15        where
16             name like '%' || replace(city, ' ', '_') || '%'
17     ) as data;
18
19  return new;
20
21  end;
22
23  $$
```

So if we run our query again:

city	country	size_rank	time_zone	time_zone_abbrev
Delhi	India	2		
São Paulo	Brazil	4		
Mexico City	Mexico	5	America/Mexico_City	CST
Shanghai	China	3	Asia/Shanghai	CST
Tokyo	Japan	1	Asia/Tokyo	JST

Now as we can see we were able to update Mexico City but none of the others. And we would have to cover a ton of edge cases to accomplish this. First off we would have to address accent marks, and the fact that India has one time zone for the country not tied to major city names and Brazil has regionally defined time zones.

1.9   UDFs

As mentioned above, user defined functions, or UDFs can greatly extend the capabilities of PostgreSQL by building a function out of multiple parts of a statement or even adding in other languages like Python. Once again these use PL/pgSQL or SQL Procedural Language and PL/Python. There are also procedural languages for Java, Perl, Javascript, R, and more.

For our purposes we will stick to SQL and also implement some functions in Python later in the book. The advantages of using SQL is that you can take a potentially lengthy chunk of code that you are running or something that requires multiple functions or steps that you are using on a regular or recurring basis. User defined functions can be programmed do any number of things including:

- Storing a code that can be used like any other function
- Performing things like if, case, and loops
- Defining parameters and constant variables
- Create stored procedures which have the added capability of running table modifications

PL/pgSQL has a ton of options, and you can create very complex functions and procedures to manage analytical workflows as well as create complex data management processes. Let's create two functions that we can use, the first will calculate the tip percentage of the NYC Taxi Dataset and the second will look at our NYC 311 Data to create a function to search specific values in the data.

As we know we can calculate our tip percentage in our taxis data by running a query such as:

```
tip_amount/total_amount
```

So to do so we can create a function that will return a new column of data from that table. Our function structure will look like this:

Listing 1.58: UDF structure

```
1  create or replace function function_name(param_list)
2      returns return_type
3      language plpgsql
4      as $$ declare -- variable declaration
5      begin
6      -- logic
7      end;
8  $$
```

Let's break down the parts of this function:

- **create [or replace] function**
    - Statement to create a new function or replace an existing function
- **function_name(param_list)**
    - The function_name can be replaced with the function name we want to use
    - The param_list is our parameters which will be written using "parameter_name data_type", for example tip_amount numeric
- **returns return_type**
    - What data type the function will return
- **language plpgsql**
    - Defines the procedural language we will use
- **as**
    - Starts the function
- **$$**
    - The functional code is written between the double dollar signs
- **declare**
    - Space to declare any constant variables
- **begin**
    - Where the function code starts
- **end;**
    - Where the function code ends (make sure to include the semicolon)
- **$$**
    - Closes the functional code

So let's take a look at the code we want to write:

Listing 1.59: Creating a tip calculation function

```
1  create
2  or replace function tip_percentage(tip_column float, total_column float)
3  returns numeric
4  language plpgsql
5  as $$
6
7  declare tip_percentage numeric;
8
```

```
9    begin if total_column = 0 then tip_percentage = 0;
10
11   elsif total_column is null then tip_percentage = 0;
12
13   elsif total_column > 0 then tip_percentage = tip_column / total_column;
14
15   end if;
16
17   return tip_percentage;
18
19   end;
20
21   $$
```

So what did we do here?

- We created a function that defines the inputs and column data types which match the data types which are float8 or numbers with decimal places
- We declare a return variable which is tip_percentage and the data type is numeric
- We use an if/else statement to handle edge cases:
  - If the total_column is 0 or null then we can just return 0 since we can't divide by 0 or null, rather than a calculation (this is a very small gain but in more complex functions and queries this can save a lot of time)
  - In each step we end it with a semicolon and set our declared value of tip_percentage to the value we want
- If the total_column is greater than 0 then we can run our calculation
- We then end the if statement and return the tip_percentage variable

Let's give this a test and see if it works, using our new function just like any other function:

Listing 1.60: Testing the new function

```
1    select
2        total_amount,
3        tip_amount,
4        tip_percentage(tip_amount, total_amount)
5    from
6        nyc_yellow_taxi_0601_0615_2016
7    order by
8        pickup_datetime desc
9    limit
10       10 offset 10000
```

total_amount	tip_amount	tip_percentage
25.3	0	0
10.55	1.75	0.165876777251185
21.8	1.5	0.0688073394495413
23.3	0	0
9.8	0	0
14.75	2.45	0.166101694915254
15.8	0	0
7.56	1.26	0.166666666666667
23.8	2.5	0.105042016806723

...continued on next page

total_amount	tip_amount	tip_percentage
7.3	1	0.136986301369863

Great! Okay let's try this again, but we can actually use a function to return a subset of results just like a query, but abstract the logic away from the query into one compact function. In this case we want to:

- Query the NYC 311 table and return text matches of terms in the columns
    - complaint_type
    - descriptor
    - location_type

This function will look a bit different:

Listing 1.61: Building our text match function

```
1   create
2   or replace function find_311_text_match(search_term text) returns table (
3       id integer,
4       agency text,
5       complaint_type text,
6       descriptor text,
7       location_type text
8   ) language plpgsql as
9   $$
10  #variable_conflict use_column
11  begin
12          return query
13          select id, agency, complaint_type, descriptor, location_type
14          from nyc_311
15          where location_type ilike '%' || search_term || '%'
16          or complaint_type ilike '%' || search_term || '%'
17          or descriptor ilike '%' || search_term || '%';
18  end;
19  $$
```

So our new changes:

- **returns table (id integer, agency text, complaint_type text, descriptor text, location_type text)**
    - We have to define a new return type of a table and we have to implicitly define our columns and data types we are returning
- **#variable_conflict use_column**
    - Since we use the same column names from the original table as the output table names we can use this to resolve conflicts
- Then we simply write our query!

Now instead of a complex query I can just write:

Listing 1.62: Testing the text match function

```
1   select
2       *
3   from
4       find_311_text_match('food')
5   limit
6       5
```

id	agency	complaint_type	descriptor	location_type
48544884	DOHMH	Food Poisoning	1 or 2	Restaurant/Bar/Deli/Bakery
48547794	DOHMH	Food Establishment	Food Contaminated	Restaurant/Bar/Deli/Bakery
48547817	DOHMH	Food Establishment	Food Temperature	Restaurant/Bar/Deli/Bakery
48546543	DOHMH	Food Establishment	Rodents/Insects/Garbage	Restaurant/Bar/Deli/Bakery
48544624	DOHMH	Food Establishment	Food Spoiled	Restaurant/Bar/Deli/Bakery

There are so many more use cases for user defined functions, but these should give you some tools and starting points for basic functions to help you speed up your workflows.

As of this chapter you should have all the building blocks in SQL that you need to start writing spatial SQL. So now we can finally move onto the core topic we want to cover: spatial SQL!

1.10   Expert Voices: Fawad Qureshi

Name: Fawad Qureshi **Title**: Industry Field CTO

How/where did you learn spatial SQL?

Started as a hobby playing with geo data and then started using it in different projects.

Why do you enjoy using spatial SQL?

I always think Spatial SQL allows you to discover patterns in data that otherwise you might miss. The new patterns unlocked using Spatial SQL are always fascinating.

Can you share an interesting way or use case that you are using spatial SQL for today?

At the beginning of the pandemic, I combined data between multiple telecoms and used complex Spatial SQL (using tessellation indexing) to perform COVID contact tracing.

2. Using the GEOMETRY

Now that we have learned the basic and advanced use cases, functions, and tools for using SQL, we are finally ready to move onto the core topic of this book: spatial SQL. The rest of this book will be dedicated to the spatial side of SQL, but before we move on I want to briefly pause to reflect and also address one point.

First off, you have, in the past few chapters, built a very solid foundation for understanding SQL and put yourself in a position to be able to create a database, load data, query data, and write a full range of queries. This alone is an achievement and one that you could cover in one or many books or courses. So give yourself a high five, pat on the back, or a well deserved reward. You earned it.

Next, I want to reflect on why spatial SQL has been somewhat of an under utilized tool for the analytics side of geospatial. If you come from more of a traditional GIS background you can start to see why the barrier of entry is so high for a tool like PostGIS or spatial SQL as a language. To fully make use of it you need a foundation in the language before you can proceed with using the spatial aspects of that language. SQL alone is a big skill to learn and something that people work years on to perfect and master, so learning it alone is a challenge.

The other side of this is that traditional education generally treats SQL as a more advanced skill. Most GIS programs start at the desktop tool level since they are purpose built for GIS and spatial data, and only when you need to move on to more advanced use cases or to use more data should you introduce spatial SQL and databases because of the additional complexity they come with. But I hope to prove to you through the rest of the book, with ideas and practical examples, why spatial SQL is very valuable and critical to modern GIS and expanding the use of spatial analytics beyond those in GIS.

2.1 Understanding the GEOMETRY and GEOGRAPHY

The single thing that differentiates SQL from spatial SQL are the two data types that contain spatial data. These are the GEOMETRY and the GEOGRAPHY. In effect these two data types are mostly the same as they store things like points, lines, and polygons with one key difference.

The GEOMETRY uses a flat, projected or Cartesian surface, and the GEOGRAPHY, uses the curved earth for functions that need to account for the curvature of the earth. Let's say that for distances from one side of a country to another, you will get a more accurate measure when you use the GEOGRAPHY. However, at a city of local level, the GEOMETRY will work just fine. A few other key points to highlight here:

- The GEOMETRY can be transformed into other projection systems just as you would in other tools using a function called ST_Transform. The GEOGRAPHY has no SRID since it is the curved earth.
- There are performance considerations for the two as well. There can be some delay in performance when using the GEOGRAPHY which is well documented in this StackOverflow post[78] which runs two tests and finds a 2.6 to 4.5 times increase in function time when using geometries. You can also see other testing benchmarks in this post[79].

- The very rough best practice is that if you have data at a large continental scale you may want

---

[78] https://loc8.cc/sql/gis.stackexchange

[79] https://loc8.cc/sql/medium-postgis-performance

157

to consider using GEOGRAPHY if you are using operations that require it, otherwise more likely GEOMETRY will be sufficient.

In addition there are only a handful of functions that will support the GEOGRAPHY type in PostGIS. Those are listed here and are borrowed from the PostGIS documentation[80]:

- Parser functions
  - ST_GeographyFromText(text) returns geography
  - ST_AsBinary(geography) returns bytea
  - ST_GeogFromWKB(bytea) returns geography
  - ST_AsSVG(geography) returns text
  - ST_AsGML(geography) returns text
  - ST_AsText(geography) returns text
  - ST_AsKML(geography) returns text
  - ST_AsGeoJson(geography) returns text
- Transformation functions
  - ST_Buffer(geography, float8) returns geography 1
  - ST_Intersection(geography, geography) returns geography 1
- Measurement functions
  - ST_Distance(geography, geography) returns double
  - ST_Area(geography) returns double
  - ST_Length(geography) returns double
- Spatial relationship functions
  - ST_Covers(geography, geography) returns boolean
  - ST_DWithin(geography, geography, float8) returns boolean
  - ST_CoveredBy(geography, geography) returns boolean
  - ST_Intersects(geography, geography) returns boolean

But with all that said it is very easy to move from one type to the other. All you have to do is cast the data just like you would with any other data type. A sample query would look like this:

Listing 2.1: Using GEOGRAPHY

```
1   select
2       id,
3       geom,
4       geom :: geography as geog
5   from
6       table_name
```

So you likely won't have to worry much about this as you have the ability to change these as needed. If you want to find what data type your data is using you can simply use the *pg_typeof()* function. No special functions just normal functions from SQL.

2.2   GEOMETRY Types

Now not all geometries are created the same, and there are many types of geometry data that can be stored and queried in PostGIS. So let's start to take a look at some of the data we loaded to understand this data type. We can query our NYC Building Footprint data to get started:

---

[80]https://loc8.cc/sql/postgis-intro

Listing 2.2: Exploring the GEOMETRY

```
1   select
2       geom
3   from
4       nyc_building_footprints
5   limit
6       1
```

geom
0106000020E61000...

Confused yet? Not to worry, we can explain this. What you are looking at is called Well Known Binary, one of two accepted geometric representations defined by OpenGIS[81]. The other is Well Known Text which is far more readable to the human eye. We can see that by using the following query:

Listing 2.3: Geometry as text

```
1   select
2       st_astext(geom) as wkt
3   from
4       nyc_building_footprints
5   limit
6       5
```

wkt
MULTIPOLYGON(((-73.96664570466969 40.62599676998366...

As you can see here we have what is known as a MULTIPOLYGON, or a polygon of multiple parts. Each sub-POLYGON is contained within parentheses and is defined by points separated by commas. Each point is separated not by a comma but by a space. This makes up the basics of a geometry in PostGIS. While the full geometry text is not in the example above, there is actually only one polygon, not multiple, in the above result. We will cover that later in the next section.

With that let's cover the different types of geometries that PostGIS, and most of the other spatial databases support. First we have our base geometries of which all others are made up of (all will be represented in Well Known Text, or WKT which we will use henceforth):

- **Point**: 'POINT(0 0)'
- **Line**: 'LINESTRING(0 0,1 1,1 2)'
- **Polygon** 'POLYGON((0 0,4 0,4 4,0 4,0 0),(1 1,2 1,2 2,1 2,1 1))'

We can actually see these on a map by creating a table and inserting that data into it:

```
create table geometries (name text, geom geometry)
```

Then we can insert our data:

Listing 2.4: Inserting GEOMETRIES

```
1   insert into
2       geometries
3   values
4       ('point', st_geomfromtext('POINT(0 0)')),
```

---

[81]https://postgis.net/docs/manual-2.3/using_postgis_dbmanagement.html#RefObject

```
 5      (
 6          'line',
 7          st_geomfromtext('LINESTRING(0 0,1 1,1 2)')
 8      ),
 9      (
10          'polygon',
11          st_geomfromtext(
12              'POLYGON((0 0,4 0,4 4,0 4,0 0),(1 1, 2 1, 2 2, 1 2,1 1))'
13          )
14      )
```

Then query it and see the geometries on a map using the geometry viewer in pgAdmin:

```
select * from geometries
```

Simply click the little map icon in the query results (Figure 2.1):

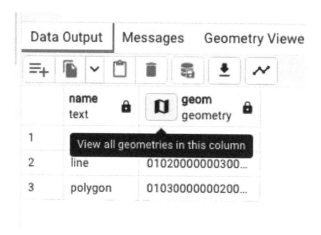

Figure 2.1: Visualizing the geometry in pgAdmin

And you should see something like this (Figure 2.2, on the next page):

Note that we have not assigned a coordinate system to our data, but we can do that later. Let's continue on to look at some other geometry types, this time the "multi" geometry family.

- **Multi-point**: 'MULTIPOINT((0 0),(1 2))'
- **Multi-line**: 'MULTILINESTRING((0 0,1 1,1 2),(2 3,3 2,5 4))'
- **(Multi-polygon)**: 'MULTIPOLYGON(((0 0,4 0,4 4,0 4,0 0),(1 1,2 1,2 2,1 2,1 1)), ((-1 -1,-1 -2,-2 -2,-2 -1,-1 -1)))'
- **Geometry collection**: 'GEOMETRYCOLLECTION(POINT(2 3),LINESTRING(2 3,3 4))'

Now most of these are the same as they are a group of one or more geometries of the same type, points, lines, or polygons, apart from the Geometry collection which can hold one or more of any geometry type, including multi-geometries. Let's add these to our table to see them on the map too (Figure 2.3, on page 162).

Listing 2.5: Multi-geometries

```
1   insert into
2       geometries
3   values
4       (
```

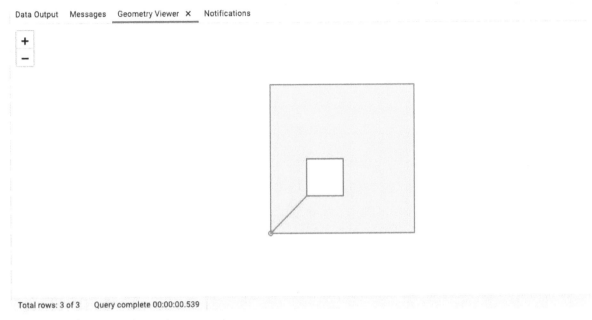

Figure 2.2: The geometries we just created

```
5            'multipoint',
6            st_geomfromtext('MULTIPOINT((0 0),(1 2))')
7        ),
8        (
9            'multiline',
10           st_geomfromtext('MULTILINESTRING((0 0,1 1,1 2),(2 3,3 2,5 4))')
11       ),
12       (
13           'multipolygon',
14           st_geomfromtext(
15               'MULTIPOLYGON(((0 0,4 0,4 4,0 4,0 0),(1 1,2 1,2 2,1 2,1 1)), ((-1 -1,-1 -2,-2 -2,-2 -1,-1 -1)))'
16           )
17       ),
18       (
19           'geometry collection',
20           st_geomfromtext(
21               'GEOMETRYCOLLECTION(POINT(2 3),LINESTRING(2 3,3 4))'
22           )
23       )
```

The next set of geometry functions also use Well Known Binary (WKB) and Well Known Text (WKT) as well but in a format known as Extended Well Known Binary and Extended Well Known Text (EWKB and EWKT respectively). This allows for:

- 3 dimensional data with an X and Y dimension and either an Z (height) or M (other dimension, most commonly time, but can be distance marker or upstream distance)[82]

- 4 dimensional data with X, Y, Z, M
- Embedded Spatial Reference ID or SRID

These new data types include but are not limited to:

---

[82]https://postgis.net/workshops/postgis-intro/3d.html

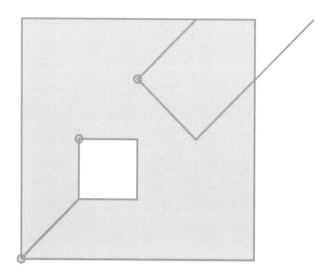

Figure 2.3: Additional geometry types

- **3D Point**: `POINT(0 0 0) -- XYZ`
- **Point with embedded SRID**: `SRID=32632;POINT(0 0) -- XY with SRID`
- **3D PointM**: `POINTM(0 0 0) -- XYM`
- **4D Point**: `POINT(0 0 0 0) -- XYZM`
- **3D Multi-PointM**: `SRID=4326;MULTIPOINTM(0 0 0,1 2 1) -- XYM with SRID`
- **3D Multi-linestring**: `MULTILINESTRING((0 0 0,1 1 0,1 2 1),(2 3 1,3 2 1,5 4 1))`
- **3D Polygon**: `POLYGON((0 0 0,4 0 0,4 4 0,0 4 0,0 0 0),(1 1 0,2 1 0,2 2 0,1 2 0,1 1 0))`
- **3D Multipolygon**: `MULTIPOLYGON(((0 0 0,4 0 0,4 4 0,0 4 0,0 0 0),(1 1 0,2 1 0,2 2 0,1 2 0,1 1 0)),((-1 -1 0,-1 -2 0,-2 -2 0,-2 -1 0,-1 -1 0)))`
- **3D Geometry Collection**: `GEOMETRYCOLLECTIONM( POINTM(2 3 9), LINESTRINGM(2 3 4, 3 4 5) )`

We will do some work with 3D data later in the book but for now we dont need to add these to our table. There are also several other types of data that PostGIS supports that we will not be using in this book. I have not used any of these types myself but they are available should you need or want to use them. These are generally curved lines or polygons, triangular data, and `POLYHEDRALSURFACE` or effectively a 3D polygon/shape. Generally in a 2D map this data cannot be rendered unless you use a function to turn these into one of the primary geometry types. For example running this query:

Listing 2.6: Other geometry types in PostGIS

```
1  select
2      st_curvetoline(
3          st_geomfromtext('CIRCULARSTRING(0 0, 4 0, 4 4, 0 4, 0 0)')
4      ) as geom
```

Will render a small circle (Figure 2.4):

Figure 2.4: CIRCULARSTRING visualized

Below are the different geometry types[83]:

- **Circular string**: CIRCULARSTRING(0 0, 4 0, 4 4, 0 4, 0 0)
- **Compound curve**: COMPOUNDCURVE(CIRCULARSTRING(0 0, 1 1, 1 0),(1 0, 0 1))
- **Curve polygon**: CURVEPOLYGON(CIRCULARSTRING(0 0, 4 0, 4 4, 0 4, 0 0), (1 1, 3 3, 3 1, 1 1))
- **Multi-surface**: MULTISURFACE(CURVEPOLYGON(CIRCULARSTRING(0 0, 4 0, 4 4, 0 4, 0 0), (1 1, 3 3, 3 1, 1 1)), ((10 10, 14 12, 11 10, 10 10), (11 11, 11.5 11, 11 11.5, 11 11)))
- **Multi-curve**: MULTICURVE((0 0, 5 5), CIRCULARSTRING(4 0, 4 4, 8 4))
- **Polyhedral Surface**: POLYHEDRALSURFACE(((0 0 0, 0 0 1, 0 1 1, 0 1 0, 0 0 0)), ((0 0 0, 0 1 0, 1 1 0, 1 0 0, 0 0 0)), ((0 0 0, 1 0 0, 1 0 1, 0 0 1, 0 0 0)), ((1 1 0, 1 1 1, 1 0 1, 1 0 0, 1 1 0)), ((0 1 0, 0 1 1, 1 1 1, 1 1 0, 0 1 0)), ((0 0 1, 1 0 1, 1 1 1, 0 1 1, 0 0 1)))
- **Triangle**: TRIANGLE ((0 0, 0 9, 9 0, 0 0))
- **Triangulated Irregular Network**: TIN(((0 0 0, 0 0 1, 0 1 0, 0 0 0)), ((0 0 0, 0 1 0, 1 1 0, 0 0 0)))

Outside of PostGIS, most other databases or data warehouses support the first set of geometries we discussed, and sometimes only support a GEOGRAPHY, and many of the data warehouses will only support EPSG 4326. PostGIS also supports raster data as well which we will cover in a later chapter.

2.3   Size of GEOMETRY data

It is important to understand that in almost all cases the size of spatial data, meaning the amount of disk space (or bytes) it takes to store a geometry, is much larger than any other data type in your database. There is an easy function to measure this which we can use to look at our NYC Zip Code polygons to take a look at this.

Before we do that let's understand why this matters. There are three main reasons why you want to know the sizing of your geometry data. The first is for storage. Taking the example of Polygon data, as the number of points increases in a polygon, each of those points will increase the disk size of that polygon. Let's test some examples out with our data. First let's check out the size of a single point:

---

[83]https://postgis.net/docs/using_postgis_dbmanagement.html

Listing 2.7: Geometry storage size

```
1  select
2      st_memsize(st_geomfromtext('POINT(0 0)')) as geom
```

Note that this query is effectively selecting this single item of data on the fly. This is not stored anywhere, but this allows us to test on simple geometries effectively.

The query returns "32" which represents 32 bytes of data. So how exactly does it get to that number? Now we can take a look at the PostgreSQL documentation for the size of the primitive geometric data types[84] to see that a point requires 16 bytes of storage. But what are the other 16 bytes that make up the total of 32 for? This post[85] from Dan Baston explains how this works for a point for the other 16 bytes:

"4 bytes to tell Postgres how large the PostGIS object is

4 bytes to store the SRID and various flags

4 bytes to store the geometry type (Point)

4 bytes to tell us how many points are in our geometry"

So now let's test this out with some other data types. First a LINESTRING:

Listing 2.8: Linestring size

```
1  select
2      st_memsize(st_geomfromtext('LINESTRING(0 0, 0 1)')) as geom
```

This returns 48 bytes or:

- 16 for each point (or 32 bytes)
- 16 for the base data as described above.

And now a POLYGON:

Listing 2.9: Polygon size

```
1  select
2      st_memsize(
3          st_geomfromtext('POLYGON((0 0, 0 1, 1 1, 1 0, 0 0))')
4      ) as geom
```

This returns 120 bytes. A bit more than you may have thought but here is the explanation:

- 4 points in the polygon which means 16 * 4 which means 64 bytes
  - But we also have to account for an additional point for the repeated first point to close the polygon, which adds 16 bytes one more time
- The POLYGON has a base of 40 bytes on its own, which is defined in the PostgreSQL docs[86].

So 16 * 5 = 80 and when we add 40 we get 120.

Let's try this with one geometry from out New York City Neighborhoods dataset.

Listing 2.10: Complex polygon size

---

[84]https://www.postgresql.org/docs/current/datatype-geometric.html

[85]https://loc8.cc/sql/danbaston-max-geometry

[86]https://www.postgresql.org/docs/current/datatype-geometric.html

```
1  select
2      st_memsize(geom)
3  from
4      nyc_neighborhoods
5  where
6      neighborhood = 'College Point'
```

This is a particularly complex geometry in north Queens, and it returns 17,488 bytes or 17.4 KB. So let's first figure out how to get to this number. To do so we can see how many points are in the polygon, the geometry type, and the number of geometries that are in the polygon in case it is a multi-polygon.

Listing 2.11: Investigating polygon memory size

```
1  select
2      st_npoints(geom) as points,
3      st_geometrytype(geom) as type,
4      st_numgeometries(geom) as geometries
5  from
6      nyc_neighborhoods
7  where
8      neighborhood = 'College Point'
```

points	type	geometries
1090 | ST_MultiPolygon		1

It is a multi-polygon with 1 geometry and 1,090 points. So based on what we know from above:

- 40 bytes for the base polygon
- 16 bytes * 1,090 points or 17,440 bytes
- 16 bytes for the closing point

17440 + 40 + 16 = 17,496, which means we somehow have 8 extra bytes. So why did it end up with extra data in our calculation? To break this down we can revisit our base polygon which has 120 bytes, but this time with a multi-polygon:

Listing 2.12: Size of a simple multi-polygon

```
1  select
2      st_memsize(
3          st_geomfromtext('MULTIPOLYGON(((0 0, 1 0, 1 1, 0 1, 0 0)))')
4      ) as geom
```

Now we get 128 bytes. Let's try again with another polygon in the multi-polygon:

Listing 2.13: Another multi-polygon

```
1  select
2      st_memsize(
3          st_geomfromtext(
4              'MULTIPOLYGON(((0 0, 1 0, 1 1, 0 1, 0 0)), ((1 1, 2 1, 2 2, 1 2, 1 1)))'
5          )
6      ) as geom
```

This time we get 224 bytes, when we expected 256 (128 * 2). So what exactly is going on? Let's try and break this down for our first multi-polygon:

- First we have 5 points here (4 + 1 closing point) which gives us 80 bytes, 48 bytes remain
- Then we have the base 40 to store our base polygon, 8 remain

Let's look back at the elements needed for our 16 base bytes from before:

"4 bytes to tell Postgres how large the PostGIS object is

4 bytes to store the SRID and various flags

4 bytes to store the geometry type (Point)

4 bytes to tell us how many points are in our geometry"

Within that 40 bytes to store the base polygon, other overhead is already stored, namely the SRID and the geometry type, in this case a MULTIPOLYGON. However since this is a set of POLYGONS, the other data (number of points and size of the geometry object) still needs to be stored on the rest of the polygons. That gives us our last remaining 8 bytes.

So, let's try and apply this to the second example with 224 bytes:

- First we have 10 points here (4 + 1 closing point for two polygons) which gives us 160 bytes, 64 bytes remain
- Then we have the base 40 to store our base polygon, 24 remain
    - For each polygon in the multi-polygon, we need 8 bytes to store the size of the PostGIS object and how many points are in the geometry. 8 * 2 = 16. 8 bytes remain
- The last 8 belong to the multi-polygon and the SRID and other flags and the geometry type. All bytes are accounted for.

And one more time to prove our theory for the neighborhood polygon:

- 16 bytes * 1,090 points or 17,440 bytes, 72,376 - 72,320 = 48 bytes remain
    - Note that when we use ST_NPoints it counts the closing point for us so no need to add that in
- 40 bytes for the base polygon. 8 bytes remain
- The last 8 belong to the multi-polygon and the SRID and other flags and the geometry type. All bytes are accounted for.

So that was a very deep dive into the disk storage required to store geometries in PostGIS. Why did we spend so much time on this? To answer that let's take a look at how much disk space is required to store other data types in PostgreSQL:

- **smallint**: 2 bytes (range of -32768 to +32767)
- **Integer**: 4 bytes (range of -2147483648 to +2147483647)
- **bigint** 8 bytes (range of -9223372036854775808 to +9223372036854775807)
- **character**: 1 byte + 1 byte per character
- **date**: 4 bytes
- **timestamp**: 8 bytes
- **boolean**: 1 byte

As you can see these data types in PostgreSQL, with the exception of a few such as UUID and JSON, are very small volumes of data storage. And nothing gets into the range of KB or MB which is often the case with geometry data. This matters not just for storage, but as your data increases in size (number of rows), it becomes important to store your geometries in a separate table and join them as needed especially if your geometry data repeats.

This also increases the operation time on things like spatial joins and intersections (sometimes called clipping). The more data you have the longer the operation takes. We will look at some options for this using spatial indexes like H3 later in the book as well as database indexes, but for now the issue of storage and operation time is important to consider at the base data level which cannot be changed in all cases, but this will help you understand where some scalability issues will originate.

2.4 A note on PostGIS documentation

One key skill that I have always reiterated as a critical to becoming self-sufficient in spatial SQL or any SQL programming is the ability to read and use documentation, and in my opinion, is one of the most important things you can do to become truly self-sufficient. For example, if you hit an issue, the first place you might look is by searching online, looking through issues on StackOverflow, or even using ChatGPT to see if it can help solve the issue. But one sure way is to go to the source to see what input the function requires, what the outputs are, and what you can expect the function to perform.

You can find the PostGIS documentation at **postgis.net/documentation**[87] which will have several versions depending on the release of PostGIS that you are using. It is important to make sure you have the right version so you know those match to the current set of functions you are using as there may be minor difference between the versions. The docs have a built-in search function, but the documentation pages are well indexed by search engines like Google so you can certainly use Google to navigate to what you are looking for. In addition, you can sometimes even search generally for what you want to do if you do not know the exact function you need and Google will sometimes point you in the right direction.

On a side note this is one area where a tool like ChatGPT can be helpful as it does a fairly decent job of indexing PostGIS and other documentation pages well. Keep in mind that while ChatGPT can help you assemble some code, it is not perfect, so I really like to use it when looking something up when I want to structure a question in a more human way.

Now there are two notes when you are reading the docs that I think are important to call out. First is the reading of the function in the docs which we have covered a bit in the book already. This is the first thing that I always start with when looking at any documentation. Let's take a look at a function we will cover later in this chapter as they are described in PostGIS docs.

ST_Length

```
float ST_Length(geometry a_2dlinestring);
float ST_Length(geography geog, boolean use_spheroid=true);
```

First we see the word **float** and this tells us the data type that is being returned from the function, in this case a numeric float value or a number with decimals. Next we can see that there are two different function signatures with one and two arguments respectively. The first is:

```
ST_Length(geometry a_2dlinestring);
```

This first part tells us that the function will take in a GEOMETRY data type, specifically a 2D linestring, so not a 3D value and not a point or a polygon. The second:

```
ST_Length(geography geog, boolean use_spheroid=true);
```

This tells us this time that it take a GEOMETRY data type followed by geog which means any geography data type and another parameter to use a BOOLEAN which will allow you to use a spheroid or sphere

---

[87] https://postgis.net/documentation/

depending on the boolean value. The second value says that the default argument here is true. This means that you only need to add false if you explicitly do not want to use a spheroid. Spheroid will be a more accurate representation of the globe but may be a bit slower than using a sphere.

The next portion is to read the description. I like to read this to make sure that my interpretation of the functions was correct and to make sure I am not missing any "gotchas" or potential parts of the function that may return an odd value. From the PostGIS docs:

For geometry types: returns the 2D Cartesian length of the geometry if it is a LineString, MultiLineString, ST_Curve, ST_MultiCurve. For areal geometries 0 is returned; use ST_Perimeter instead. The units of length is determined by the spatial reference system of the geometry.

For geography types: computation is performed using the inverse geodesic calculation. Units of length are in meters. If PostGIS is compiled with PROJ version 4.8.0 or later, the spheroid is specified by the SRID, otherwise it is exclusive to WGS84. If use_spheroid=false, then the calculation is based on a sphere instead of a spheroid.

Currently for geometry this is an alias for ST_Length2D, but this may change to support higher dimensions.

Based on the description this looks like we have a good understanding of ST_Length. We can also see that this function acts as an alias for ST_Length2D but in the future it may have added support for 3D or 4D lines.

Next we can see a warning which is called out by a red stop sign (Figure 2.5):

 Changed: 2.0.0 Breaking change -- in prior versions applying this to a MULTI/POLYGON of type geography would give you the perimeter of the POLYGON/MULTIPOLYGON. In 2.0.0 this was changed to return 0 to be in line with geometry behavior. Please use ST_Perimeter if you want the perimeter of a polygon

Figure 2.5: Warning in the PostGIS docs

Changed: 2.0.0 Breaking change -- in prior versions applying this to a MULTI/POLYGON of type geography would give you the perimeter of the POLYGON/MULTIPOLYGON. In 2.0.0 this was changed to return 0 to be in line with geometry behavior. Please use ST_Perimeter if you want the perimeter of a polygon

And this validates that we can only use this function with linestrings but in a previous version (below 2.0.0) that this did support other geometry types.

There is also a note called out in a yellow box with a stick note icon (Figure 2.6):

 For geography the calculation defaults to using a spheroidal model. To use the faster but less accurate spherical calculation use ST_Length(gg,false);

Figure 2.6: Note in the PostGIS docs

For geography the calculation defaults to using a spheroidal model. To use the faster but less accurate spherical calculation use ST_Length(gg,false);

And this validates that we can use the sphere for a faster calculation. Everything that is contained in PostGIS docs is there for a reason, there is no erroneous or extra information, so it all can be considered important.

Every example in PostGIS is written so you do not have to have any data in your database to run them, meaning that they use WKT string polygons to show the functionality and cast them to a GEOMETRY like we have in previous examples using ST_GeomFromText or ST_GeogFromText. This means that you can copy/paste these examples in pgAdmin and run them right from the docs.

Let's look at the first example:

Return length in feet for line string. Note this is in feet because EPSG:2249 is Massachusetts State Plane Feet

Listing 2.14: Using transformations

```
1  select
2      st_length(
3          st_geomfromtext(
4              'LINESTRING(743238 2967416,743238 2967450,743265 2967450,
5              743265.625 2967416,743238 2967416)',
6              2249
7          )
8      );
9
10  -- Transforming WGS 84 LINESTRING to Massachusetts State Plane Meters
```

Listing 2.15: Example PostGIS documentation

```
1  select
2      st_length(
3          st_transform(
4              st_geomfromewkt(
5                  'srid=4326;linestring(-72.1260 42.45, -72.1240 42.45666, -72.123 42.1546)'
6              ),
7              26986
8          )
9      );
```

We can actually run these examples or the GEOGRAPHY based examples on the page below to get the same responses as we can see in the docs. We will refer to the docs multiple times in the book, so it is a good practice to start to use and become fluent with the docs.

Another great feature in the PostGIS documentation are the Workshops. These are more hands on guided tutorials that you can test out to go deeper into specific topics. You can find these on postgis.net/workshops[88] and they often have some other detail if you are looking for some specific workflows too.

2.5 Working with GEOMETRY data

In this section we are going to dive into working with the GEOMETRY itself. These functions allow you to do everything from creating geometries or geographies, manipulating them, changing them, and more. While they are a component of spatial analysis, they are very important to the data engineering and process. We will use them sporadically such as finding the nearest point on a line to another point, but overall these functions are ones that you can generally keep in your back pocket to use as needed for analysis purposes.

This section also groups the functions by their overall functional purpose as described in the PostGIS documentation here[89]. I will also add an opinionated view of the functions that I believe are the most important to know based on my usage of them over the years. This may very well be different for you depending on your use case so please keep that in mind. The function names and descriptions are from

---

[88]https://postgis.net/workshops/postgis-intro/

the PostGIS documentation directly so as not to add any extra flavor to the descriptions. With that let's dive in.

2.6 Constructors

My top functions

- **ST_Collect** — Creates a GeometryCollection or Multi* geometry from a set of geometries.
- *'ST_MakeEnvelope'* — Creates a rectangular Polygon from minimum and maximum coordinates.
- **ST_MakePoint** — Creates a 2D, 3DZ or 4D Point.
- **ST_MakeLine** — Creates a LineString from Point, MultiPoint, or LineString geometries.

The rest

- Line creation functions
  - **ST_LineFromMultiPoint** — Creates a LineString from a MultiPoint geometry.
- Point creation functions
  - **ST_MakePointM** — Creates a Point from X, Y and M values.
  - **ST_Point** — Creates a Point with X, Y and SRID values.
  - **ST_PointZ** — Creates a Point with X, Y, Z and SRID values.
  - **ST_PointM** — Creates a Point with X, Y, M and SRID values.
  - **ST_PointZM** — Creates a Point with X, Y, Z, M and SRID values.
- Polygon creation functions
  - **ST_MakePolygon** — Creates a Polygon from a shell and optional list of holes.
  - **ST_Polygon** — Creates a Polygon from a LineString with a specified SRID.
- **ST_TileEnvelope** — Creates a rectangular Polygon in Web Mercator (SRID:3857) using the XYZ tile system.
- **ST_HexagonGrid** — Returns a set of hexagons and cell indices that completely cover the bounds of the geometry argument.
- **ST_Hexagon** — Returns a single hexagon, using the provided edge size and cell coordinate within the hexagon grid space.
- **ST_SquareGrid** — Returns a set of grid squares and cell indices that completely cover the bounds of the geometry argument.
- **ST_Square** — Returns a single square, using the provided edge size and cell coordinate within the square grid space.
- **ST_Letters** — Returns the input letters rendered as geometry with a default start position at the origin and default text height of 100.

There are three functions I think you definitely need to know out of this list.

ST_Collect

This function allows you to take several geometries and turn them into a geometry collection. This can be useful for aggregations and other use cases. Let's test this out using this query:

Listing 2.16: ST_Collect

```
1  with a as (
2      select
3          geom
```

---
[89]https://postgis.net/docs/reference.html

```
4      from
5          nyc_zips
6      limit
7          5
8  )
9  select
10     st_collect(geom)
11 from
12     a
```

If we wanted to include additional data here we would have to aggregate it somehow:

Listing 2.17: ST_Collect

```
1  with a as (
2      select
3          geom,
4          population,
5          zipcode
6      from
7          nyc_zips
8      limit
9          5
10 )
11 select
12     string_agg(zipcode, ',') as zips,
13     sum(population) as total_pop,
14     st_collect(geom)
15 from
16     a
```

This function will not union your geometries into a single geometry just turn them into a collection of one or many geometries.

ST_MakeEnvelope

This creates a geometry from two different points: an X Min/Y Min, and X Max/Y Max pair. I use a web based bounding box tool to give me the data that goes into the function here that also has a search capability integrated with OpenStreetMap to search anything in OSM[90].

In the image below I searched for San Juan, Puerto Rico and selected the CSV option from the dropdown to create this query (Figure 2.7, on the following page):

Listing 2.18: ST_MakeEnvelope

```
1  select
2      st_makeenvelope(-66.125091, 18.296531, -65.99142, 18.471986) as geom
```

You can also add in the projection EPSG code to see it on the map, in this case that is 4326 (Figure 2.8, on page 173).

Listing 2.19: Envelope with SRID

```
1  select
2      st_makeenvelope(
3          -66.125091,
4          18.296531,
5          -65.99142,
6          18.471986,
```

---

[90]https://boundingbox.klokantech.com/

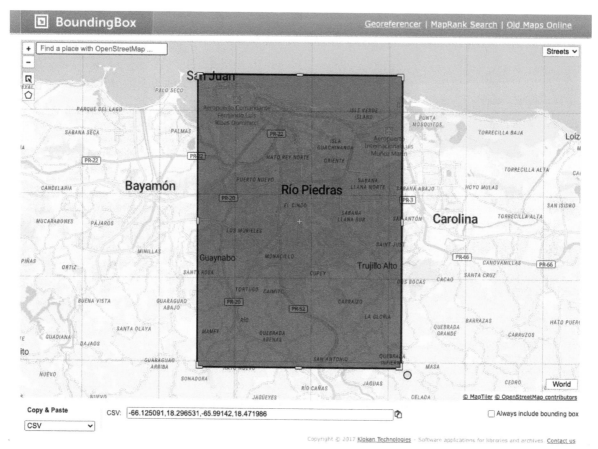

Figure 2.7: Creating a bounding box on boundingbox.klokantech.com

```
7            4326
8    ) as geom
```

ST_MakePoint

This function allows you to create points from data in your table such as latitude and longitude data.
I have used this many times as will we for data that does not have a geometry in it such as our NYC
Taxi Data. Let's try it with a few rows now.

Listing 2.20: ST_MakePoint

```
1   select
2       st_makepoint(pickup_longitude, pickup_latitude) as geom
3   from
4       nyc_yellow_taxi_0601_0615_2016
5   limit
6       100
```

Now if you try to see this data on the map you will notice that it doesn't since you have to manually
set the SRID which we can do with this query (Figure 2.9, on page 174):

Listing 2.21: Make point with SRID

```
1   select
2       ogc_fid,
```

Figure 2.8: Creating an envelope in PostGIS

```
3      st_setsrid(
4          st_makepoint(pickup_longitude, pickup_latitude),
5          4326
6      ) as geom
7   from
8      nyc_yellow_taxi_0601_0615_2016
9   limit
10      100
```

Now this is something we will be doing several more times during the course of this book. Is there a way we can make this more efficient? If you guessed user defined function then you would be correct! Try to write a UDF called *BuildPoint* to do so. If you need some hints:

- You will need three arguments:
    - X coordinate
    - Y coordinate
    - SRID integer

Okay so here is how to build our UDF to save us some typing later on:

Listing 2.22: BuildPoint function

```
1   create or replace function BuildPoint(x numeric, y numeric, srid int)
```

Figure 2.9: Using our new UDF

```
2       returns geometry
3       language plpgsql
4       as $$
5           begin
6               return st_setsrid(st_makepoint(x, y), srid);
7           end;
8       $$;
```

And with our original query:

Listing 2.23: Using our new function
```
1   select
2       ogc_fid,
3       buildpoint(
4           pickup_longitude :: numeric,
5           pickup_latitude :: numeric,
6           4326
7       ) as geom
8   from
9       nyc_yellow_taxi_0601_0615_2016
10  limit
11      100
```

Now just for fun you may have noticed a function called ST_Letters. Go ahead and give this a try:

Listing 2.24: Just for fun

```
1  SELECT
2      st_setsrid(
3          ST_Translate(ST_Scale(ST_Letters('Spatial SQL'), 1, 1), 0, 0),
4          4326
5      );
```

I have personally never used this function until now but hey, why not! See the results in 2.10.

Figure 2.10: Letters using Spatial SQL!

2.7 Accessors

There are many different accessor functions, so I am only going to list my top functions here, but you can see the full list using the link in the footnote[91]. There are only a handful that I have found helpful to keep in memory on a regular basis, but keep in mind that if there is something you want to do there is almost always a function for it in PostGIS.

My top functions

- **ST_Dump** — Returns a set of geometry_dump rows for the components of a geometry.
- **ST_GeometryType** — Returns the SQL-MM type of a geometry as text.
- **ST_MemSize** — Returns the amount of memory space a geometry takes.
- **ST_NPoints** — Returns the number of points (vertices) in a geometry.
- **ST_PointN** — Returns the Nth point in the first LineString or circular LineString in a geometry.
- **ST_X** — Returns the X coordinate of a Point.

---

[91]https://postgis.net/docs/reference.html#Geometry_Accessors

- **ST_Y** — Returns the Y coordinate of a Point.

ST_Dump

The first function is call ST_Dump which basically dumps out the individual geometries from a compound geometry like a *MULTIPOLYGON* or *GEOMETRYCOLLECTION* as rows called a *geometry_dump* (more on this later). As we can see in our NYC Neighborhoods data the City Island neighborhood is made up of several shapes or islands. We can use this to see what the ST_Dump will do (Figure 2.11).

Listing 2.25: ST_Dump

```
1  select
2      st_dump(geom) as geom
3  from
4      nyc_neighborhoods
5  where
6      neighborhood = 'City Island'
```

	geom geometry_dump 🔒
1	({1},0103000020...
2	({2},0103000020...
3	({3},0103000020...
4	({4},0103000020...
5	({5},0103000020...
6	({6},0103000020...
7	({7},0103000020...
8	({8},0103000020...

Figure 2.11: Geometry dump

As you can see this returns a column with the data type *geometry_dump* which is basically what is known as a composite, or combined, data type. From the PostGIS docs:

geometry_dump is a composite data type containing the fields:

geom - a geometry representing a component of the dumped geometry. The geometry type depends on the originating function.

path[] - an integer array that defines the navigation path within the dumped geometry to the geom component. The path array is 1-based (i.e. path[1] is the first element.)

So how can we access the actual geometries and get that data back. We basically need to treat it as JSON. We can access the geometry by adding parenthesis around the function and .geom on to the end of the parenthesis as so (Figure 2.12):

Listing 2.26: ST_Dump extraction

```
1  select
2      (st_dump(geom)).geom as geom
3  from
4      nyc_neighborhoods
5  where
6      neighborhood = 'City Island'
```

Figure 2.12: Extracting geometries from a geometry dump

From here you can join this back to any original data and access these geometries as individual geometries.

ST_GeometryType

A simple function that tells you the geometry type of your data:

Listing 2.27: ST_GeometryType

```
1  select
```

```
2        st_geometrytype(geom)
3  from
4        nyc_neighborhoods
5  where
6        neighborhood = 'City Island'
```

st_geometrytype
ST_MultiPolygon

ST_MemSize

We have used this function earlier which this tells you the disk memory to store you geometry data:

Listing 2.28: ST_MemSize

```
1  select
2        st_memsize(geom)
3  from
4        nyc_neighborhoods
5  where
6        neighborhood = 'City Island'
```

st_memsize
21088

ST_NPoints

Find the number of points in a geometry (we have also used this before):

Listing 2.29: ST_NPoints

```
1  select
2        st_npoints(geom)
3  from
4        nyc_neighborhoods
5  where
6        neighborhood = 'City Island'
```

st_npoints
1314

ST_PointN

Function to find a specific point at a specific position in a LINESTRING geometry. We can try this with our NYC Bike Routes:

select

Listing 2.30: ST_PointN

```
1  select
2        st_pointn(geom, 1) as geom
3  from
```

```
4      nyc_bike_routes
5   where
6      segmentid = '331385'
```

Well this returned null. So what happened? Here is a coding debugging challenge for you to figure out. Take a look at the docs and try to see what the issue might be? This is a common one so no hints here.

Okay so if you took a look at the docs you can see that the function signature is:

```
geometry ST_PointN(geometry a_linestring, integer n);
```

It very clearly calls for a LINESTRING and an integer representing the point position. We know that 1 is in fact an integer, so the issue must be with the geometry data. Let's take a look and see by checking our geometry type:

Listing 2.31: Checking ST_PointN

```
1   select
2      st_geometrytype(geom) as geom
3   from
4      nyc_bike_routes
5   where
6      segmentid = '331385'
```

geom
ST_MultiLineString

Aha! We have a Multi-linestring, so it was an issue with the geometry. So how can we make this one single linestring? We know we can dump the parts out the linestring then select them individually, but how can we turn them into one? If you checked the docs, or better yet Googled what you could do, then you may have come across the function ST_LineMerge which has this signature and description:

```
geometry ST_LineMerge(geometry amultilinestring);
```

Returns a LineString or MultiLineString formed by joining together the line elements of a MultiLineString. Lines are joined at their endpoints at 2-way intersections. Lines are not joined across intersections of 3-way or greater degree.

So this looks like it would work for us. Our final function (Figure 2.13, on the following page):

Listing 2.32: Final output

```
1   select
2      st_pointn(st_linemerge(geom), 1) as geom
3   from
4      nyc_bike_routes
5   where
6      segmentid = '331385'
```

Why go through all this trouble? If you ever need to get the starting/ending points of all your line data, now you know how!

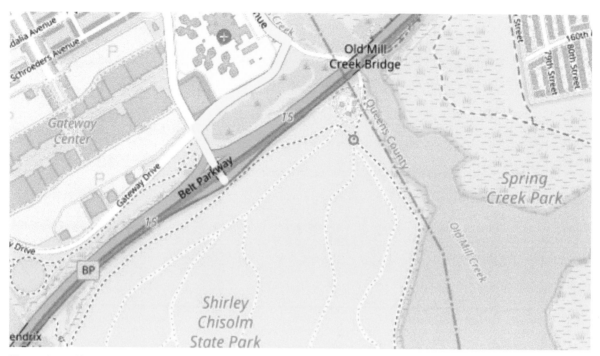

Figure 2.13: None

2.8 Editors

This set of functions allows you to edit and modify your geometries on a very granular level like adding or removing points, snapping, forcing 2/3D geometries, and more. I won't mention these here since there isn't a ton of analytical value, but it is good to know of their existence. For those who are maintaining geometries only in SQL this is a core set of functions to understand. You can see the full set of functions in the PostGIS reference[92].

2.9 Validators

https://postgis.net/docs/reference.html#Geometry_Validation[93]

Out of all the different spatial formats that are available there are bound to be some issues with our geometries. The geometry validators provide the best place to start to check if you have invalid geometries. Let's see if we have any in our data!

- **ST_IsValid** — Tests if a geometry is well-formed in 2D.
- **ST_IsValidDetail** — Returns a valid_detail row stating if a geometry is valid or if not a reason and a location.
- **ST_IsValidReason** — Returns text stating if a geometry is valid, or a reason for invalidity.
- **ST_MakeValid** — Attempts to make an invalid geometry valid without losing vertices.

ST_IsValid

We can take a look at the geometries in our NYC Buildings data:

---

[92]https://postgis.net/docs/reference.html#Geometry_Editors
[93]https://postgis.net/docs/reference.html#Geometry_Validation

Listing 2.33: ST_IsValid

```
1  select
2      *
3  from
4      nyc_building_footprints
5  where
6      st_isvalid(geom) is false
```

And in fact we have three geometries that have invalid geometries:

mpluto_bbl
1022430261
1016710039
4039760001

Instead of looking for all the invalid geometries each time we can just query these three IDs.

ST_IsValidDetail

So let's see the valid detail from our three geometries above:

Listing 2.34: ST_IsValidDetail

```
1  select
2      mpluto_bbl,
3      st_isvaliddetail(geom)
4  from
5      nyc_building_footprints
6  where
7      mpluto_bbl in ('1022430261', '1016710039', '4039760001')
```

mpluto_bbl	st_isvaliddetail
4039760001	(t)
1016710039	(f, "Ring Self-intersection", 01010000007F4EC1DA6E7C52C0DCF0906B9F644440)
4039760001	(f, "Ring Self-intersection", 01010000009C8C8F29BB7552C0323B56A12C654440)
1022430261	(t)
4039760001	(t)
1022430261	(f, "Ring Self-intersection", 0101000000D9494DB2957A52C01C07C27A6F6F4440)
1016710039	(t)

What this tells us is that these are MULTIPOLYGON geometries and that one part of each has a self-intersection error.

ST_IsValidReason

Better yet we can use this function to get a more readable detail:

Listing 2.35: ST_IsValidReason

```
1  select
2      mpluto_bbl,
```

```
3       st_isvalidreason(geom)
4    from
5       nyc_building_footprints
6    where
7       mpluto_bbl in ('1022430261', '1016710039', '4039760001')
```

mpluto_bbl	st_isvalidreason
4039760001	Valid Geometry
1016710039	Valid Geometry
1016710039	Ring Self-intersection[-73.9442660224686 40.7861151178092]
4039760001	Ring Self-intersection[-73.8395484830712 40.7904245062877]
1022430261	Valid Geometry
4039760001	Valid Geometry
1022430261	Ring Self-intersection[-73.9153867487688 40.8705895850564]

ST_MakeValid

Fortunately fixing these geometries is generally easy using this function.

Listing 2.36: ST_MakeValid

```
1    select
2       mpluto_bbl,
3       st_isvalid(st_makevalid(geom))
4    from
5       nyc_building_footprints
6    where
7       mpluto_bbl in ('1022430261', '1016710039', '4039760001')
```

And now we have valid geometries!

Spatial Reference

https://postgis.net/docs/reference.html#SRS_Functions[94]

Of course no geospatial system will be complete without projection support and PostGIS has three simple functions to manage your projections.

- **ST_SetSRID** — Set the SRID on a geometry.
- **ST_SRID** — Returns the spatial reference identifier for a geometry.
- *'ST_Transform'* — Return a new geometry with coordinates transformed to a different spatial reference system.

ST_SetSRID

If you have a geometry without an SRID you can add one using this function, which we already used in an earlier example. Keep in mind some other functions may let you set the SRID in the creation a geometry.

---

[94]https://postgis.net/docs/reference.html#SRS_Functions

ST_SRID

To find the SRID of a geometry we can use ST_SRID:

Listing 2.37: ST_SRID

```
1  select
2      st_srid(geom)
3  from
4      nyc_building_footprints
5  limit
6      3
```

st_srid
4326
4326
4326

ST_Transform

And finally this function is the one you might use the most if you need to transform your SRID:

Listing 2.38: ST_Transform which will be used often

```
1  select
2      ogc_fid,
3      st_transform(geom, 2263) as geom
4  from
5      nyc_building_footprints
6  limit
7      3
```

Creators

Sometimes you need to create, or export, geometries from other types of data that you have imported into your database. For that we have the creator functions that can turn some data into a geometry and vice-versa. We don't need to look at each one of these in detail, but we see one example from each group. Overall the WKT and WKB formats are the most common but there are plenty of others you can use such as GeoJSON, KML, and more.

2.10 Inputs

This set of functions takes an argument and then returns a geometry or geography:

Listing 2.39: Points from text

```
1  select
2      st_geomfromtext('POINT(-73.9772294 40.7527262)', 4326) as geom
```

This will return a point at Grand Central Station in New York City.

- **ST_GeogFromText** — Return a specified geography value from Well-Known Text representation or extended (WKT).
- **ST_GeographyFromText** — Return a specified geography value from Well-Known Text representation or extended (WKT).

- **ST_GeogFromWKB** — Creates a geography instance from a Well-Known Binary geometry representation (WKB) or extended Well Known Binary (EWKB).
- **ST_GeomFromWKB** — Creates a geometry instance from a Well-Known Binary geometry representation (WKB) and optional SRID.

Others

- **ST_Box2dFromGeoHash** — Return a BOX2D from a GeoHash string.
- **ST_GeomFromGeoHash** — Return a geometry from a GeoHash string.
- **ST_GeomFromGML** — Takes as input GML representation of geometry and outputs a PostGIS geometry object
- **ST_GeomFromGeoJSON** — Takes as input a geojson representation of a geometry and outputs a PostGIS geometry object
- **ST_GeomFromKML** — Takes as input KML representation of geometry and outputs a PostGIS geometry object
- **ST_GeomFromTWKB** — Creates a geometry instance from a TWKB ("Tiny Well-Known Binary") geometry representation.
- **ST_GMLToSQL** — Return a specified ST_Geometry value from GML representation. This is an alias name for ST_GeomFromGML
- **ST_LineFromEncodedPolyline** — Creates a LineString from an Encoded Polyline.
- **ST_PointFromGeoHash** — Return a point from a GeoHash string.
- **ST_FromFlatGeobufToTable** — Creates a table based on the structure of FlatGeobuf data.
- **ST_FromFlatGeobuf** — Reads FlatGeobuf data.

2.11 Outputs

We have seen the *ST_AsText* function earlier but you can also output geometries as different formats:

Listing 2.40: ST_AsGeoJSON

```
1  select
2      st_asgeojson(geom)
3  from
4      nyc_building_footprints
5  limit
6      3
```

st_asgeojson
{"type":"MultiPolygon", "coordinates":[[[[-73.925006409, 40.623351698]...
{"type":"MultiPolygon", "coordinates":[[[[-73.753816555, 40.674630114]...
{"type":"MultiPolygon", "coordinates":[[[[-73.721306282, 40.734020454]...

- **ST_AsEWKT** — Return the Well-Known Text (WKT) representation of the geometry with SRID meta data.
- **ST_AsText** — Return the Well-Known Text (WKT) representation of the geometry/geography without SRID metadata.
- **ST_AsBinary** — Return the OGC/ISO Well-Known Binary (WKB) representation of the geometry/geography without SRID meta data.
- **ST_AsEWKB** — Return the Extended Well-Known Binary (EWKB) representation of the geometry with SRID meta data.

Other Formats

- **ST_AsEncodedPolyline** — Returns an Encoded Polyline from a LineString geometry.

- **ST_AsFlatGeobuf** — Return a FlatGeobuf representation of a set of rows.
- **ST_AsGeobuf** — Return a Geobuf representation of a set of rows.
- **ST_AsGeoJSON** — Return a geometry as a GeoJSON element.
- **ST_AsGML** — Return the geometry as a GML version 2 or 3 element.
- **ST_AsKML** — Return the geometry as a KML element.
- **ST_AsLatLonText** — Return the Degrees, Minutes, Seconds representation of the given point.
- **ST_AsMARC21** — Returns geometry as a MARC21/XML record with a geographic datafield (034).
- **ST_AsMVTGeom** — Transforms a geometry into the coordinate space of a MVT tile.
- **ST_AsMVT** — Aggregate function returning a MVT representation of a set of rows.
- **ST_AsSVG** — Returns SVG path data for a geometry.
- **ST_AsTWKB** — Returns the geometry as TWKB, aka "Tiny Well-Known Binary"
- **ST_AsX3D** — Returns a Geometry in X3D xml node element format: ISO-IEC-19776-1.2-X3DEncodings-XML
- **ST_GeoHash** — Return a GeoHash representation of the geometry.

Manipulating and transforming geometries

This set of functions allows you to turn your geometry or geometries into a new geometry. This includes many common operations like buffers, centroids, concave/convex hulls, simplification and more.

My top functions

- **ST_Buffer** — Computes a geometry covering all points within a given distance from a geometry.
- **ST_Centroid** — Returns the geometric center of a geometry.
- **ST_ChaikinSmoothing** — Returns a smoothed version of a geometry, using the Chaikin algorithm
- **ST_ConcaveHull** — Computes a possibly concave geometry that encloses all input geometry vertices
- **ST_ConvexHull** — Computes the convex hull of a geometry.
- **ST_DelaunayTriangles** — Returns the Delaunay triangulation of the vertices of a geometry.
- **ST_GeneratePoints** — Generates random points contained in a Polygon or MultiPolygon.
- **ST_LineMerge** — Return the lines formed by sewing together a MultiLineString.
- **ST_Simplify** — Returns a simplified version of a geometry, using the Douglas-Peucker algorithm.
- **ST_SimplifyPreserveTopology** — Returns a simplified and valid version of a geometry, using the Douglas-Peucker algorithm.

Others

- **ST_BuildArea** — Creates a polygonal geometry formed by the linework of a geometry.
- **ST_FilterByM** — Removes vertices based on their M value
- **ST_GeometricMedian** — Returns the geometric median of a MultiPoint.
- **ST_MaximumInscribedCircle** — Computes the largest circle contained within a geometry.
- **ST_MinimumBoundingCircle** — Returns the smallest circle polygon that contains a geometry.
- **ST_MinimumBoundingRadius** — Returns the center point and radius of the smallest circle that contains a geometry.
- **ST_OrientedEnvelope** — Returns a minimum-area rectangle containing a geometry.
- **ST_OffsetCurve** — Returns an offset line at a given distance and side from an input line.
- **ST_PointOnSurface** — Computes a point guaranteed to lie in a polygon, or on a geometry.
- **ST_Polygonize** — Computes a collection of polygons formed from the linework of a set of geometries.

- **ST_ReducePrecision** — Returns a valid geometry with points rounded to a grid tolerance.
- **ST_SharedPaths** — Returns a collection containing paths shared by the two input linestrings/-multilinestrings.
- **ST_VoronoiPolygons** — Returns the cells of the Voronoi diagram of the vertices of a geometry.
- **ST_SimplifyPolygonHull** — Computes a simplified topology-preserving outer or inner hull of a polygonal geometry.
- **ST_SimplifyVW** — Returns a simplified version of a geometry, using the Visvalingam-Whyatt algorithm
- **ST_SetEffectiveArea** — Sets the effective area for each vertex, using the Visvalingam-Whyatt algorithm.
- **ST_TriangulatePolygon** — Computes the constrained Delaunay triangulation of polygons
- **ST_VoronoiLines** — Returns the boundaries of the Voronoi diagram of the vertices of a geometry.

ST_Buffer

This function will perform a very popular analysis: creating a buffer around a geometry. A few important notes:

- There are many stylistic options such as different end-caps (round, mitre, etc.) and you can choose to have the buffer one one side of the polygon or line
- For geometries the measurement uses the unit of measurement of the projection (keep this in mind as we proceed)
- You can also control the number of points per quarter circle

For our example we will create some points with the user defined function then turn those into geographies and create a ½ kilometer buffer (Figure 2.14, on the next page):

Listing 2.41: ST_Buffer

```
1  select
2      st_buffer(
3          buildpoint(longitude, latitude, 4326) :: geography,
4          500
5      )
6  from
7      nyc_311
8  limit
9      10
```

For polygons you can also create buffers, as well as negative buffers (Figure 2.15, on page 188):

Listing 2.42: Negative buffer

```
1  select
2      st_buffer(st_transform(geom, 4326) :: geography, -200)
3  from
4      nyc_zips
5  limit
6      10
```

ST_Centroid

This creates a centroid at the geographic center of mass (Figure 2.16, on page 188):

Listing 2.43: ST_Centroid

```
1  select
2      st_centroid(st_transform(geom, 4326) :: geography)
```

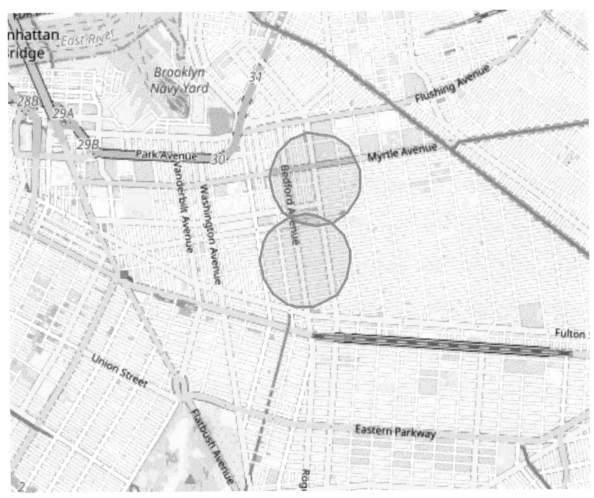

Figure 2.14: Creating a buffer

```
3  from
4      nyc_zips
5  limit
6      10
```

ST_ChaikinSmoothing

This is a smoothing function that uses the Chaikin Smoothing algorithm:

Listing 2.44: ST_ChaikinSmoothing

```
1  select
2      st_transform(geom, 4326) as original,
3      st_chaikinsmoothing(st_transform(geom, 4326), 1) as one,
4      st_chaikinsmoothing(st_transform(geom, 4326), 5) as five
5  from
6      nyc_zips
7  limit
8      10
```

Here we can check each of the different results in Chaikin algorithm which double the number of

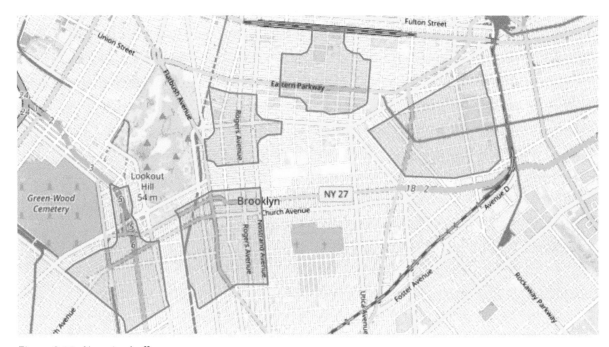

Figure 2.15: Negative buffer

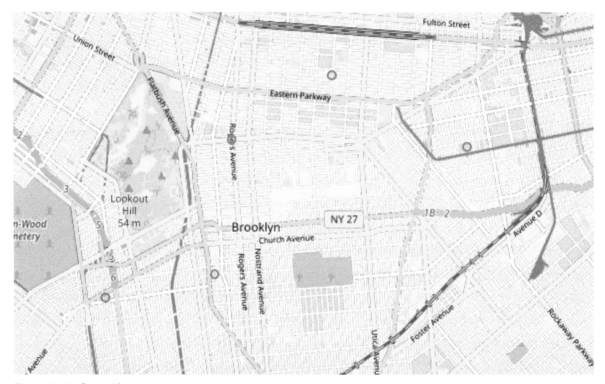

Figure 2.16: Centroids

vertices to create a smoothed polygon. Below are the original polygons (Figure 2.17, on page 189):

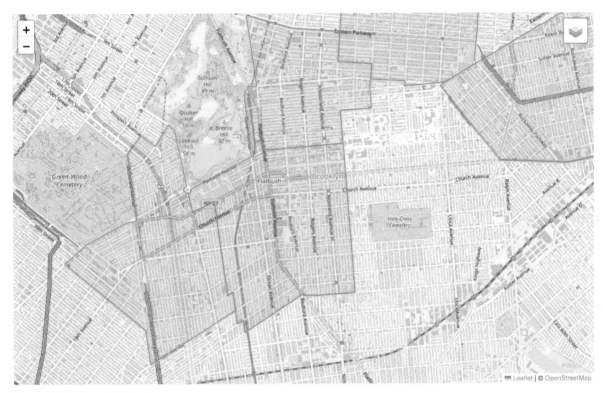

Figure 2.17: Smoothed polygons

Then the with the base number of iterations or 1 (Figure 2.18, on page 189):

Then with the max iterations or 5 (Figure 2.19, on page 190):

ST_ConcaveHull

You can also create concave hull polygons around geometries. You need to add a float as a second argument to define the amount of "concave-ness". 0 is the most concave and 1 will produce a convex hull so something around 0.3 or 0.5 will likely work for most use cases. To demonstrate this we will grab 10 points from our NYC 311 dataset and create a geometry collection from them to build a single concave hull (Figure 2.20, on the next page):

Listing 2.45: ST_ConcaveHull

```
1   -- Find the first 50 trees in Fort Greene with the
2   -- Latitude and longitude columns
3   with a as (
4       select
5           latitude,
6           longitude
7       from
8           nyc_2015_tree_census
9       where
10          nta_name = 'Fort Greene'
11      limit
12          50
13  ),
14
```

Figure 2.18: Smoothed polygons with one iteration

Figure 2.19: Smoothed polygons with five iterations

```
15  -- Turn the latitude/longitude columns into geometries
16  b as (
17    select
18        st_collect(
19            buildpoint(longitude :: numeric, latitude :: numeric, 4326)
20        ) as geom
21    from
22        a
23  )
24
25  -- Create multiple concave hulls with various concave-ness
26  -- and use UNION to turn them into a single table
27  select
28      st_concavehull(geom, 0.1) as hull
29  from
30      b
31  union
32  select
33      st_concavehull(geom, 0.3) as hull
34  from
35      b
36  union
37  select
38      st_concavehull(geom, 0.7) as hull
39  from
40      b
```

ST_ConvexHull

And you can do the same with a convex hull (Figure 2.21, on the facing page):

Listing 2.46: Creating a convex hull

```
1   with a as (
2     select
3         latitude,
4         longitude
5     from
6         nyc_2015_tree_census
7     where
8         nta_name = 'Fort Greene'
9     limit
10        50
11  ), b as (
12    select
13        st_collect(
14            buildpoint(longitude :: numeric, latitude :: numeric, 4326)
15        ) as geom
16    from
17        a
18  )
19  select
20      st_convexhull(geom) as hull
21  from
22      b
```

ST_DelaunayTriangles

This function allows you to triangulate polygons using the Delauny triangulation method[95]. The result is a *GEOMETRY COLLECTION* of multiple polygons (using the 0 flag) which can be used as needed.

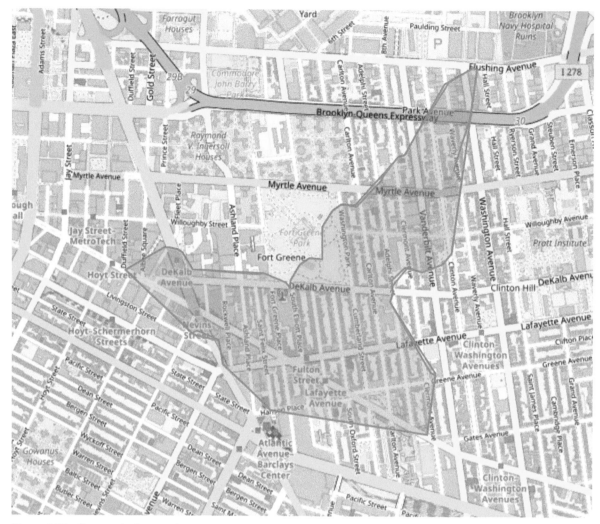

Figure 2.20: Concave hull examples

There is a great use case for this which we will review in a later chapter but for now here is the query:

Listing 2.47: ST_DelaunayTriangles

```
1  select
2      st_delaunaytriangles(st_transform(geom, 4326)) as triangles
3  from
4      nyc_zips
5  where
6      zipcode = '10009'
```

You can include a parameter for tolerance (float) in the second argument and type flag in the third argument but if you just want polygons you don't need the extra arguments (Figure 2.22, on page 194).

---

[95]https://en.wikipedia.org/wiki/Delaunay_triangulation

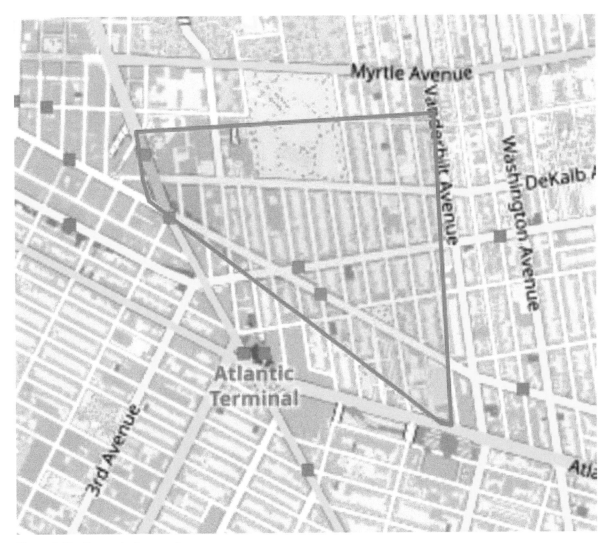

Figure 2.21: Convex hull examples

ST_GeneratePoints

This function allows you to generate a random set of points within a polygon. The second argument is the number of points you want to generate (Figure 2.23, on page 195):

Listing 2.48: ST_GeneratePoints

```
1   select
2       st_generatepoints(st_transform(geom, 4326), 500) as points
3   from
4       nyc_zips
5   where
6       zipcode = '10009'
```

ST_LineMerge

This is a quick and easy way to merge several linestrings together, which is perfect for our NYC Bike Routes which are all individual linestrings. Let's join one path into a complete line using this query:

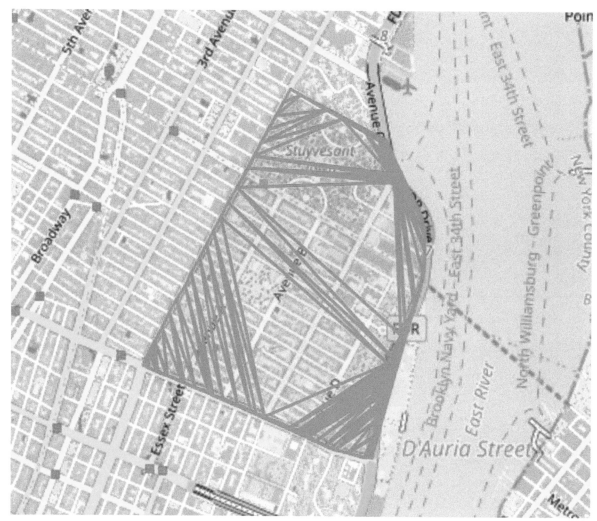

Figure 2.22: Delaunay triangles

Listing 2.49: ST_LineMerge

```
1   select
2   st_linemerge(geom) as geom from
3   nyc_bike_routes
4   where
5   street = '7 AV'
6   and fromstreet = '42 ST'
7   and tostreet = '65 ST'
```

ST_Simplify

This is the first of two functions to simplify geometries using the Douglas-Peucker algorithm. This one focuses on just simplification with two arguments, one for the geometry and one for the tolerance of simplification. We will run the same query 4 times with different tolerance levels to see the changes to the geometry on one map, and union the using the UNION operator since they have one column with the same name (Figure 2.24, on page 196).

Listing 2.50: ST_Simplify

Figure 2.23: Random generated points

```
1    -- Create multiple geometries with different simplification levels
2    -- and UNION them into one table
3    select
4        st_transform(geom, 4326) as geom
5    from
6        nyc_zips
7    where
8        zipcode = '11693'
9    union
10   select
11       st_transform(st_simplify(geom, 1), 4326) as geom
12   from
13       nyc_zips
14   where
15       zipcode = '11693'
16   union
17   select
18       st_transform(st_simplify(geom, 10), 4326) as geom
19   from
20       nyc_zips
21   where
22       zipcode = '11693'
23   union
24   select
25       st_transform(st_simplify(geom, 50), 4326) as geom
26   from
27       nyc_zips
28   where
29       zipcode = '11693'
```

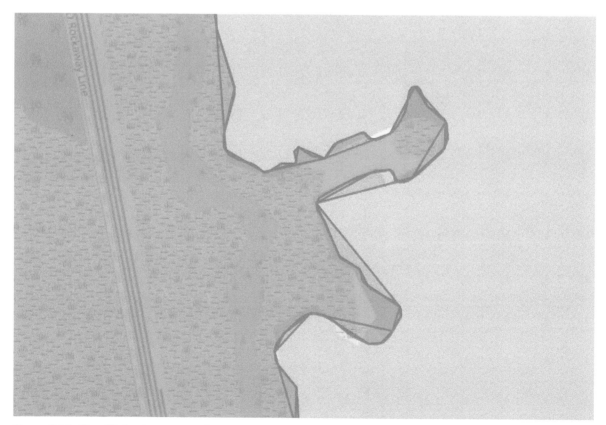

Figure 2.24: Simplified polygon examples

ST_SimplifyPreserveTopology

This is the same function as above but in this case it preserves the topology, or the touching parts of the geometry. We can test this out using a new operator we will see in the next chapter on spatial relationships called *ST_Touches*. We will get all the zip codes that touch 11434 (where JFK Airport is located) and 11434 too (Figure 2.25, on page 198).

Listing 2.51: ST_SimplifyPreserveTopology

```
1   -- Create multiple geometries that share borders with different
2   -- simplification levels and UNION them into one table
3   select
4       st_transform(geom, 4326) as geom
5   from
6       nyc_zips
7   where
8       zipcode = '11434'
9       or st_touches(
10          geom,
11          (
12              select
13                  geom
14              from
15                  nyc_zips
16              where
17                  zipcode = '11434'
18          )
19      )
20  union
21  select
22      st_transform(st_simplifypreservetopology(geom, 1), 4326) as geom
23  from
24      nyc_zips
25  where
26      zipcode = '11434'
27      or st_touches(
28          geom,
29          (
30              select
31                  geom
32              from
33                  nyc_zips
34              where
35                  zipcode = '11434'
36          )
37      )
38  union
39  select
40      st_transform(st_simplifypreservetopology(geom, 10), 4326) as geom
41  from
42      nyc_zips
43  where
44      zipcode = '11434'
45      or st_touches(
46          geom,
47          (
48              select
49                  geom
50              from
51                  nyc_zips
52              where
53                  zipcode = '11434'
54          )
55      )
```

```
56   union
57   select
58       st_transform(st_simplifypreservetopology(geom, 50), 4326) as geom
59   from
60       nyc_zips
61   where
62       zipcode = '11434'
63       or st_touches(
64           geom,
65           (
66               select
67                   geom
68               from
69                   nyc_zips
70               where
71                   zipcode = '11434'
72           )
73       )
```

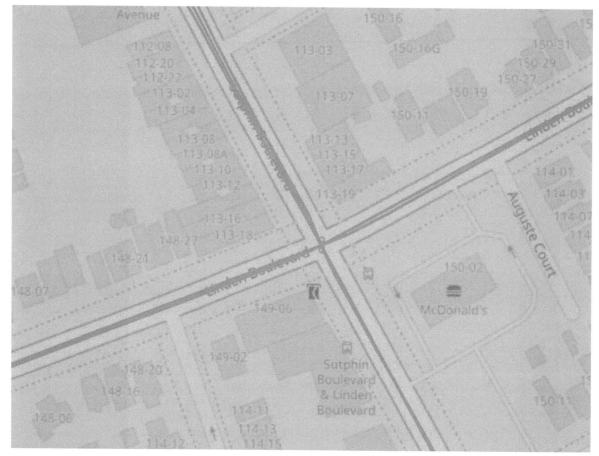

Figure 2.25: Simplified polygon examples with preserved topology

2.12   Measurements in spatial SQL

There are many different ways to measure a geometry, and PostGIS comes with a complete set of functions to measure all types of geometries.

My top functions

- **ST_Area** — Returns the area of a polygonal geometry.
- **ST_ClosestPoint** — Returns the 2D point on g1 that is closest to g2. This is the first point of the shortest line from one geometry to the other.
- **ST_Distance** — Returns the distance between two geometry or geography values.
- **ST_Length** — Returns the 2D length of a linear geometry.
- **ST_Perimeter** — Returns the length of the boundary of a polygonal geometry or geography.
- **ST_ShortestLine** — Returns the 2D shortest line between two geometries

Other functions

- **ST_Azimuth** — Returns the north-based azimuth of a line between two points.
- **ST_Angle** — Returns the angle between two vectors defined by 3 or 4 points, or 2 lines.
- **ST_3DClosestPoint** — Returns the 3D point on g1 that is closest to g2. This is the first point of the 3D shortest line.
- **ST_3DDistance** — Returns the 3D cartesian minimum distance (based on spatial ref) between two geometries in projected units.
- **ST_DistanceSphere** — Returns minimum distance in meters between two lon/lat geometries using a spherical earth model.
- **ST_DistanceSpheroid** — Returns the minimum distance between two lon/lat geometries using a spheroidal earth model.
- **ST_FrechetDistance** — Returns the Fréchet distance between two geometries.
- **ST_HausdorffDistance** — Returns the Hausdorff distance between two geometries.
- **ST_Length2D** — Returns the 2D length of a linear geometry. Alias for ST_Length
- **ST_3DLength** — Returns the 3D length of a linear geometry.
- **ST_LengthSpheroid** — Returns the 2D or 3D length/perimeter of a lon/lat geometry on a spheroid.
- **ST_LongestLine** — Returns the 2D longest line between two geometries.
- **ST_3DLongestLine** — Returns the 3D longest line between two geometries
- **ST_MaxDistance** — Returns the 2D largest distance between two geometries in projected units.
- **ST_3DMaxDistance** — Returns the 3D cartesian maximum distance (based on spatial ref) between two geometries in projected units.
- **ST_MinimumClearance** — Returns the minimum clearance of a geometry, a measure of a geometry's robustness.
- **ST_MinimumClearanceLine** — Returns the two-point LineString spanning a geometry's minimum clearance.
- **ST_Perimeter2D** — Returns the 2D perimeter of a polygonal geometry. Alias for ST_Perimeter.
- **ST_3DPerimeter** — Returns the 3D perimeter of a polygonal geometry.
- **ST_Project** — Returns a point projected from a start point by a distance and bearing (azimuth).
- **ST_3DShortestLine** — Returns the 3D shortest line between two geometries

ST_Area

This allows us to find the area of a polygon. This will return in the unit of measure from the SRID for geometries and is square meters for geographies:

Listing 2.52: ST_Area

```
1  select
2      st_area(geom) as area
3  from
4      nyc_building_footprints
5  limit
6      5
```

1.4428577997126009e-09
7.891702476768148e-09
6.695094119757017e-09
1.2662729366160693e-08
2.4262124438870062e-09

When casting to geography we can see the answer in square meters:

Listing 2.53: Area in meters

```
1  select
2      st_area(geom :: geography) as area
3  from
4      nyc_building_footprints
5  limit
6      5
```

13.556961725698784
74.09368502616417
62.80374527350068
119.01674082968384
22.811112018302083

ST_ClosestPoint

This function takes two geometries and finds the closest point from the first geometry to the second geometry:

Listing 2.54: ST_ClosestPoint

```
1  with one as (
2      select
3          geom
4      from
5          nyc_zips
6      where
7          zipcode = '10009'
8  ),
9  two as (
10     select
11         geom
12     from
13         nyc_zips
14     where
15         zipcode = '10001'
16 )
17 select
18     st_closestpoint(one.geom, two.geom) as point
19 from
20     one,
21     two
```

ST_Distance

Similarly, we can find the difference between two geometries, once again in the spatial reference units for geometries and meters for geographies.

Listing 2.55: ST_Distance

```
1  with one as (
2      select
3          geom
4      from
5          nyc_zips
6      where
7          zipcode = '10009'
8  ),
9  two as (
10     select
11         geom
12     from
13         nyc_zips
14     where
15         zipcode = '10001'
16 )
17 select
18     st_distance(one.geom, two.geom) as dist
19 from
20     one,
21     two
```

dist
3855.56160052085

Since this returns a number, this case the distance in feet, we can easily turn this into a different unit of measure using simple math, in this case miles:

Listing 2.56: Distance in miles

```
1  with one as (
2      select
3          geom
4      from
5          nyc_zips
6      where
7          zipcode = '10009'
8  ),
9  two as (
10     select
11         geom
12     from
13         nyc_zips
14     where
15         zipcode = '10001'
16 )
17 select
18     st_distance(one.geom, two.geom) / 5280 as dist
19 from
20     one,
21     two
```

dist
0.7302200000986458

So almost a quarter of a mile. We can also compare the difference between geometry and geography here too:

Listing 2.57: Distance with GEOGRAPHY

```
1  with one as (
2      select
3          geom :: geography as geog
4      from
5          nyc_zips
6      where
7          zipcode = '10009'
8  ),
9  two as (
10     select
11         geom :: geography as geog
12     from
13         nyc_zips
14     where
15         zipcode = '10001'
16 )
17 select
18     st_distance(one.geog, two.geog) / 1609 as dist
19 from
20     one,
21     two
```

Whoops. That seems odd. Here is the response that we got back from the query we just ran:

ERROR: Only lon/lat coordinate systems are supported in geography.

SQL state: 22023

So it appears there is some issue with our geometry? Enter another coding challenge. See if you can figure out how to solve this problem using some functions we just explored in this chapter.

———————————

So if we read our error closely it appears that there may be an error with our coordinate system. Let's first see what our projection that we are using with our data is currently:

Listing 2.58: Checking our SRID

```
1  select
2      st_srid(geom)
3  from
4      nyc_zips
5  limit
6      1
```

st_srid
2263

So it looks like our SRID is 2263 which is the North American Datum 1983 (NAD 83) for New York Long Island[96]. And in this case the unit of measurement is in feet. So we need a coordinate system such as WGS 84 or 4326. Once we perform the transformation we can cast this to a GEOGRAPHY and we can get our measurement in meters.

Listing 2.59: Casting to GEOGRAPHY

```
1   with one as (
2       select
3           st_transform(geom, 4326) :: geography as geog
4       from
5           nyc_zips
6       where
7           zipcode = '10009'
8   ),
9   two as (
10      select
11          st_transform(geom, 4326) :: geography as geog
12      from
13          nyc_zips
14      where
15          zipcode = '10001'
16  )
17  select
18      st_distance(one.geog, two.geog) / 1609 as dist
19  from
20      one,
21      two
```

dist
0.7303799424922313

And with that we can see that we have a very similar, but not totally exact answer.

ST_Length

To measure the length of a line we can use ST_Length. In this case we can turn the geometry, in SRID 4326, to a geometry to get a measurement in meters.

Listing 2.60: ST_Length

```
1   select
2       st_length(geom :: geography)
3   from
4       nyc_bike_routes
5   limit
6       1
```

st_length
40.163645298747284

ST_Perimeter

We can also determine the perimeter length of a polygon:

---

[96]https://epsg.io/2263

Listing 2.61: Measuring a perimeter

```
1  select
2      st_perimeter(geom)
3  from
4      nyc_zips
5  where
6      zipcode = '10009'
```

st_perimeter
16247.124894682644

ST_ShortestLine

This function returns a line that represents the shortest line between two geometries. We can reuse our query and then transform the return value to SRID 4326 to make sure it renders on the map.

Listing 2.62: ST_ShortestLine

```
1  with one as (
2      select
3          geom
4      from
5          nyc_zips
6      where
7          zipcode = '10009'
8  ),
9  two as (
10     select
11         geom
12     from
13         nyc_zips
14     where
15         zipcode = '10001'
16 )
17 select
18     st_transform(st_shortestline(one.geom, two.geom), 4326) as line
19 from
20     one,
21     two
```

3. Spatial Relationships

Now that we have the fundamental spatial SQL elements in our toolkit, we can now move into some of the more advanced topics around spatial relationships which include spatial joins and aggregations, overlay functions which can do things like spatial unions and clipping, clustering, and some special spatial operators which you can use in your spatial SQL.

3.1 Relationship Functions

Spatial relationship functions[97] provide capabilities to understand how different geometries interact in space, and includes a widely used function and likely my most used spatial SQL function, ST_Intersects. Some characteristics of these functions are that:

- Almost all of these functions return a boolean, so either a true or false condition
- Most functions take two geometries that will be evaluated
    - These can come from a single table, two tables, a table and a static geometry, etc.
- You can use these functions in a few different areas in your query such as
    - As a new column in your data
    - As a condition in a WHERE clause
    - As a condition for a table join (more on this later)

Below are a list of all the different spatial relationship functions. We will review the top list as well as the relationships between the functions since many have very similar functionality with slight differences, so there are some that overlap functionality (no pun intended):

My top functions

- **ST_Contains** — Tests if no points of B lie in the exterior of A, and A and B have at least one interior point in common.
- **ST_Disjoint** — Tests if two geometries are disjoint (they have no point in common).
- **ST_Intersects** — Tests if two geometries intersect (they have at least one point in common).
- **ST_Overlaps** — Tests if two geometries intersect and have the same dimension, but are not completely contained by each other.
- **ST_Touches** — Tests if two geometries have at least one point in common, but their interiors do not intersect.
- **ST_Within** — Tests if no points of A lie in the exterior of B, and A and B have at least one interior point in common

Other functions

- **ST_3DIntersects** — Tests if two geometries spatially intersect in 3D - only for points, linestrings, polygons, polyhedral surface (area).
- **ST_ContainsProperly** — Tests if B intersects the interior of A but not the boundary or exterior.
- **ST_CoveredBy** — Tests if no point in A is outside B
- **ST_Covers** — Tests if no point in B is outside A

---

[97]https://postgis.net/docs/reference.html#Spatial_Relationships

- **ST_Crosses** — Tests if two geometries have some, but not all, interior points in common.
- **ST_Equals** — Tests if two geometries include the same set of points.
- **ST_LineCrossingDirection** — Returns a number indicating the crossing behavior of two LineStrings.
- **ST_OrderingEquals** — Tests if two geometries represent the same geometry and have points in the same directional order.
- **ST_Relate** — Tests if two geometries have a topological relationship matching an Intersection Matrix pattern, or computes their Intersection Matrix
- **ST_RelateMatch** — Tests if a DE-9IM Intersection Matrix matches an Intersection Matrix pattern.

3.2   Ways to use spatial relationship functions

As I mentioned before, there are several ways to use spatial relationship functions all of which produce different yet equally useful results. We will use ST_Intersects as the function here as it covers the most common spatial relationship question which is if two polygons touch or overlap in some way. Below are the most common ways that I have used these functions, but as with all things in spatial SQL, you have the full control of SQL to build and write queries as you want.

As a column

The first way of using spatial relationship functions is using the returned result of the spatial relationship, or the boolean value, as a new column in your query. For this we can use our NYC Neighborhoods and our NYC Taxis data from the previous chapters:

Listing 3.1: Relationship functions as a column

```
1    select
2        ogc_fid,
3        trip_distance,
4        total_amount,
5
6        -- ST_Intersects will return a boolean in a column
7        st_intersects(
8
9            -- First geometry is at the pickup location using the buildpoint function
10           buildpoint(
11               pickup_longitude :: numeric,
12               pickup_latitude :: numeric,
13               4326
14           ),
15
16           -- This selects the geometry for the West Village
17           (
18               select
19                   geom
20               from
21                   nyc_neighborhoods
22               where
23                   neighborhood = 'West Village'
24           )
25       )
26   from
27       nyc_yellow_taxi_0601_0615_2016
28   order by
29       pickup_datetime asc
30   limit
31       10
```

Now this query is a bit busy because we are using a subquery to extract one specific geometry from the Neighborhoods table, and we have to turn our pickup locations to geometries, but this returns data that looks like this:

ogc_fid	trip_distance	total_amount	st_intersects
1803838	2.3	16.6	false
1543344	1.3	11.4	false
2983958	2.59	18.8	false
1239517	5.9	24.96	false
247513	0.9	6.3	false

Now you can use this to add a new column to your dataset and then update that column with the return results from that function too if you want to store that data too.

In a WHERE clause

Let's say we want to filter results rather than add them as a column:

Listing 3.2: Using a WHERE clause

```
1  select
2      ogc_fid,
3      trip_distance,
4      total_amount
5  from
6      nyc_yellow_taxi_0601_0615_2016
7  where
8
9      -- Using ST_Intersects in the WHERE clause
10     st_intersects(
11
12         -- Using ST_Intersects in the WHERE clause, first with the pick up point
13         buildpoint(
14             pickup_longitude :: numeric,
15             pickup_latitude :: numeric,
16             4326
17         ),
18
19         -- Selecting the geometry for the West Village
20         (
21             select
22                 geom
23             from
24                 nyc_neighborhoods
25             where
26                 neighborhood = 'West Village'
27         )
28     )
29 order by
30     pickup_datetime asc
31 limit
32     10
```

We can find only the trips that start in the West Village and limit that to 10 results.

ogc_fid	trip_distance	total_amount
2541221	1.4	12.35
2199905	2.76	14.76
5611817	1.39	8.8
4043047	3.07	18.36
5291922	2.49	12.8
4088179	5.92	20.8
2428947	9	31.8
5356494	1.89	12.8
3072080	0.03	4.3
3995644	1.56	9

Hold on a minute. If you take a look at our query you can see that where we would normally have some sort of equality evaluation after our `WHERE` operator we simply have the function and nothing more. Think about it for a minute about why this works as our next challenge.

Did you figure it out? If you recall from our earlier chapters our `WHERE` condition allows us to filter our rows based on a condition of equality, or in short true or false (it can also evaluate to unknown but for now let's focus on true and false). So for a normal `WHERE` conditional we might have some condition like:

```
WHERE neighborhood = 'West Village'
```

And if the row matches the condition, or `neighborhood = 'West Village'`, will evaluate to `true` or `false`. If you read the above section about spatial relationship functions closely you can see that the return value of `ST_Intersects` is in fact a boolean, or true/false, in which case the return value of the function is enough for us to evaluate the equality of our spatial relationship.

Before we proceed you may have noticed that the last query took some time to run. That is because we are still creating our geometries on the fly using our `BuildPoint` user defined function. A good rule of thumb is that a `GEOMETRY` or `GEOGRAPHY` stored on the database will be far more efficient to query than those generated on the fly. This is because when we create it on the fly it takes time to run that function for every point being evaluated. In the case of our first query we return the first 100 rows no matter what they are but in our second we may have to query through 500, 1,000, or 10,000 rows to reach the 100 desired results that match our condition. If you recall from our section on CRUD tasks, to fix this we have to:

- Add new columns for our geometry
- `UPDATE` our new columns with the geometry values created from the latitude and longitudes

Since we have a set of lat/longs for pickup and drop-off we can create two different geometries. This is a nice advantage of PostGIS where we can have multiple geometries in the same table.

First we can add the columns to our table:

Listing 3.3: Update the taxis table

```
1   alter table
```

```
2       nyc_yellow_taxi_0601_0615_2016
3   add
4       column pickup geometry,
5   add
6       column dropoff geometry
```

Then UPDATE the table with the new values. This process took 6 minutes and 26 seconds on my computer so don't be surprised if this takes a long time.

Listing 3.4: Update the pickup and drop-off locations

```
1   update
2       nyc_yellow_taxi_0601_0615_2016
3   set
4       pickup = st_setsrid(
5           st_makepoint(pickup_longitude, pickup_latitude),
6           4326
7       ),
8       dropoff = st_setsrid(
9           st_makepoint(pickup_longitude, pickup_latitude),
10          4326
11      )
```

To test our new columns out let's see if our last query using ST_Intersects runs any faster this time around:

Listing 3.5: Testing with the new geometry columns

```
1   select
2       ogc_fid,
3       trip_distance,
4       total_amount
5   from
6       nyc_yellow_taxi_0601_0615_2016
7   where
8       st_intersects(
9           pickup,
10          (
11              select
12                  geom
13              from
14                  nyc_neighborhoods
15              where
16                  neighborhood = 'West Village'
17          )
18      )
19  order by
20      pickup_datetime asc
21  limit
22      10
```

On my computer using the GEOMETRY stored as a column my query finished in 14 seconds compared to 2 minutes and 7 seconds creating the geometries on the fly. This translates into about a 907% perfomance increase, so definitely worth the effort to create the geometries.

Within a JOIN

Within a JOIN we can perform our previous queries with some cleaner code, as well as perform spatial aggregations with joins. First let's rewrite our first query but this time as a join:

Listing 3.6: Within a JOIN

```
1   select
2       a.ogc_fid,
3       a.trip_distance,
4       a.total_amount,
5       st_intersects(a.pickup, b.geom)
6   from
7       nyc_yellow_taxi_0601_0615_2016 a,
8       nyc_neighborhoods b
9   where
10      b.neighborhood = 'West Village'
11  order by
12      a.pickup_datetime asc
13  limit
14      100
```

Since we want to check all the values we can perform a cross join since we have no condition apart from the WHERE clause so our Neighborhoods table is only one after the filter.

We can do the same with our second query to move the intersection parameter from the WHERE operator into the JOIN:

Listing 3.7: Cleaning up the query

```
1   select
2       a.ogc_fid,
3       a.trip_distance,
4       a.total_amount
5   from
6       nyc_yellow_taxi_0601_0615_2016 a
7
8       -- Since ST_Intersects will return true or false
9       -- we can use it to evaluate the join
10      join nyc_neighborhoods b on st_intersects(a.pickup, b.geom)
11  where
12      b.neighborhood = 'West Village'
13  order by
14      a.pickup_datetime asc
15  limit
16      10
```

Once again this results in a cleaner query. You can also use this same structure to add columns from your second data source as well now that we have that table joined to our other data:

Listing 3.8: A few more adjustments

```
1   select
2       a.ogc_fid,
3       a.trip_distance,
4       a.total_amount,
5       b.neighborhood
6   from
7       nyc_yellow_taxi_0601_0615_2016 a
8       join nyc_neighborhoods b on st_intersects(a.pickup, b.geom)
9   where
10      b.neighborhood = 'West Village'
11  order by
12      a.pickup_datetime asc
13  limit
14      10
```

ogc_fid	trip_distance	total_amount	ntaname	boro_name
2199905	2.76	14.76	West Village	Manhattan
5611817	1.39	8.8	West Village	Manhattan
2541221	1.4	12.35	West Village	Manhattan
4043047	3.07	18.36	West Village	Manhattan
5291922	2.49	12.8	West Village	Manhattan

Finally, we can use a spatial join to perform aggregate joins. Now I will demonstrate this with the total and average trip values for a few neighborhoods in New York, but you can use any aggregation method that we have covered in previous chapters:

Listing 3.9: Spatial join with aggregations

```
1   select
2
3       -- Here we can aggregate other data that all falls within our
4       -- joined geometry data
5       a.neighborhood,
6       sum(b.total_amount) as sum_amount,
7       avg(b.total_amount) as avg_amount
8   from
9       nyc_neighborhoods a
10      join nyc_yellow_taxi_0601_0615_2016 b on st_intersects(b.pickup, a.geom)
11  where
12          a.neighborhood = 'West Village'
13  group by
14      a.neighborhood
15  limit
16      5
```

In a CTE

Another way to use a spatial relationship function is in the context of a CTE that can then be joined to other data. This may make the query a bit cleaner and potentially help with performance depending on the scenario. In particular in cloud data warehouses, it is likely that you will not be able to GROUP BY the geometry to visualize your data, and in general this is a frowned upon practice since even if one point is in a different order despite the polygons matching, they will not match in the GROUP BY clause. Let's modify our query to join it back to the geometry data to map it:

Listing 3.10: JOIN with a CTE

```
1   with a as (
2       select
3           a.neighborhood,
4           sum(b.total_amount) as sum_amount
5       from
6           nyc_neighborhoods a
7           join nyc_yellow_taxi_0601_0615_2016 b on st_intersects(b.pickup, a.geom)
8       where
9           a.neighborhood = 'West Village'
10      group by
11          a.neighborhood
12  )
13  select
14      a.sum_amount,
15      b.*
16  from
17      a
```

```
18    join nyc_neighborhoods b using (neighborhood)
```

This allows us to join the aggregate back to the original data and view the results for the neighborhood tabulation areas.

Using a LATERAL JOIN

This is one of my favorite uses for a spatial relationship function, and we will cover it in more detail later in the book, but for now you can see a quick preview of how to use this to analyze, row by row, the values of the other table. In this case we are using the same table. Note that we don't need to group by since the SQL in the CROSS LATERAL JOIN is running once for each row so keep that in mind.

Listing 3.11: LATERAL JOIN

```
1   select
2       zipcode,
3       population,
4       z.neighbor_sum
5   from
6       nyc_zips a
7
8       -- This join will join across to each row of data above
9       -- but can also reference data from the outer query
10      cross join lateral (
11          select
12              sum(population) as neighbor_sum
13          from
14              nyc_zips
15          where
16              st_intersects(geom, a.geom)
17              and a.zipcode != zipcode
18      ) z
```

Two things should stand out to you here. First is that you can preform these lateral queries very effectively with this method and also move between the main table and the joined table to grab different data components from each. Second ,is that this is a very fast operation and highly efficient approach for this type of query.

3.3   Spatial relationship functions

Next, we can take a look at the various spatial relationship functions that are available. Each one does a slightly different task, but all serve the purpose of analyzing the relationships between two or more geometries. We will review each of these in detail, but they can also be explained visually, which the PostGIS Documentation Exercises section does a great job of. You can find that link at the link in the footnotes[98], but below is the example for ST_Intersects (Figure 3.1, on the next page):

ST_Contains

This function will return true if all vertices overlap or fall within the other geometry. If any point falls outside, it will return false. We will showcase this with some sample data from our NYC Buildings dataset and see how many buildings are contained by a 200-meter buffer of Madison Square Garden:

Listing 3.12: ST _Contains

```
1   select
```

---

[98]https://loc8.cc/sql/postgis-spatial-relationships

Intersects

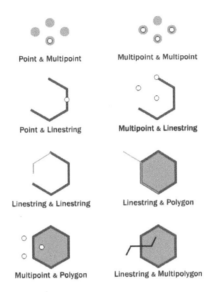

Figure 3.1: Visualizing intersections between different geometry types (postgis.net)

```
2       name,
3       geom
4   from
5       nyc_building_footprints
6   where
7       st_contains(
8           (
9               select
10                  st_buffer(
11                      buildpoint(-73.993584, 40.750580, 4326) :: geography,
12                      200
13                  ) :: geometry
14              ),
15              geom
16          )
```

You may notice this part of the query which creates the point and buffer around the centroid of Madison Square Garden:

```
st_buffer(buildpoint(-73.993584, 40.750580, 4326)::geography, 200)::geometry
```

Since our source data is in a 4326 projection we create our point in that projection, however the ST_Buffer function asks for the buffer distance to be in the units of the source projection, which in this case is degrees. So to use meters we cast this to a geography, but since our ST_Contains function, and most of the spatial relationship functions, accept only geometries as their arguments, we then need to turn it back into a geometry. A lot of work indeed, but we will see a different way of doing this later in the chapter.

We also want to wrap it in a subquery since this will generate the geometry one time rather than every single time the function needs to evaluate (Figure 3.2, on the following page).

Figure 3.2: Using ST_Contains

Since Madison Square Garden is in the middle of the Midtown neighborhood which is home to many large buildings, let's us a different location with smaller buildings to test all the edge cases of the spatial relationship functions, in this case the Stonewall Inn National Monument (Figure 3.3, on the next page).

We can see that our query has returned 349 buildings that are totally contained by the buffer. It is also important to note the function signature as well:

```
boolean ST_Contains(geometry geomA, geometry geomB);
```

Returns TRUE if geometry B is completely inside geometry A. A contains B if and only if no points of B lie in the exterior of A, and at least one point of the interior of B lies in the interior of A.

Since we have our 200 meter buffer first this makes sense. If we flipped this around we would have no rows returned since the buffer is not contained completely any single building. As we will see later ST_

Figure 3.3: Buildings within 200 meters of the Stonewall Inn National Monument

Within is the inverse of this, meaning we would reverse the order of our geometries to lead with our buildings followed by our buffer. The names of the functions are helpful to remember which is which:

- Does our buffer **contain** this building?
- Does this building fall **within** our buffer?

Keep this in mind as you use these functions as there are two with very similar properties!

ST_Crosses

This function will return true if one part of the geometry crosses the other, but does not simply overlap with the other. The illustration of ST_Crosses in the PostGIS documentation are the best visual representations of this function, so I will defer to those which are referenced in the footnotes[99].

We can test this out with our NYC Bike Routes and Buildings to see if there are any bike routes that cross over or under a building in New York.

Listing 3.13: ST_Crosses

```
1  select
2      a.ogc_fid,
3      a.name,
4      st_centroid(st_transform(a.geom, 4326)),
5      b.ogc_fid as b_id,
6      st_transform(b.geom, 4326)
7  from
8      nyc_building_footprints a
9      join nyc_bike_routes b on st_crosses(a.geom, b.geom)
```

Here we can see that there are several bike paths that cross totally through buildings, mostly on Roosevelt Island (Figure 3.4, on the facing page).

ST_Disjoint

This function is the opposite of ST_Intersects and returns everything that does not intersect and this will return true if the polygons do not intersect, and in this case order of the geometries is irrelevant. In this query let's find the first 200 buildings that do not intersect our 200 meter buffer that are closest to the Stonewall Inn using ST_Distance:

Listing 3.14: ST_Disjoint

```
1  select
2      name,
3      geom
4  from
5      nyc_building_footprints
6  where
7      st_disjoint(
8          (
9              select
10                 st_buffer(
11                     buildpoint(-74.002222, 40.733889, 4326) :: geography,
12                     200
13                 ) :: geometry
14          ),
15          geom
16      )
```

---

[99]https://postgis.net/docs/ST_Crosses.html

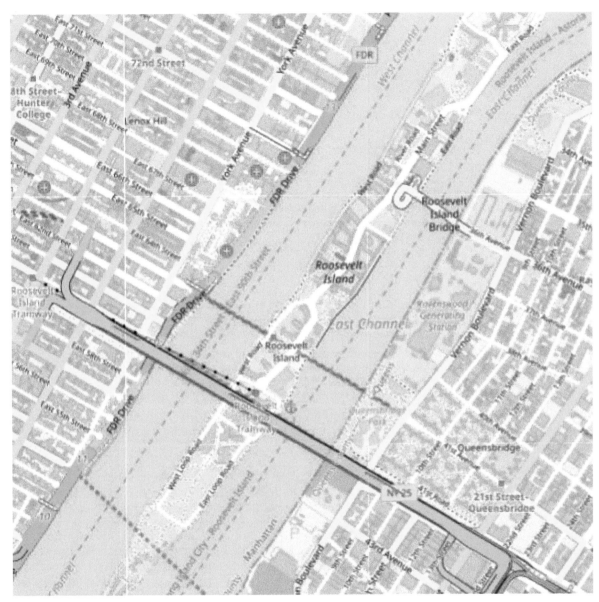

Figure 3.4: Bike routes that cross a building

```
17   order by
18       st_distance(
19           (
20               select
21                   st_buffer(
22                       buildpoint(-74.002222, 40.733889, 4326) :: geography,
23                       200
24                   ) :: geometry
25           ),
26           geom
27       ) asc
28   limit
29       200
```

Here we used ST_Distance to calculate the distance between the buildings and the centroid of the Stonewall Inn, then ordered that in ascending order from smallest to largest until we get our target of 200 buildings (Figure 3.5, on the next page).

ST_Intersects

This function will return all the buildings that intersect the buffer including ones that overlap the buffer. An interesting side note about ST_Intersects is that it will return true even if your geometries do not touch in the case that they fall within 0.00001 meters (or 0.00039 inches/0.01 millimeters). This only really applies in a few scenarios but is good to know should your analysis fall into that category.

This is also the function you will likely use the most if you want to evaluate if two geometries overlap. It has had a lot of work and resources put into it over the years that have increased the speed some 5 times[100]. So it is a great function to use as you know it has great engineering power behind it. But it is also important to understand how this function works, so you can make it work better for you and your needs.

This post[101] by Paul Ramsey does a good job of explaining this and how, depending on the size and complexity of your geometries, you can use some techniques (some of which are now baked into Post-GIS) such as subdividing the geometries to make them smaller, but baked into that explanation is a subtle detail you may have missed about how bounding boxes are used within this function.

What this means is that if you have a spatial index on your dataset then the function will first run a bounding box comparison to see if the bounding box touches the other geometry, then it will perform the intersection. The bounding box step efficiently removes any non-matches and then will help the join run faster. The next step is to evaluate if any part of the geometries you are comparing touch. This effectively includes making a comparison across all the various vertices in your geometries, thus the more vertices it needs to compare the longer it will take.

So what does this mean for you?

1. First, is that you should use spatial indexes on tables that will commonly have spatial relationship analysis performed on them.

2. Next, for larger or complex geometries make sure to try and decrease the number of vertices in your polygons or use less complex geometries if possible

---

[100]https://blog.cleverelephant.ca/2020/12/waiting-postgis-31-1.html

[101]https://blog.cleverelephant.ca/2019/11/subdivide.html

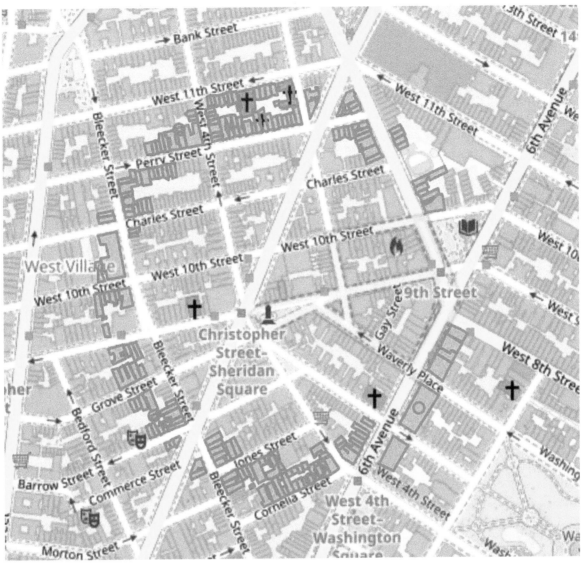

Figure 3.5: ST_Disjoint or an anti-intersection with the 200 buildings nearest to the Stonewall Inn National Monument

3. Also, if you need, you can use the subdivide method in the blog post in the previous footnote especially for large geometries. In PostGIS 3.1 there are native improvements that have boosted this even further.

Apart from that we will explore two other approaches, using spatial indexes (different from a spatial *database* index which is how we have used the term so far) such as H3 hexagons as well as using triangulated polygons which is similar to the subdivide method.

ST_Overlaps

The next function returns TRUE when a spatial relationship has at least one part that overlaps equally with the geometry, but that are not totally contained or crossing. It also includes the concept of dimension meaning that the two geometries should be the same such as Polygon to Polygon. We can validate this by using the following query:

Listing 3.15: ST_Overlaps

```
1   select
2       st_geomfromtext(
3           'GEOMETRYCOLLECTION(LINESTRING(0 0, 3 3), POLYGON((0 0, 0 1, 1 1, 1 0, 0 0)))'
4       ) as geom,
5       st_overlaps(
6           st_geomfromtext('LINESTRING(0 0, 0 3)'),
7           st_geomfromtext('POLYGON((0 0, 0 1, 1 1, 1 0, 0 0))')
8       )
```

Here even though the two geometries overlap, they do not share the same dimension. The next two queries will return TRUE since they share the same dimension:

Listing 3.16: Overlaps test

```
1   select
2       st_geomfromtext(
3           'GEOMETRYCOLLECTION(POLYGON((1 0, 1 1, 1 2, 0 2, 1 0)), POLYGON((0 0, 0 1, 1 1, 1 0, 0 0)))'
4       ) as geom,
5       st_overlaps(
6           st_geomfromtext('POLYGON((1 0, 1 1, 1 2, 0 2, 1 0))'),
7           st_geomfromtext('POLYGON((0 0, 0 1, 1 1, 1 0, 0 0))')
8       )
```

Listing 3.17: Overlaps test 2

```
1   select
2       st_geomfromtext(
3           'GEOMETRYCOLLECTION(LINESTRING(1 0, 1 1, 0 1, 0 0), LINESTRING(2 1, 1 1, 0 1, 1 2))'
4       ) as geom,
5       st_overlaps(
6           st_geomfromtext('LINESTRING(1 0, 1 1, 0 1, 0 0)'),
7           st_geomfromtext('LINESTRING(2 1, 1 1, 0 1, 1 2)')
8       )
```

ST_Touches

This function will return TRUE if the two geometries share one or more points in common, but do not intersect in their interiors. Basically they share a border but do not overlap. This means that the geometries have to have a perfect match and even a slight overlap will return false. We can check and see if this is the case with our NYC Zip Codes:

Listing 3.18: ST_Touches

```
1   select
2       *
3   from
4       nyc_zips
5   where
6       st_touches(
7           geom,
8           (
9               select
10                  geom
11              from
12                  nyc_zips
13              where
14                  zipcode = '10009'
15          )
16      )
```

And we can see that the three zip codes that border 10009 are returned (Figure 3.6):

Figure 3.6: ST_Touches for all zip codes touching 10009

ST_Within

Finally closing out this section is ST_Within, which has two arguments and asks if geometry A is completely inside of geometry B. We can test this by modifying our Stonewall National Monument query (Figure 3.7, on the next page):

Listing 3.19: ST_Within

```
1   select
2       name,
```

```
3      geom
4    from
5      nyc_building_footprints
6    where
7      st_within(
8         geom,
9         (
10           select
11             st_buffer(
12                buildpoint(-74.002222, 40.733889, 4326) :: geography,
13                200
14             ) :: geometry
15         )
16      )
```

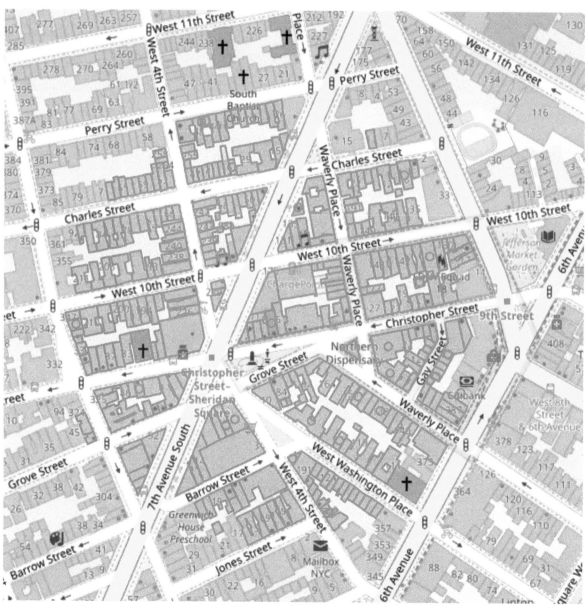

Figure 3.7: Using ST_Dwithin

3.4   Distance Relationship Functions

For distance relationships there are five total functions that you can use to analyze the relationship of features based on distance. The two we will focus on are ST_DFullyWithin and ST_DWithin.

These functions take three arguments, two geometries and a distance in meters. Now in a classic GIS sense we think of this as a buffer analysis and this is a very common point of confusion. Let's take a look at our most recent query but using the ST_Intersects relationship:

Listing 3.20: Distance functions

```
1    select
2        name,
3        geom
4    from
5        nyc_building_footprints
6    where
7        st_intersects(
8            geom,
9            (
10                select
11                    st_buffer(
12                        buildpoint(-74.002222, 40.733889, 4326) :: geography,
13                        200
14                    ) :: geometry
15            )
16        )
```

So here you can see we have three steps:

- Create our point from a latitude and longitude pair (and cast to a geography)
- Create our 200-meter buffer (and cast back to a geometry)
- Run our intersection

With ST_DWithin we can cut the middle step out completely. Let's expand our buffer to 10 kilometers in the first query and see how long it takes to run:

Listing 3.21: ST_DWithin

```
1    select
2        name,
3        geom
4    from
5        nyc_building_footprints
6    where
7        st_intersects(
8            geom,
9            (
10                select
11                    st_buffer(
12                        buildpoint(-74.002222, 40.733889, 4326) :: geography,
13                        10000
14                    ) :: geometry
15            )
16        )
```

On my computer this took 14.81 seconds and returned 224,392 rows. Let's see how this performs using the same query, but this time with ST_DWithin. Note that we will want to use a projection that measures in meters. To do so we will use ST_Transform to turn the geometries into the 3857 projection, and we can test this with our original 200 meter radius first:

Listing 3.22: Testing another distance query

```
1   select
2       name,
3       geom
4   from
5       nyc_building_footprints
6   where
7       st_dwithin(
8           st_transform(geom, 3857),
9           buildpoint(-74.002222, 40.733889, 3857),
10          200
11      )
```

Surprised? On my computer I stopped the query at 3 minutes since it was taking so long. Why is this query, with a more efficient function **and** our original 200 meter radius, taking far longer?

Here is another coding challenge for you. We will cover one way to speed this up, but there is actually an error in this code that is causing the issue. Think back to your GIS basics and projections, and if you need a hint I would take a look at the information about the 3857 projection

---

So if you remember when we created our *buildpoint()* function we used this code:

```
st_setsrid(st_makepoint(-74.002222, 40.733889), 3857)
```

So in theory this should work, but the devil is in the details, and if we look at the units the projection uses, which are used by most other WGS84 and NAD83 projections, they actually use different units that are not latitude and longitude. So we need to first create our point in the 4326 projection which uses degrees and then transform that to 3857.

```
st_transform(st_setsrid(st_makepoint(-74.002222, 40.733889), 4326), 3857)
```

Now that is a lot of code to generate one point. I tested this query on its own, and it took 0.218 seconds to run. Now running that a handful of times isn't too difficult but the more times you have to run it the more costly it will be. Let's try it out and see how much time it will take in 200 meters by transforming each point.

Listing 3.23: Generating our point

```
1   select
2       name,
3       geom
4   from
5       nyc_building_footprints
6   where
7       st_dwithin(
8           st_transform(geom, 3857),
9           st_transform(
10              st_setsrid(st_makepoint(-74.002222, 40.733889), 4326),
11              3857
12          ),
13          200
14      )
```

This took 28 seconds for 200 meters which took me under 2 seconds using our buffer and intersection query. To speed this up let's add a new geometry column for each row of our buildings dataset using the 3857 projection, so we don't have to create one each time. First altering our table and then updating our table.

Listing 3.24: Update the table

```
1   alter table
2       nyc_building_footprints
3   add
4       column geom_3857 geometry;
5
6   update
7       nyc_building_footprints
8   set
9       geom_3857 = st_transform(geom, 3857);
```

Now we can run this query:

Listing 3.25: Getting better

```
1   select
2       name,
3       geom
4   from
5       nyc_building_footprints
6   where
7       st_dwithin(
8           geom_3857,
9           st_transform(
10              st_setsrid(st_makepoint(-74.002222, 40.733889), 4326),
11              3857
12          ),
13          200
14      )
```

Okay this went down to 12 seconds, still better but not perfect. Another approach that might work is creating our point that represents the Stonewall National Monument in a subquery, and then running a cross join since it is only joining to the one row:

Listing 3.26: Using a CTE

```
1   with a as (
2       select
3           st_transform(
4               st_setsrid(st_makepoint(-74.002222, 40.733889), 4326),
5               3857
6           ) as geo
7   )
8   select
9       name,
10      geom
11  from
12      nyc_building_footprints,
13      a
14  where
15      st_dwithin(geom_3857, a.geo, 200)
```

This brings us down to 9 seconds, still too slow. Now there is a bit of a secret here that is important to note. When we originally brought this data in using our ogr2ogr method the command added a very helpful database component known as a database index. This is, in simple terms, a data structure that allows the database to organize the table on a specific column in a way that makes it know the data structure and to make it more searchable ahead of time. And many spatial relationship functions take advantage of indexes, and they are quite easy to create. Let's add one for our new *geom_3857* column:

Listing 3.27: Creating an index

```
1   create index geom_3857_idx on
2   nyc_building_footprints using gist(geom_3857)
```

This will create an index with the name *geom_3857_idx* on our buildings table using the GiST method which is for generalized text[102]. Once you have run this you will get a message that it has been created. Now give the previous query a try again. Using the subquery method my time went down to 0.15 seconds which is far faster than our 1 second time. Trying this again with a 10 kilometer radius:

Listing 3.28: Finally optimized

```
1   with a as (
2       select
3           st_transform(
4               st_setsrid(st_makepoint(-74.002222, 40.733889), 4326),
5               3857
6           ) as geo
7   )
8   select
9       name,
10      geom
11  from
12      nyc_building_footprints,
13      a
14  where
15      st_dwithin(
16          geom_3857,
17          (
18              select
19                  geo
20              from
21                  a
22          ),
23          10000
24      )
```

This brings it down to just a hair under 5 seconds total, down from 14.81 seconds. Using indexes are a major boost, but thinking through your queries logically and trying to reduce the number of operations your query needs to run are both good practices.

3.5 Spatial Joins

As one of the most frequent operations that I have used over the course of time I agave been using spatial SQL, I think it is important to dedicate a bit of space to the spatial join. For the most part there are two common spatial joins:

- A true spatial join where one joins some data from one table to another based on a spatial relationship (ex. Adding the name of a county to a set of points) which may also be known as "Join points by location"
- A "point in polygon" join, although this could be any type of geometry to polygon, where the results are aggregated into a count, sum, or any other aggregation.

We reviewed some of these approaches at the beginning of the chapter but let's take a look at the

---
[102]https://www.postgresql.org/docs/9.1/textsearch-indexes.html

performance of these to compare. Both are important and there are a number of different ways that you can achieve each. First let's take a look at the spatial join, and then let's review the aggregation spatial join.

Pure spatial joins

For these use cases we will use the same data for each, a tree census and our neighborhoods. Ignoring the fact that we can perform a string join here that would be more efficient, this will give us a good idea on how you can perform a variety of joins. We will also limit our query to have trees that include the name Maple in them.

First let's test out a query with a WHERE clause, which represents one of the most common mistakes when performing a spatial join.

Listing 3.29: Spatial cross join

```
1  select
2      a.ogc_fid,
3      a.health,
4      a.spc_common,
5      b.neighborhood
6  from
7      nyc_2015_tree_census a,
8      nyc_neighborhoods b
9  where
10     st_intersects(a.geom, b.geom)
11     and a.spc_common ilike '%maple%'
```

This took ~41 seconds on my computer and the reason for that is as you can see we are performing a cross join, or every row to every row. This is not the most efficient way to accomplish this, and we can take a look at what is happening in the database using the Explain Analyze tool within pgAdmin. You can do this by clicking the small graph button in pgAdmin next to the button with the "E" on it with these settings in the dropdown (Figure 3.8).

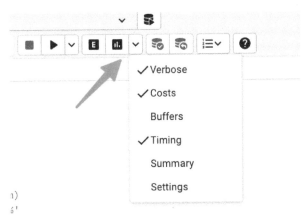

Figure 3.8: Running explain analyze in pgAdmin

That big red box (Figure 3.9, on the next page) indicates that there is one operation that is taking particularly long which is the join we are performing. Now let's try this again and move this into a table join with the condition of the join being our spatial intersection:

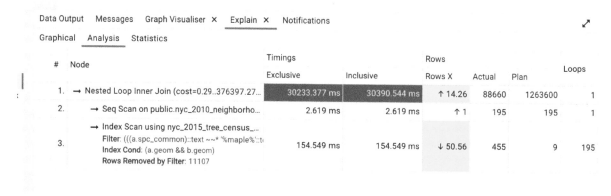

Figure 3.9: Explain analyze showing a high cost nested loop inner join

Listing 3.30: Regular join

```
1  select
2      a.ogc_fid,
3      a.health,
4      a.spc_common,
5      b.neighborhood
6  from
7      nyc_2015_tree_census a
8      join nyc_neighborhoods b on st_intersects(a.geom, b.geom)
9      and a.spc_common ilike '%maple%'
```

This query came in at ~35 seconds on my computer, and we can check to see if there was a difference in our query plan again using the same Explain Analyze feature (Figure 3.10):

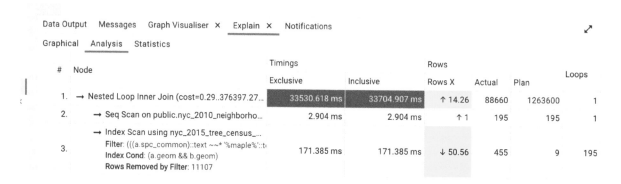

Figure 3.10: Same result as before

So no not really.

Let's test out subdividing our geometries:

Listing 3.31: Subdividing our geometries

```
1  create table nyc_2010_neighborhoods_subdivide as
2  select
3      st_subdivide(geom) as geom,
4      neighborhood
5  from
6      nyc_neighborhoods
```

Listing 3.32: Subdividing our geometries

```
1   with trees as (
2        select
3             ogc_fid,
4             health,
5             spc_common,
6             geom
7        from
8             nyc_2015_tree_census
9        where
10            spc_common ilike '%maple%'
11       )
12  select
13       trees.ogc_fid,
14       trees.health,
15       trees.spc_common,
16       b.neighborhood
17  from
18       trees
19       join nyc_neighborhoods_subdivide b on st_intersects(trees.geom, b.geom)
```

This improved our query time to 19 seconds! The other strategy you can use is to create an index on the columns you need to use in your query. Remember that when we imported our data using `ogr2ogr` an index on the `GEOMETRY` column automatically. However we can create an index on our new subdivided geometries here too.

Listing 3.33: Creating an index

```
1   create index nyc_neighborhoods_subdivide_geom_idx
2   n nyc_neighborhoods_subdivide using gist(geom)
```

From here we can also cluster our geometry data using the index, which effectively organizes the data based on the index which can also improve query time.

Listing 3.34: Clustering on the index

```
1   cluster nyc_neighborhoods_subdivide using nyc_neighborhoods_subdivide_geom_idx;
2
3   cluster nyc_2015_tree_census using nyc_2015_tree_census_geom_geom_idx;
```

This improved the query to 16 seconds. While you don't need to optimize every table and every query, using these tools strategically can help you make some significant gains in your query time.

Aggregations and spatial joins

Adding aggregations to your query only takes a few extra steps. We can run our same query as above, but this time return a count of maples per neighborhood and a percentage of all trees in the neighborhood (note that we are casting the numbers to numeric to make sure it divides accurately since `COUNT` returns an integer and the result will always be 0 or 1):

Listing 3.35: Aggregations and spatial joins

```
1   select
2        count(a.ogc_fid) filter (
3            where
4                a.spc_common ilike '%maple%'
5        ) :: numeric / count(a.ogc_fid) :: numeric as percent_trees,
6        count(a.ogc_fid) filter (
7            where
8                a.spc_common ilike '%maple%'
9        ) as count_maples,
```

```
10      b.neighborhood
11   from
12      nyc_2015_tree_census a
13      join nyc_neighborhoods_subdivide b on st_intersects(a.geom, b.geom)
14   group by
15      b.neighborhood
```

Now as you notice we did not add in a geometry here. While we could do so, if we did we would need to GROUP BY our geometry. There are two issues with that, one is that the GEOMETRY column is quite large as we know and this makes for a cleaner operation since we can always quickly join the GEOMETRY to our results using the common neighborhood name column. The other reason is that if we group by a geometry, even though in this case we know we have one unique geometry per neighborhood, this could present issues if we have more than one geometry and if our geometries are slightly different, even if their points (or start/end points) are out of order. This means that even though we perceive two geometries to be the same, the database does not, and it will group them as such.

3.6 Overlay Functions

The next group of functions includes overlay functions which allows us to analyze and create new geometries from our existing geometries. These functions perform common GIS tasks generally known as clipping, subdividing, unioning, and desolving and geometries. It's important to know that these functions do not take advantage of database indexes and will be quite slower than the previous set of spatial relationship examples that we just took a look at.

ST_Difference

The ST_Difference function allows you to take two geometries and return the difference of geometry A minus geometry B. Order is important in this function as the first geometry will be the geometry with the remainder (that is with the overlap subtracted) returned and none of the remainder of geometry B will be returned.

We can test this out by subtracting the geometry that represents the West Village from its accompanying zip code, 10014 (Figure 3.11, on the next page):

Listing 3.36: ST_Difference

```
1   select
2      st_difference(a.geom, st_transform(b.geom, 4326)) as geom
3   from
4      nyc_neighborhoods a,
5      nyc_zips b
6   where
7      b.zipcode = '10014'
8      and a.neighborhood = 'West Village'
```

As you can see, the arrows point out some discrepancies between the geometries beyond just the docks which were not included in the neighborhood file.

ST_Intersection

ST_Intersection returns just the area that intersects the two geometries. We can see this by running a query to find the intersection between the Gramercy neighborhood and zip code 10003.

Listing 3.37: ST_Intersection

```
1   select
```

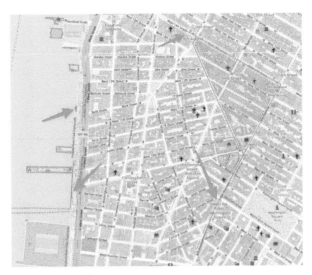

Figure 3.11: Extra geometries using ST_Difference

```
2      st_intersection(a.geom, st_transform(b.geom, 4326)) as geom
3  from
4      nyc_neighborhoods a,
5      nyc_zips b
6  where
7      b.zipcode = '10003'
8      and a.neighborhood = 'Gramercy'
```

And you can use the following query to perform a table union to combine the three different geometries together to see how they overlay on the map (Figure 3.12, on the following page):

Listing 3.38: Comparing intersection results

```
1  select
2      st_intersection(a.geom, st_transform(b.geom, 4326)) as geom
3  from
4      nyc_neighborhoods a,
5      nyc_zips b
6  where
7      b.zipcode = '10003'
8      and a.neighborhood = 'Gramercy'
9  union
10 select
11     geom
12 from
13     nyc_neighborhoods
14 where
15     neighborhood = 'Gramercy'
16 union
17 select
18     st_transform(geom, 4326)
19 from
20     nyc_zips
21 where
22     zipcode = '10003'
```

Figure 3.12: Result of ST_Intersection

ST_Split

This function does exactly what it sounds like, it splits a geometry using a linestring or multi-linestring. We can do this by joining some of the various linestrings from our bike routes dataset using ST_Union which we will learn more about shortly, then split the West Village Neighborhood using the bike path that runs along Hudson St/8th Avenue. This path is split into two parts, the part that runs from W Houston St to Bank St, and from Bank St to W 39th St.

Listing 3.39: ST_Split

```
1   -- Query all the street segments between W 39 ST and BANJ ST
2   with a as (
3       select
4           st_union(geom) as geom
5       from
6           nyc_bike_routes
7       where
8           fromstreet IN ('W HOUSTON ST', 'BANK ST')
9           or tostreet IN ('BANK ST', 'W 39 ST', 'W HOUSTON ST')
10  )
11  select
12      st_split(
13          -- Select the geometgry for the West Village
14          (
15              select
16                  st_transform(geom, 4326)
17              from
18                  nyc_neighborhoods
19              where
20                  neighborhood = 'West Village'
21          ),
22
23          -- Split it with our geometry in our CTE above
```

```
24          (
25              select
26                  geom
27              from
28                  a
29          )
30      )
```

This will return a split geometry right along the bike path (Figure 3.13):

Figure 3.13: Result of ST_Split

ST_Subdivide

We have seen this function already as we used it to try and improve our spatial join times, so as you may recall this function will split geometries such as lines and polygons into different parts based on a threshold of max vertices passed into the function, resulting ins smaller geometries.

We can test this out with the same West Village neighborhood using 50 vertices (Figure 3.14, on the following page):

Listing 3.40: ST_Subdivide

```
1   select
2       st_subdivide(st_transform(geom, 4326), 50) as geom
3   from
4       nyc_neighborhoods
5   where
6       neighborhood = 'West Village'
```

Then 25 (Figure 3.15, on the next page):

And 10 (Figure 3.16, on page 235):

Figure 3.14: ST_Subdivide with 50 verticies

Figure 3.15: ST_Subdivide with 25 verticies

Figure 3.16: ST_Subdivide with 10 verticies

ST_Union and ST_UnaryUnion

ST_Union, as we saw earlier, merges two or more geometries together to create a single geometry. The variant ST_UnaryUnion applies this to a single, multi-part geometry, creating one geometry from the input. We can test this with all neighborhoods that intersect the zip code 10001 (Figure 3.17, on the next page):

Listing 3.41: ST_Union

```
 1  select
 2      st_union(geom) as geom
 3  from
 4      nyc_neighborhoods
 5  where
 6      st_intersects(
 7          geom,
 8          (
 9              select
10                  st_transform(geom, 4326)
11              from
12                  nyc_zips
13              where
14                  zipcode = '10009'
15          )
16      )
```

3.7 Cluster Functions

The next set of functions allow us to create spatial clusters from our data. These functions, which can also be used for clustering non-spatial data, allow us to see how the data is clustered spatially. It is also worth noting that these are some of the only spatial specific window functions that are available.

Figure 3.17: Unioned geometries

ST_ClusterDBSCAN

The DBSCAN method will build an appropriate number of clusters based on the data it is provided, so we do not know how many clusters we will end up with when our query is complete. We can test this out by making a view so we can see our data in QGIS and style it. We will create clusters with a minimum of 30 points and within 30 meters of each other (we will have to translate the projection again to make sure we can provide the measurements for this).

First, we need to add a geometry using the latitude and longitude columns in our table:

Listing 3.42: Updating our 311 table

```
1   alter table
2       nyc_311
3   add
4       column geom geometry;
5
6   update
7       nyc_311
8   set
9       geom = buildpoint(longitude, latitude, 4326);
```

Listing 3.43: ST_ClusterDBSCAN

```
1   create
2   or replace view nyc_311_dbscan_noise as
3
4   -- Create the clustering functon using the Window function syntax
5   select
```

```
 6      id,
 7      ST_ClusterDBSCAN(st_transform(geom, 3857), 30, 30) over () AS cid,
 8      geom
 9  from
10      nyc_311
11  where
12
13      -- Find just the complaints with "noise" in the description
14      -- and that are in zip code 10009
15      st_intersects(
16          geom,
17          (
18              select
19                  st_transform(geom, 4326)
20              from
21                  nyc_zips
22              where
23                  zipcode = '10009'
24          )
25      )
26      and complaint_type ilike '%noise%'
```

From here we can add our view and style it in QGIS which will result in this map, where I removed the points that were null, or not a part of a specific cluster (Figure 3.18):

Figure 3.18: Results of ST_ClusterDBSCAN

As you can see there are 71 different compact clusters using these parameters. As you can see most of the data is very dense, so depending on your data you may need to play with the parameters a bit to build appropriate clusters.

ST_ClusterKMeans

KMeans differs from DBSCAN in that you provide KMeans with a desired number of clusters and all features are assigned to a cluster. Let's use the same data and choose 7 clusters, once again creating a view, so we can see and style the data in QGIS.

Listing 3.44: ST_ClusterKMeans

```
1   create
2   or replace view nyc_311_kmeans_noise as
3
4   -- Create the clustering functon using the Window function syntax
5   select
6       id,
7       ST_ClusterKMeans(st_transform(geom, 3857), 7, 1609) over () AS cid,
8       geom
9   from
10      nyc_311
11  where
12
13      -- Find just the complaints with "noise" in the description
14      -- and that are in zip code 10009
15      st_intersects(
16          geom,
17          (
18              select
19                  st_transform(geom, 4326)
20              from
21                  nyc_zips
22              where
23                  zipcode = '10009'
24          )
25      )
26      and complaint_type ilike '%noise%'
```

And the data in QGIS (Figure 3.19, on the next page):

ST_ClusterWithin

The final clustering method is one that clusters points within a specific distance of separation. For this we will test this at 25 meters:

Listing 3.45: ST_ClusterWithin

```
1   create table nyc_311_clusterwithin_noise as
2
3   -- Find the 311 calls in the 10009 zip code
4   with a as (
5       select
6           geom
7       from
8           nyc_311
9       where
10          st_intersects(
11              geom,
12              (
13                  select
14                      st_transform(geom, 4326)
15                  from
16                      nyc_zips
17                  where
18                      zipcode = '10009'
19              )
```

Figure 3.19: Results of ST_ClusterKMeans

```
20          )
21          and complaint_type ilike '%noise%'
22  ),
23
24  -- In CTE "b", we have to unnest the results since it returns
25  -- geometries in an array
26  b as (
27      select
28          st_transform(
29              unnest(ST_ClusterWithin(st_transform(geom, 3857), 25)),
30              4326
31          ) AS geom
32      from
33          a
34  )
35
36  -- row_number() over() creates an id for each row starting at 1
37  select
38      row_number() over() as id,
39      geom
40  from
41      b
```

In my results I ended up with 256 clusters. Since our data is so dense and since we used such a low distance, this actually makes sense, but other datasets will likely be different so make sure to test the distance parameter. And here is our resulting map (Figure 3.20, on the following page):

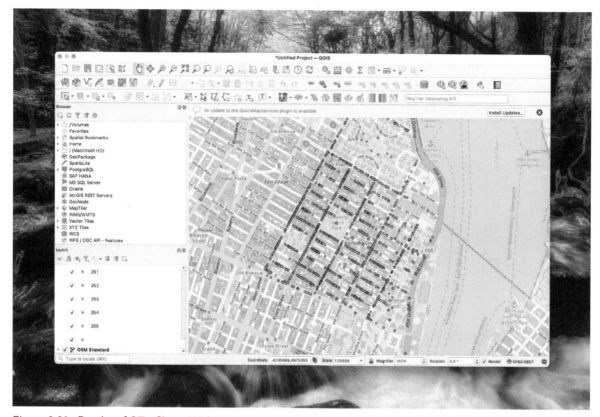

Figure 3.20: Results of ST_ClusterWithin

3.8 Special Operators

Now from time to time you may see some of these special operators within a PostGIS query. Post-greSQL has these special operators such as <> which is the equivalent of not equal. In the case of PostGIS there are a handful that we will review that can come in handy and save some keystrokes.

&&

This function works the same as ST_Intersects but instead of finding the overlap of the two geometries, it simply finds if the bounding boxes of the two geometries overlap. For example:

Listing 3.46: Using the && operator

```
1   select
2       zipcode,
3       st_transform(geom, 4326)
4   from
5       nyc_zips
6   where
7       st_transform(geom, 4326) && (
8           select
9               geom
10          from
11              nyc_neighborhoods
12          where
13              neighborhood = 'East Village'
14      )
```

```
15   UNION
16   select
17       'None' as zipcode,
18       st_envelope(
19           (
20               select
21                   geom
22               from
23                   nyc_neighborhoods
24               where
25                   neighborhood = 'East Village'
26           )
27       )
```

Note that we are drawing the bounding box of the East Village neighborhood as reference using the UNION operator to join the data together (Figure 3.21).

Figure 3.21: Visual representation of the && operator

&< and &>

These functions check if the bounding box of the first geometry overlaps or is to the left for *&<* or to the right for *&>* of the second geometry.

Here we can query all the neighborhood bounding boxes that fall to the left of the East Village (Figure 3.22, on the following page):

Listing 3.47: Using the right/left shorthand expression

```
1   select
2       geom
3   from
4       nyc_neighborhoods
5   where
6       geom &< (
7           select
8               geom
9           from
10              nyc_neighborhoods
```

```
11        where
12            neighborhood = 'East Village'
13      )
```

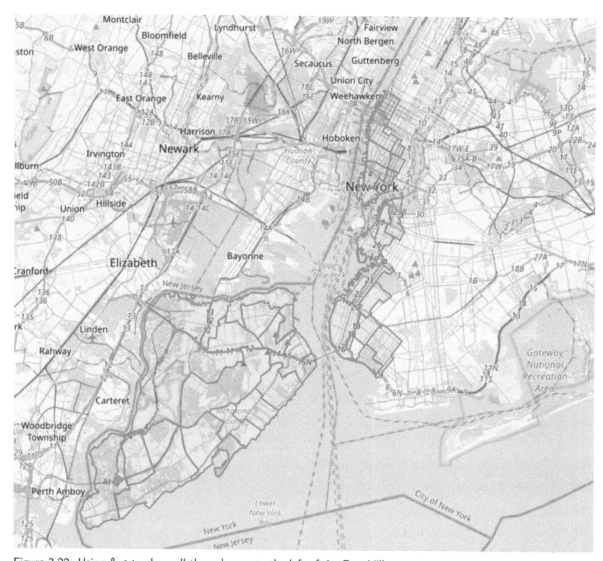

Figure 3.22: Using &< to show all the polygons to the left of the East Village

<->

Finally, this operator returns the 2D Distance between two geometries. We can compare the results of this and the ST_Distance function below:

Listing 3.48: <->

```
1  with ev as (
2      select
3          geom
4      from
5          nyc_neighborhoods
6      where
7          neighborhood = 'East Village'
```

```
8  ),
9  ues as (
10    select
11        geom
12    from
13        nyc_neighborhoods
14    where
15        neighborhood = 'Upper East Side'
16  )
17 select
18    ev.geom <-> ues.geom,
19    st_distance(ev.geom, use.geom)
20 from
21    ev,
22    ues
```

These are exactly the same result. We will see a difference if we cast the geometries to geographies since ST_Distance uses a spheroid measurement in ST_Distance by default:

Listing 3.49: Comparing ST_Distance and <->

```
1  with ev as (
2     select
3         geom :: geography
4     from
5         nyc_neighborhoods
6     where
7         neighborhood = 'East Village'
8  ),
9  ues as (
10    select
11        geom :: geography
12    from
13        nyc_neighborhoods
14    where
15        neighborhood = 'Upper East Side'
16  )
17 select
18    ev.geom <-> ues.geom as new_operator,
19    st_distance(ev.geom, ues.geom)
20 from
21    ev,
22    ues
```

new_operator	st_distance
3581.510728297563	3580.0905042

And with that we have wrapped up our chapters on the foundation elements of spatial SQL. Obviously we did not touch on everything, but in almost every circumstance when I needed a function to do something I often found it, and even when I don't, it was a matter of using SQL to create the right query to do so. In our next chapters, we will be going over some fundamental spatial analysis problems in spatial SQL, some various use cases and examples, and advanced use cases.

3.9 Expert Voices: Justin Chang

Name: Justin Chang **Title**: GIS Analyst

How/where did you learn spatial SQL?

I learned it after my organization started using QGIS/PostGIS to create multi-user environment to draw telecommunication design. We now have approximately 200 users using QGIS/PostGIS set up and learned about spatial SQL naturally as we try to do more analysis in a robust way using QGIS.

Why do you enjoy using spatial SQL?

I like how fast it is and how instantly I can acquire analysis using SQL. Although it requires some knowledge of GIS and the logics behind it, it is very good at getting results quickly. PostGIS comes with handy spatial functions such as ST_Intersects, ST_DWithin and ST_Length, which enables users to use their spatial knowledge with SQL. Furthermore, spatial SQL allows users to do GIS without the visuals in a quick way and the queries can be repeated and shared among users, which makes it quite useful.

Can you share an interesting way or use case that you are using spatial SQL for today?

In Telecommunication design we need to do a lot of analysis within a FSA (Fibre Serving Areas) like counting how many items are there and how much length of certain cables are within the boundary. Spatial SQL enables users to get analysis quickly and reliably. In essence, it's a modification of "select by location" in a GIS desktop program like QGIS and Spatial SQL allows users to customize their queries by using Spatial SQL to find the data they need.

Listing 3.50: Samples from Justin's work

```
1   /* Calculate all the NEW splice which is either  B4, C5 and D5 within FSA 101-1 HALIFAX */
2
3   SELECT b.fsa, b.exchange, COUNT(CASE WHEN a.status = 'NEW'
4    AND (a.closure_type LIKE '%A5' OR a.closure_type LIKE '%B5' OR a.closure_type LIKE '%C5')THEN 1 END )
5   FROM t_mobia.splice AS a
6   JOIN t_mobia.adminboundary AS b
7   ON ST_intersects(a.geom,b.geom)
8   WHERE fsa = '101-1' AND exchange = 'HALIFAX'
9   GROUP by b.fsa, b.exchange;
10
11  /* Calculate all the NEW FDH vaults which is either  30x48 or 36x60 within FSA 102-1 HALIFAX*/
12
13  SELECT b.fsa, b.exchange,
14   COUNT(CASE WHEN a.status = 'NEW' AND a.ped_type  IN('VAULT 30x48','VAULT 36x60')  THEN 1 END  )
15  FROM t_mobia.structures AS a
16  JOIN t_mobia.adminboundary AS b
17  ON ST_intersects(a.geom, b.geom)
18  WHERE fsa = '102-1' AND exchange = 'HALIFAX'
19  GROUP by b.fsa, b.exchange;
20
21  /* Calculate all the NEW FSA vaults which is either  17x30, 24x36 or 30x48 within FSA 107-1 DARTMOUTH */
22
23  SELECT b.fsa, b.exchange,
24  COUNT(CASE WHEN a.status = 'NEW' AND a.ped_type='VAULT 17x30'  THEN 1 END) AS v1730_count,
25  COUNT(CASE WHEN a.status = 'NEW' AND a.ped_type='VAULT 24x36'  THEN 1 END) AS v2436_count,
26  COUNT(CASE WHEN a.status = 'NEW' AND a.ped_type='VAULT 30x48'  THEN 1 END) As v3048_count,
27  COUNT(CASE WHEN a.status = 'NEW' AND a.ped_type
28   IN('VAULT 17x30','VAULT 24x36','VAULT 30x48')  THEN 1 END  ) AS total_count
29  FROM t_mobia.structures AS a
30  JOIN t_mobia.adminboundary AS b
31  ON ST_intersects(a.geom, b.geom)
32  WHERE fsa = '107-1' AND exchange = 'DARTMOUTH'
33  GROUP by b.fsa, b.exchange;
34
```

```
35   /* Calculate all aerial placement lines within FSA 303-1 BEDFORD */
36
37   SELECT b.fsa, b.exchange, ROUND(SUM(st_length(a.geom))::integer,2) AS aerial_length_sum
38   FROM t_mobia.aerial_placement AS a
39   JOIN t_mobia.adminboundary AS b
40   ON ST_intersects(b.geom, a.geom)
41   WHERE fsa = '303-1' AND exchange = 'BEDFORD'
42   GROUP by b.fsa, b.exchange;
43
44   /* Calculate all the conduits within each FSA with 100mm length in BEDFORD */
45
46   SELECT b.fsa, b.exchange, ROUND (SUM(st_length(
47    CASE WHEN a.status = 'NEW' AND a.category = 'HDPE-100' THEN a.geom END
48   ))::integer,2) AS length_sum,
49   COUNT(CASE WHEN a.category = 'HDPE-100'  THEN 1 END )
50   FROM t_mobia.conduit AS a
51   JOIN t_mobia.adminboundary AS b
52   ON ST_intersects(b.geom, a.geom)
53   WHERE exchange = 'BEDFORD'
54   GROUP BY b.fsa, b.exchange
55   ORDER BY b.exchange ASC;/
```

4. Spatial Analysis

Now that we have all the building blocks in place, our next step is to start applying spatial SQL to some common GIS analyses. While I think that many things you need to do in GIS or geospatial analytics can be performed with spatial SQL, most people employ some sort of hybrid approach, meaning that their toolkit consists of things like QGIS, Python, visualization libraries, and more. Spatial SQL is one part of the modern GIS ecosystem and knowing what to use when is another skill that is incredibly important.

This section is built to help you connect spatial SQL to functions that you may find in QGIS or ArcGIS' toolboxes to help you see how you can apply these analyses in spatial SQL. Many times you will use two or more of these analyses together and in the next chapter we will take a look at some common problems in spatial SQL that use several techniques in combination.

4.1 Analyses we have already seen

Some of these are analyses we have seen throughout the course of the book already since they are generally implemented with one or two functions from spatial SQL. Given that we will start with these since we know what they are and can easily draw upon what we have already learned:

- KMeans Clustering
- DBScan Clustering
- Merge or Union geometries
- Buffer
- Centroids
- Deluaney triangles
- Collect geometries
- Deluany triangulation
- Simplify
- Split with lines
- Voronoi polygons
- Count points in polygons
- Concave hull
- Convex hull
- Extract X/Y coordinates
- Smoothing lines

Add categorical labels

This one actually has nothing to do with spatial SQL as we can just use a CASE WHEN statement which we can show with our tree census dataset:

Listing 4.1: Creating labels in SQL

```
1  select
2      spc_common,
3      case
4          when spc_common ilike '%oak%' then 'Oak'
```

```
5            when spc_common ilike '%maple%' then 'Maple'
6            when spc_common ilike '%pine%' then 'Pine'
7            else NULL
8        end as tree_type
9    from
10       nyc_2015_tree_census
11   limit
12       100
```

Anything that you can write in a WHERE clause after the WHEN can be used including dates, numbers, and text data. This is also great for generating labels for your data and visualizations as well.

Distance Matrix

We reviewed this briefly when discussing cross joins, which can be used to calculate the distances from one set of points to another. We can do this by simulating a table with points located at Yankee Stadium and Citi Field, the stadiums of the New York Yankees and New York Mets of Major League Baseball, respectively. Using the centroids of the neighborhoods file, we will find which neighborhoods are closest to each, first calculating the distance of each neighborhood to each stadium.

Additionally, we will use a new syntax called a *temporary table* which will only persist the table until the session is terminated. Since we don't need to keep this in memory long term this is a great solution.

Listing 4.2: Distance matrix table

```
1   create temporary table stadiums_matrix as with stadiums as (
2       select
3           'Citi Field' as stadium,
4           buildpoint(-73.845833, 40.756944, 4326) as geom
5       union
6       select
7           'Yankees Stadium' as stadium,
8   ) buildpoint(-73.926389, 40.829167, 4326) as geom
9   select
10      a.stadium,
11      b.neighborhood,
12      st_distance(st_centroid(b.geom), a.geom)
13  from
14      stadiums a,
15      nyc_neighborhoods b
```

Now, we can write a query to find the distance for each neighborhood to see which neighborhood is closer to which stadium.

Listing 4.3: Neighborhoods to baseball stadiums

```
1   -- Find all the rows from the stadiums matrix for Citi Field
2   with mets as (
3       select
4           *
5       from
6           stadiums_matrix
7       where
8           stadium = 'Citi Field'
9   ),
10
11  -- Find all the rows from the stadiums matrix for Yankees Stadium
12  yankees as (
13      select
14          *
15      from
```

```
16        stadiums_matrix
17    where
18        stadium = 'Yankees Stadium'
19  )
20
21  select
22    a.neighborhood,
23    b.st_distance as mets,
24    c.st_distance as yankees
25  from
26    nyc_neighborhoods a
27    join mets b using (neighborhood)
28    join yankees c using (neighborhood)
```

To see all the neighborhoods closer to Yankees Stadium we can use this query (Figure 4.1, on the next page):

Listing 4.4: Neighborhoods closer to Yankees Stadium

```
1   with mets as (
2     select
3        *
4     from
5        stadiums_matrix
6     where
7        stadium = 'Citi Field'
8   ),
9   yankees as (
10    select
11       *
12    from
13       stadiums_matrix
14    where
15       stadium = 'Yankees Stadium'
16  )
17  select
18    a.neighborhood,
19    a.geom,
20    b.st_distance as mets,
21    c.st_distance as yankees
22  from
23    nyc_neighborhoods a
24    join mets b using (neighborhood)
25    join yankees c using (ntaname)
26  where
27    c.st_distance < b.st_distance
```

And for Citi Field (Figure 4.2, on page 251):

Listing 4.5: Closer to Citi Field

```
1   with mets as (
2     select
3        *
4     from
5        stadiums_matrix
6     where
7        stadium = 'Citi Field'
8   ),
9   yankees as (
10    select
11       *
12    from
13       stadiums_matrix
```

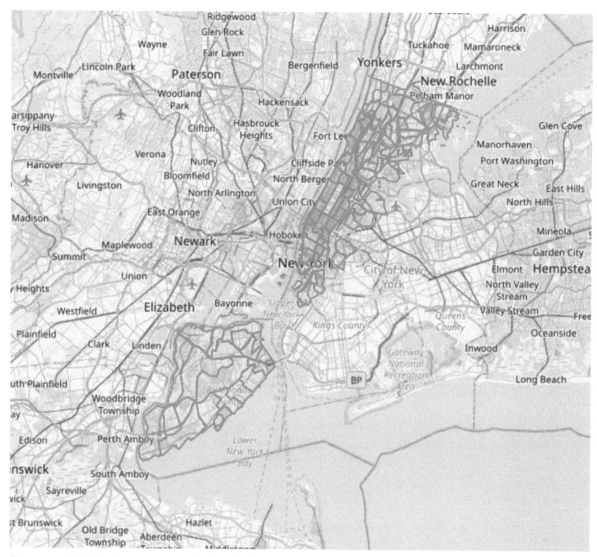

Figure 4.1: Neighborhoods closer to Yankee Stadium

```
14      where
15          stadium = 'Yankees Stadium'
16  )
17  select
18      a.ntaname,
19      a.geom,
20      b.st_distance as mets,
21      c.st_distance as yankees
22  from
23      nyc_neighborhoods a
24      join mets b using (neighborhood)
25      join yankees c using (neighborhood)
26  where
27      b.st_distance < c.st_distance
```

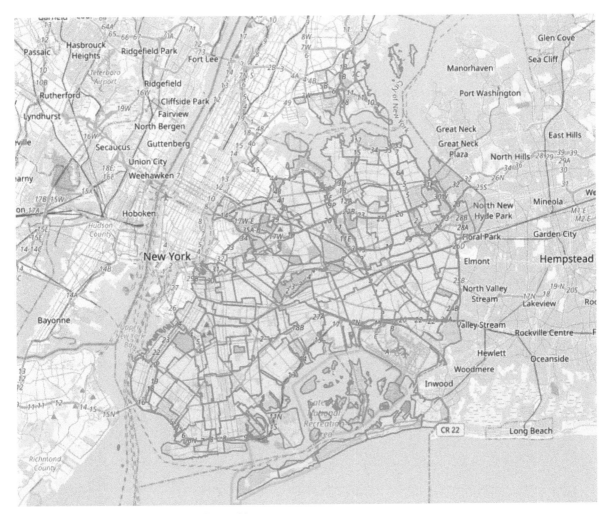

Figure 4.2: Neighborhoods closer to Citi Field

Bounding Box

There are two different methods of creating a bounding box in spatial SQL. The first is to create a bounding box from a set of coordinates, the minimum X and Y values and the maximum X and Y values. To do that we can use the function ST_MakeEnvelope to create a bounding box. If you need to find the values of a specific area I recommend using a free online tool from Klokan Technologies[103] (which I have used hundreds of times so thank you if you are reading this!) which you can access at the URL in the footnotes.

First we can make a quick bounding box over Manhattan:

Listing 4.6: Bounding box - Method 1

```
1  select
2      st_makeenvelope(-74.047196, 40.679654, -73.906769, 40.882012, 4326)
```

The other method is to extract a bounding box from a specific geometry. We can do so using this query:

---

[103] https://boundingbox.klokantech.com/

Listing 4.7: Bounding box - Method 2

```
1  select
2      st_envelope(st_transform(geom, 4326)) as geom
3  from
4      nyc_zips
5  where
6      zipcode = '11231'
```

Which results in this map (Figure 4.3):

Figure 4.3: Bounding boxes using ST_Envelope

As you can see we have not one but two bounding boxes here. For some reason, the city decided to store these geometries as two separate records. As a coding challenge how could you combine them into one?

_____

If you guessed ST_Collect then you are correct! We can validate that here (Figure 4.4, on the facing page):

Listing 4.8: Collecting our geometries!

```
1  select
2      st_collect(st_transform(geom, 4326)) as geom
3  from
4      nyc_zips
5  where
6      zipcode = '11231'
```

Figure 4.4: Combining the geometries using ST_Collect

Merge/split lines

If you recall, we can use ST_Union to merge lines or other geometries together and *ST_Split* to split a line by another geometry, or use a line to split other geometries. You can refer back to the previous chapter for some examples on this using the NYC Bike Route data.

Make valid

To make a geometry that is invalid in the database valid, which will generally return an error for any number of reasons such as an unclosed polygon or overlapping points on a polygon, you can use *ST_MakeValid*. Depending on the import method that you use you may or may not actually get to this point. For example GDAL will generally throw an error if there is an invalid geometry and you can use a flag within the ogr2ogr command, in this case `-makevalid`, to validate the geometries before they land in PostGIS.

Interpolate point on line

To accomplish the task of interpolating a point or points along a line, we can use one of two functions. First, let's grab a specific line from our dataset, in this case the longest which can be found using a query you are going to write as another coding challenge! Think of a query you can use to find the longest segment in the bike paths dataset.

So if you landed on using `ST_Length` as the function you are correct. Now the question asks us to find the longest linestring, so we know we only need one result. We can order our table by the length of the lines in descending order and simply `LIMIT` the query to return one row:

Listing 4.9: Finding the longest bike route part

```
1   select
2       *
3   from
4       nyc_bike_routes
5   order by
6       st_length(geom) desc
7   limit
8       1
```

And that will return a bike route in south Brooklyn (Figure 4.5, on the next page):

Now let's first start by interpolating a single point. We can use a function called `ST_LineInterpolatePoint` which takes two arguments, a geometry and a number between 0 and 1 representing a fraction of how far you want to place the point. For example 0 will be at the beginning of the line, 0.5 will be at the halfway point, and 1 will be at the end. Let's try this using 0.5 (note that since it is a multi-linestring we will merge it using `ST_LineMerge`) (Figure 4.6, on page 256):

Listing 4.10: Interpolate a point at the halfway mark

```
1   select
2       st_lineinterpolatepoint(st_linemerge(geom), 0.5) as geom
3   from
4       nyc_bike_routes
5   where
6       ogc_fid = 20667
```

And this is great if you know the exact fraction of the length of the line where you want to place your point, but in most cases you will want to place a point at a specified distance along the line. Let's first find the length of our line in meters:

Listing 4.11: Get the route length in meters

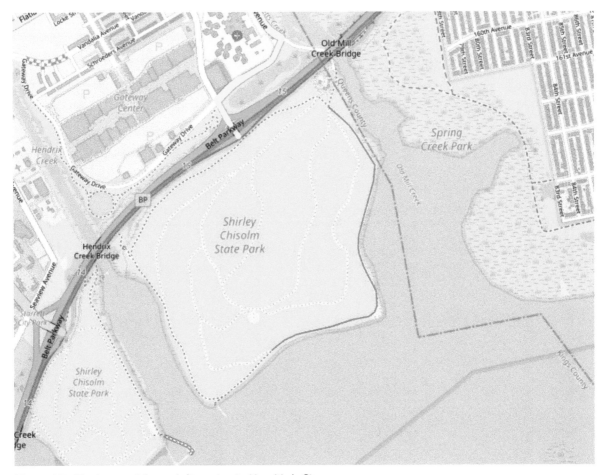

Figure 4.5: The longest bike path linestring in New York City

```
1  select
2      st_length(st_transform(geom, 3857))
3  from
4      nyc_bike_routes
5  where
6      ogc_fid = 20667
```

This shows that the line is about 2,133 meters long. So let's say we want to find a point along the line that is 500 meters from the beginning we need to find the fraction of the distance that 500 meters is compared to 2,133 meters which we can accomplish as so:

Listing 4.12: Finding a point 500m from the start

```
1  select
2      st_lineinterpolatepoint(
3          -- This is the line created from ST_LineMerge
4          st_linemerge(geom),
5
6          -- Here we divide 500 by the total length of the route
7          (
8              500 / (
9                  select
10                      st_length(st_transform(geom, 3857))
11                  from
```

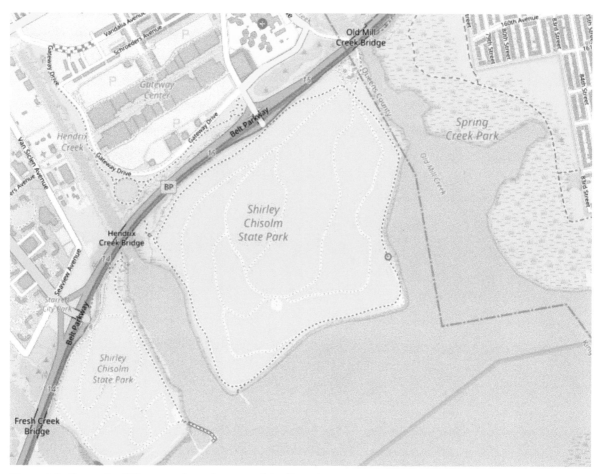

Figure 4.6: One point 500 meters from the start of the linestring

```
12                          nyc_bike_routes
13                  where
14                      ogc_fid = 20667
15            )
16        )
17      ) as geom
18  from
19      nyc_bike_routes
20  where
21      ogc_fid = 20667
```

Now instead imagine that we want to add a point every 75 meters along the line. A second function exists called ST_InterpolatePoints which we can use our same query for just swapping out our function and changing 500 for 75 (Figure 4.7, on the next page):

Listing 4.13: One point every 75 meters

```
1  select
2      st_lineinterpolatepoints(
3
4          -- Our merged geometry
5          st_linemerge(geom),
6
7          -- Dividing the length of the route by 75
```

```
 8          (
 9              75 / (
10                  select
11                      st_length(st_transform(geom, 3857))
12                  from
13                      nyc_bike_routes
14                  where
15                      ogc_fid = 20667
16              )
17          )
18      ) as geom
19  from
20      nyc_bike_routes
21  where
22      ogc_fid = 20667
```

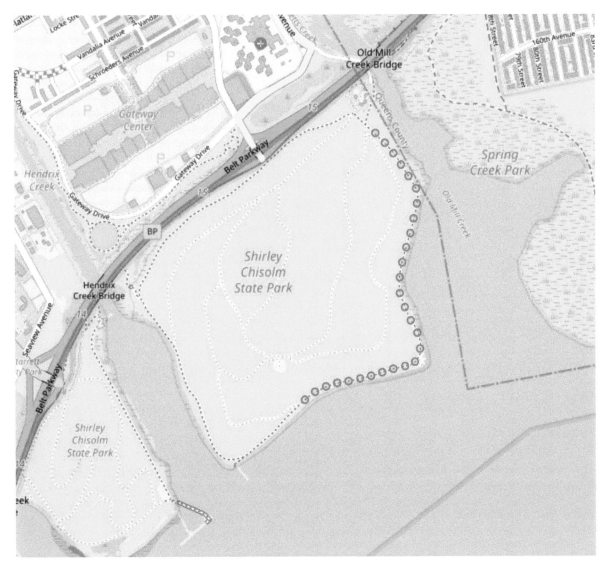

Figure 4.7: One point every 75 meters

Clip/Intersection

While there is an ST_Clip function in PostGIS it applies to raster data, so we use ST_Intersection in this case. We can clip multiple geometries using this function across all geometries in the table. We can see this in this example where we clip all the zip codes in New York City with a bounding box around Central Park (Figure 4.8, on the following page):

Listing 4.14: ST_Intersection

```
1  select
2      st_intersection(
3          st_transform(geom, 4326),
4          st_makeenvelope(-73.981667, 40.76461, -73.949314, 40.800368, 4326)
5      ) as geom
6  from
7      nyc_zips
```

Figure 4.8: Using ST_Intersection

Difference

The function to perform a difference does carry the same name as the analysis in this case, ST_Difference. We can see this using the same query as above (Figure 4.9, on the next page):

Listing 4.15: ST_Difference

```
1  select
2      st_difference(
3          st_transform(geom, 4326),
4          st_makeenvelope(-73.981667, 40.76461, -73.949314, 40.800368, 4326)
5      ) as geom
6  from
7      nyc_zips
```

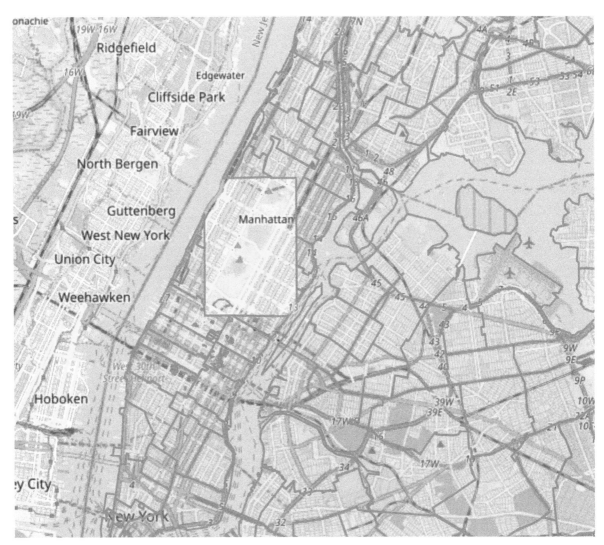

Figure 4.9: Using ST_Difference

4.2   New analyses

Create random points

We will see this function again to generate some random points for another analysis, but this can be solved using a single function, ST_GeneratePoints. This will return n-number of points and accepts two arguments, the geometry and an integer with the number of points to generate in that order.

Let's test this with out zip codes and generate 50 points in the 10001 zip code (Figure 4.10, on page 260):

Listing 4.16: ST_GeneratePoints

```
1   select
2       st_generatepoints(st_transform(geom, 4326), 50) as geom
3   from
4       nyc_zips
5   where
6       zipcode = '10001'
```

Figure 4.10: Creating random points

In the output you will see that it returns one row which means that it returns a geometry collection. To extract each point, we can use ST_Dump:

Listing 4.17: Dump the geometries

```
1   select
2       (
3           st_dump(
4               st_generatepoints(st_transform(geom, 4326), 50)
5           )
6       ).geom as geom
7   from
8       nyc_zips
9   where
10      zipcode = '10001'
```

Subdivide geometry (collection with parts or individuals)

Earlier in the book we saw how you can use ST_Subdivide to divide polygons based on the number of vertices they contain. However, another common analysis that we may want to perform is to split a polygon into a number of equal areas. To do that we need to perform a few different steps, which are outlined in this post by Paul Ramsey[104].

Let's pick one zip code in New York, one with an odd shape in Long Island City, Queens, 11101 (Figure 4.11, on the next page):

Listing 4.18: Transforming zip code 11101

```
1   select
2       st_transform(geom, 4326) as geom
3   from
4       nyc_zips
5   where
6       zipcode = '11101'
```

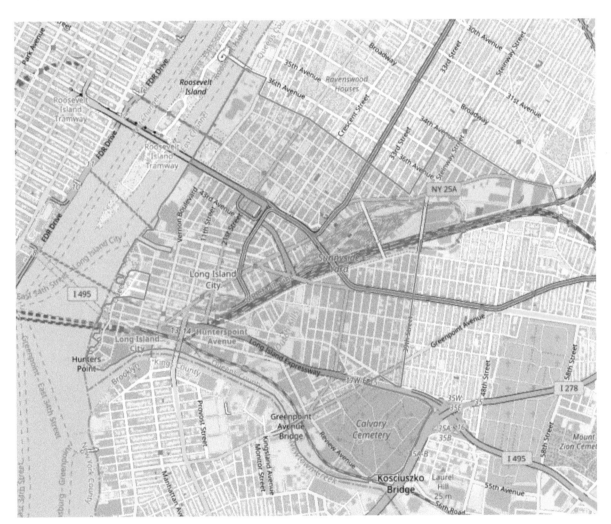

Figure 4.11: Long Island City zip code 11101

To accomplish the task first we will generate some random points inside this polygon using ST_GeneratePoints. Since this returns a geometry collection we will need to dump the individual points using ST_Dump and extract the geometry using the .geom accessor (Figure 4.12, on the following page):

Listing 4.19: Generating random points

---

[104]https://blog.cleverelephant.ca/2018/06/polygon-splitting.html

```
1   select
2     (
3         st_dump(
4             st_generatepoints(st_transform(geom, 4326), 5000)
5         )
6     ).geom as geom
7   from
8       nyc_zips
9   where
10      zipcode = '11101'
```

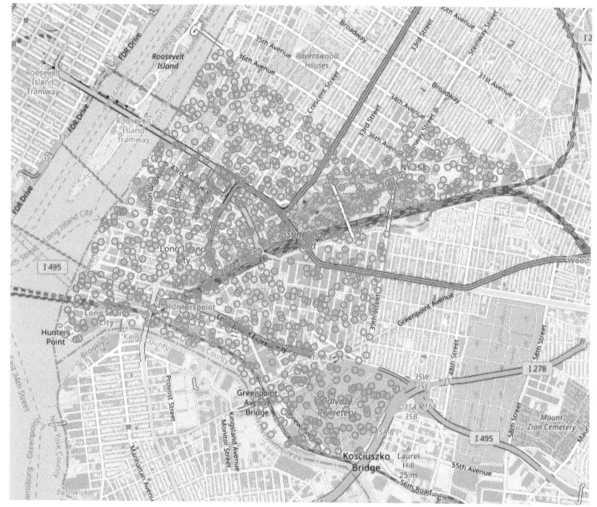

Figure 4.12: Creating random points in 11101

Next we will need to create several evenly sized clusters, which calls for ST_ClusterKMeans to group our random points. In this case let's create 6 clusters (Figure 4.13, on the next page):

Listing 4.20: Creating even clusters of points

```
1   -- The "points" CTE generates 5,000 random points in the 11101 postal code
2   with points as (
3       select
4         (
5             st_dump(
6                 st_generatepoints(st_transform(geom, 4326), 5000)
```

```
 7                  )
 8              ).geom as geom
 9      from
10          nyc_zips
11      where
12          zipcode = '11101'
13  ),
14
15  -- Create 6 even clusters using ST_ClusterKMeans
16  cluster as (
17      select
18          geom,
19          st_clusterkmeans(geom, 6) over () AS cluster
20      from
21          points
22  )
23
24  -- Group or collect each cluster and find the centroid
25  select
26      st_centroid(
27          st_collect(geom)
28      ) as geom,
29      cluster
30  from
31      cluster
32  group by
33      cluster
```

In our next to last step, we need to now create Voronoi polygons around our centroids (Figure 4.14, on page 265):

Listing 4.21: Creating Voronoi polygons around our points

```
 1  with points as (
 2      select
 3          (
 4              st_dump(
 5                  st_generatepoints(st_transform(geom, 4326), 5000)
 6              )
 7          ).geom as geom
 8      from
 9          nyc_zips
10      where
11          zipcode = '11101'
12  ),
13  cluster as (
14      select
15          geom,
16          st_clusterkmeans(geom, 6) over () AS cluster
17      from
18          points
19  ),
20  centroid as (
21      select
22          st_centroid(st_collect(geom)) as geom,
23          cluster
24      from
25          cluster
26      group by
27          cluster
28  )
29
30  -- In this step we collect the centroids
31  -- then create Voronoi polygons, then extract
```

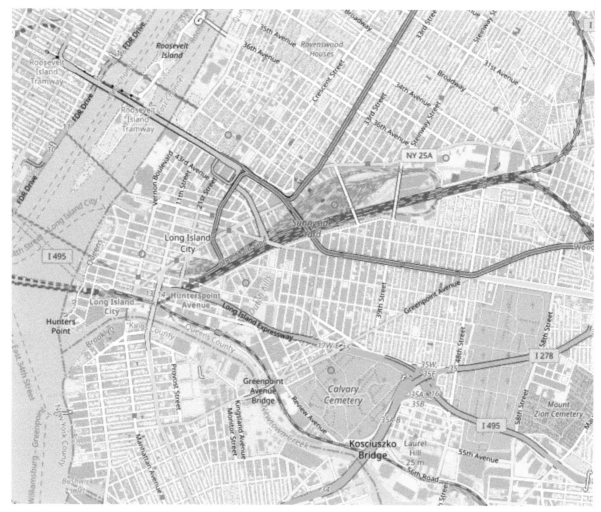

Figure 4.13: The center of each KMeans cluster

```
32   -- each individual polygon
33   select
34       (
35           st_dump(st_voronoipolygons(st_collect(geom)))
36       ).geom AS geom
37   from
38       centroid
```

And in our final step we will then clip our original polygon with our resulting Voronoi polygons (Figure 4.15, on page 266):

Listing 4.22: Clipping to produce the final product

```
1   with points as (
2       select
3           (
4               st_dump(
5                   st_generatepoints(st_transform(geom, 4326), 5000)
6               )
7           ).geom as geom
8       from
```

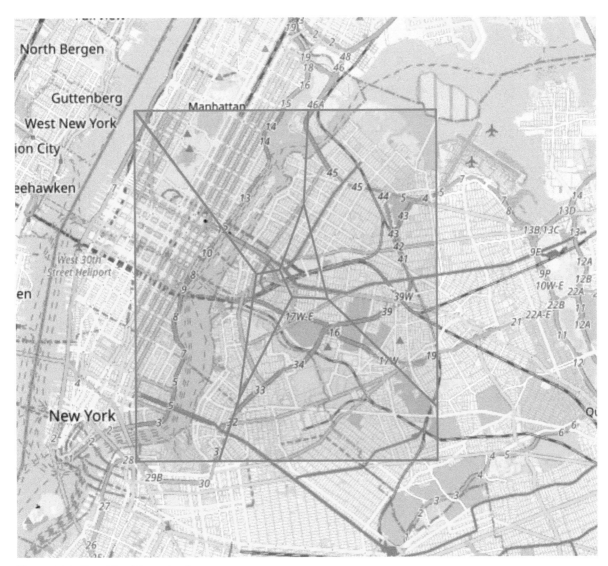

Figure 4.14: Resulting Voronoi polygons

```
9          nyc_zips
10     where
11         zipcode = '11101'
12  ),
13  cluster as (
14     select
15         geom,
16         st_clusterkmeans(geom, 6) over () AS cluster
17     from
18         points
19  ),
20  centroid as (
21     select
22         st_centroid(st_collect(geom)) as geom,
23         cluster
24     from
25         cluster
26     group by
```

```
27          cluster
28  ),
29  voronoi as (
30      select
31          (
32              st_dump(st_voronoipolygons(st_collect(geom)))
33          ).geom AS geom
34      from
35          centroid
36  )
37
38  -- In the last step, we find the intersection (or clip)
39  -- the 11101 zip code and the Voronoi polygons
40  select
41      st_intersection(
42          (
43              select
44                  st_transform(geom, 4326)
45              from
46                  nyc_zips
47              where
48                  zipcode = '11101'
49          ),
50          geom
51      )
52  from
53      voronoi
```

As you can see this is quite a chunky bit of SQL. Even if we combined this into one single query it would be difficult to read and decipher. This is a great use case for a user defined function. We can do this by adding placeholder variables in our SQL, so it can be used across multiple data types. Let's take a look at the function creation statement and break it down:

Listing 4.23: Creating a new UDF

```
1   -- Setting up our function and inputs
2   create
3   or replace function st_equalarea(
4       seed_points int,
5       tablename text,
6       polygons int,
7       unique_id text
8   )
9
10  -- Define that the function returns a table and the return values
11
12  returns table (id varchar, geom geometry) language plpgsql
13  as $$
14  begin
15  return query
16
17  -- This will run the string as a query, filling in the values
18  execute format(
19      'with points as (select %s as id,
20      (st_dump( st_generatepoints( geom , %s) )).geom as geom from %s),
21      cluster as (select geom, id, st_clusterkmeans(geom, %s)
22      over (partition by id) AS cluster from points),
23      centroid as (select id, st_centroid(st_collect(geom)) as geom,
24      cluster from cluster group by cluster, id),
25      voronoi as (select id, (st_dump( st_voronoipolygons( st_collect(geom) ) )).geom
26      AS voronoi_geom from centroid group by id)
27      select b.id, st_intersection(a.geom, b.voronoi_geom) as
28      geom from voronoi b join %s a on b.id = %s;',
29
```

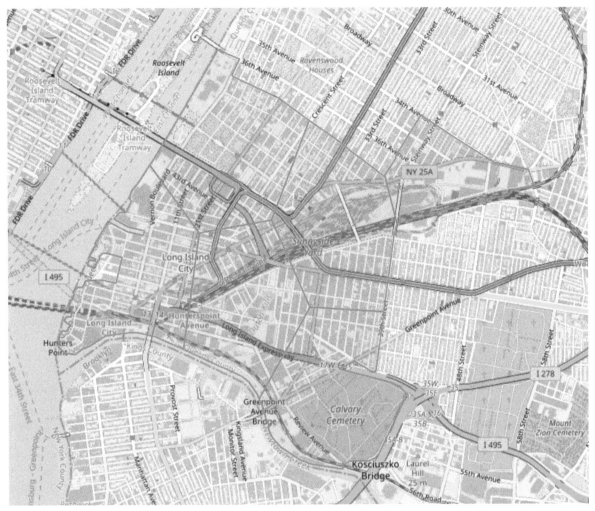

Figure 4.15: Final result with the Voronoi polygons clipped by 11101

```
30      -- These values will replace each instance of %s in the order they appear
31      unique_id,
32      seed_points,
33      tablename,
34      polygons,
35      tablename,
36      unique_id
37   );
38
39   end;
40   $$
```

Yes this is a big one but let's take it bit by bit:

```
create or replace function st_equalarea(seed_
points int, tablename text, polygons int, unique_id text)
```

This is the create function syntax that contains the different input variables. Note that `tablename` and `unique_id` are stored as text variables in this case. More on that later.

```
returns table (id varchar, geom geometry)
```

The thing we want to return from the function in this case is a table with two columns, an ID that is a VARCHAR format and a geometry, which will be our equally divided areas.

```
language plpgsql as $$ begin return query
```

The first four lines are standard for defining a stored procedure in PostgreSQL. The final line tells that the function will return a query which will in turn produce a table described in the previous section above.

```
execute format('select...rest of the query;', unique_id, seed_
points, tablename, polygons, tablename, unique_id);
```

Okay so this is where things get a bit funky. We will discuss the few changes to our query next but for now there are a few things to focus on:

- The execute format allows us to construct our query as a string and insert data from our function arguments into the query
- At the end of the query you will see this ...unique_id, seed_points, tablename, polygons, tablename, unique_id)
  - This is the order that the elements will be added to the query contained in the string. unique_id is first, followed by seed_points, so on and so forth
- Within the query you will see several instances of %s. Each time you see this that placeholder will be replaced by one of the values from above, in the order that they appear.
  - The first %s is replaced by unique_id, the second by seed_points, etc.

Finally, in our query we made a few modifications. Since we are running this query across an entire table, we will need to keep the unique ID for each original polygon intact, in this case that is the zip code. You will see that this is included in the first CTE and given the alias ID which carries through the rest of the query:

```
with points as (select %s as id,(st_dump(st_
generatepoints(geom, %s))).geom as geomfrom %s),
```

As you can see there are three instances of %s here, which are replaced by unique_id, seed_points, and tablename respectively.

The only other change comes in the section that utilizes ST_ClusterKMeans. In our original query that line looks like this:

```
st_clusterkmeans(geom, 6) over () AS cluster
```

Remember that this is one of only a few window functions that exist in PostGIS. Since we were only dealing with one geometry at the time we knew that we would get 6 total clusters back. Now since we are now passing many points across many polygons, if we used the same structure of the function we would in fact be getting 6 clusters for every single point in every zip code. But since this is a window function we can easily fix this with one quick change

```
st_clusterkmeans(geom, 6) over (partition by id) AS cluster
```

By adding the `PARTITION BY` this acts kind of like a group by meaning that the window will be applied for each ID, in this case zip code. So we will, in this example, end up with 6 clusters for each zip code.

```
end; $$
```

End the statement and close the function.

Now that we have done this let's try our new function with 6 even areas per zip code:

Listing 4.24: Testing our new function

```
1  select
2      *
3  from
4      st_equalarea(1000, 'nyc_zips', 6, 'zipcode')
```

Keep in mind we have not re-projected our data, so you should see this when you open the geometry viewer, and we are missing a large portion of Queens and Brooklyn since it will only show 1,000 geometries (Figure 4.16):

Figure 4.16: Equal areas for all NYC

However, we can add a geometry that will show on the base map like this:

Listing 4.25: Adding a geometry this time

```
1  select
2      id,
3      st_transform(geom, 4326) as geom
4  from
5      st_equalarea(1000, 'nyc_zips', 6, 'zipcode')
```

Which shows this map (Figure 4.17, on the next page):

If you zoom in you can see that this applied to even the small zip codes in midtown or downtown Manhattan, most of which are zip codes specific to a single building (Figure 4.18, on page 271):

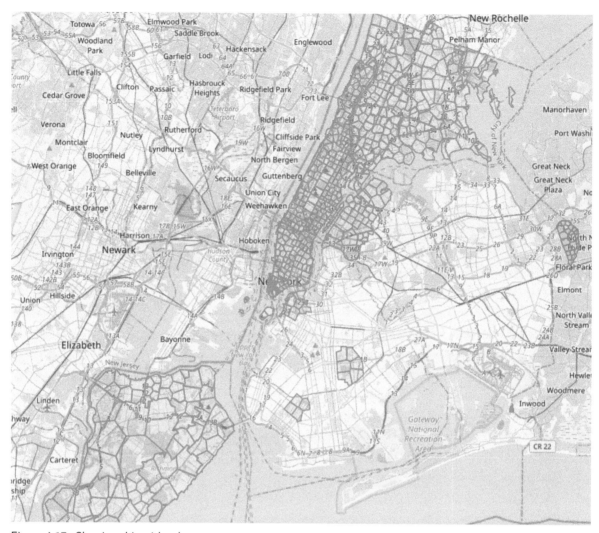

Figure 4.17: Showing this with a basemap

Now do you think we could modify our function to subdivide our polygons into areas of equal area globally, such as 50 acres, rather than 5 equal areas per polygon. If you feel a coding challenge coming up, then you are correct! Here are some hints to get you started:

- You only need to modify one line of code and add one extra CTE (this calculates the area of the original zip code polygons)
- Since you know that the small building size polygons are under this limit, make sure you account for that edge case
- The code you will be replacing takes a whole integer, so you will need to round the result
- Make the function flexible so you can divide the area of the polygon by any number

---

So if you focused in on the number of clusters in ST_ClusterKMeans then you went in the right direction. This was previously static based on the number of polygons we provided in the input. In this case we want to:

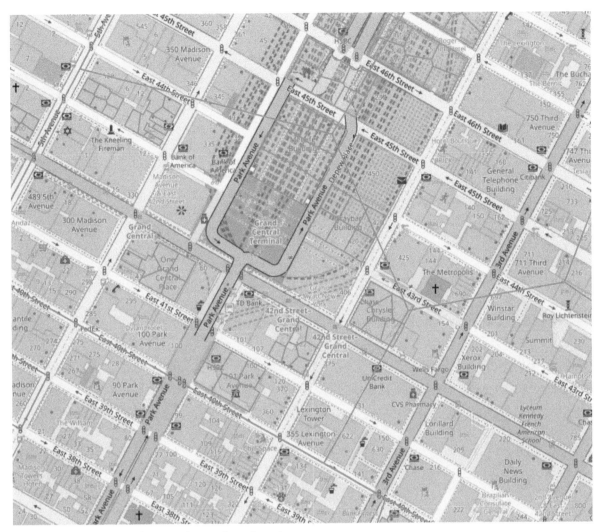

Figure 4.18: Equal areas for even the smallest zip codes

- Add a new CTE that contains the zip code and area of the polygon which we will use to join in the step where the KMeans clusters are created
- Use that number and a modified input to change the cluster size based on the area divided by the input parameter

The full code is here with the modified lines in bold:

Listing 4.26: Reformatting our function

```
1   create
2   or replace function st_equalareawithinput(
3       seed_points int,
4       tablename text,
5       polygons int,
6       unique_id text
7   ) returns table (id varchar, geom geometry) language plpgsql as $$ begin return query execute format(
8       'with points as (select %s as id, (st_dump( st_generatepoints( geom , %s) )).geom
9       as geom from %s),
10      area as (select st_area(geom) as area, zipcode from %s),
11      cluster as (select points.geom, points.id,
```

```
12        st_clusterkmeans(points.geom, ceil((a.area/(%s)))::int) over (partition by id) AS cluster
13        from points left join area a on a.zipcode = points.id),
14        centroid as (select id, st_centroid(st_collect(geom)) as geom,
15        cluster from cluster group by cluster, id),
16        voronoi as (select id,(st_dump( st_voronoipolygons( st_collect(geom) ) )).geom AS voronoi_geom
17        from centroid group by id) select b.id, st_intersection(a.geom, b.voronoi_geom) as geom
18        from voronoi b join %s a on b.id = %s;',
19        unique_id,
20        seed_points,
21        tablename,
22        tablename,
23        polygons,
24        tablename,
25        unique_id
26    );
27
28    end;
29
30    $$
```

As you can see we added this CTE to calculate the area one time rather than each time for each point:

```
area as (select st_area(geom) as area, zipcode from %s),
```

Next let's look at the KMeans portion of the query:

Listing 4.27: Focusing on the ST__KMeans modifications

```
1   cluster as (
2       select
3           points.geom,
4           points.id,
5           st_clusterkmeans(points.geom, ceil((a.area /(% s))) :: int) over (partition by id) AS cluster
6       from
7           points
8           left join area a on a.zipcode = points.id
9   )
```

The first change is that instead of the static integer we used as an input we changed it to this:

```
ceil((a.area/(%s)))::int)
```

This takes the total area of the zip code from our preceding CTE, then divides it by the input number in the function. In this case we are creating areas of 50 acres which we will see below that 43,560 square feet (our source projection in this case measures in feet) multiplied by 50. We then use CEIL which will round up to the highest nearest integer, then cast this to an integer to match the input type required by ST_ClusterKMeans.

Finally, we join the table together:

```
left join area a on a.zipcode = points.id)
```

You will also see that there are additional placeholders at the end of the function to replace one additional %s placeholder added as seen above.

With that we can run our new query (Figure 4.19, on the next page)!

Listing 4.28: Finally getting our equal areas

```
1  select
2      id,
3      st_transform(geom, 4326) as geom
4  from
5      st_equalareawithinput(1000, 'nyc_zips', (43560 * 50), 'zipcode')
```

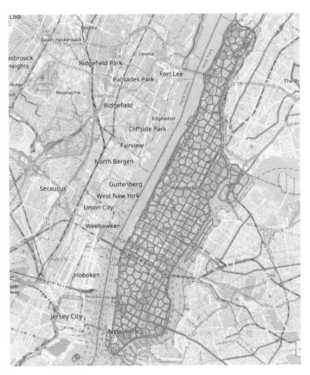

Figure 4.19: Equal areas of 50 acres in Manhattan

Since we can only see 1,000 geometries let's create a new table to view in QGIS (Figure 4.20, on page 274):

Listing 4.29: Build a table for QGIS

```
1  create table nyc_zips_50_acres as
2  select
3      id,
4      st_transform(geom, 4326) as geom
5  from
6      st_equalareawithinput(1000, 'nyc_zips', (43560 * 50), 'zipcode')
```

Overall it seems to work great apart from areas with islands which may have something to do with the random point assignment but for now this is a workable solution (Figure 4.21, on page 275)!

Connect with lines (hub and spoke)

Another common analysis is connecting points to other points with lines using a common attribute. To do this we can use our taxis dataset to find all the trips that originated within 50 meters of a specific intersection, in this case the intersection at 5th Avenue and East 59th Street at the southeast corner of Central Park next to the Plaza Hotel.

To do so we will first create a CTE with a single point, or the location of the intersection. Next we will

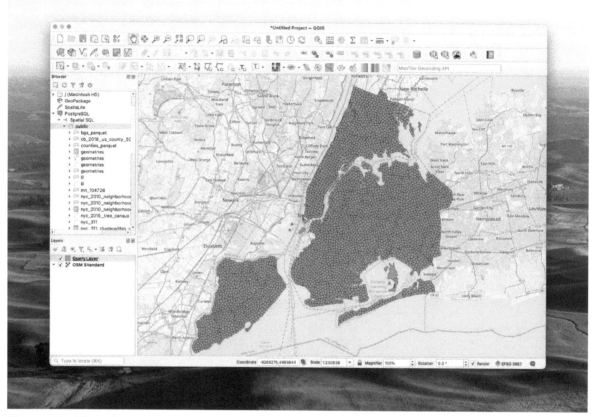

Figure 4.20: All equal areas in NYC

find all the pickups that fall within 50 meters of that point using ST_DWithin and focus on pickups on June 1st, 2016. Finally, we will build a line between the first point at the intersection and all the drop-off geometries (Figure 4.22, on page 276).

Listing 4.30: Hub and spoke

```
1   -- Create a point at the Plaza Hotel
2   with point as (
3       select
4           buildpoint(-73.9730423, 40.7642784, 4326) as geom
5   ),
6
7   -- Find all the pickups within 50 meters of the Plaza
8   -- on June 1st, 2016 and calculate distance with a cross
9   -- join. Since it is just one point the cross join is acceptable
10  -- since it is just one row in that table.
11  start as (
12      select
13          *
14      from
15          nyc_yellow_taxi_0601_0615_2016,
16          point
17      where
18          st_dwithin(pickup :: geography, point.geom :: geography, 50)
19          and pickup_datetime :: date = '06-01-2016'
20  )
21  select
```

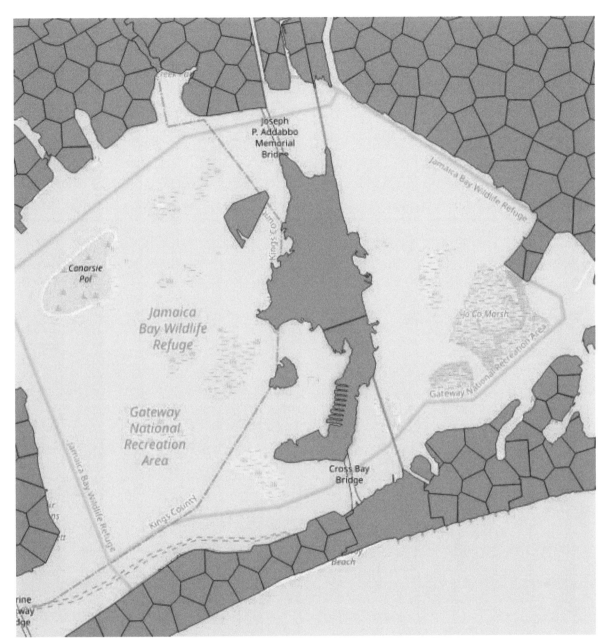

Figure 4.21: Some odd issues with specific geometries

```
22        ogc_fid,
23        trip_distance,
24        total_amount,
25
26        -- Create a line from the Plaza (in the subquery in the second argument)
27        -- and all the dropoff locations
28        st_makeline(
29            dropoff,
30            (
31                select
32                    geom
33                from
34                    point
35            )
36        ) as geom
37    from
38        start
```

Figure 4.22: Hub and spoke

You can do the same thing with multiple origin points by joining your data using a common column between your datasets. For example:

Listing 4.31: This time with data

```
1   select
```

```
2        a.id,
3        st_makeline(a.geom, b.geom) as geom
4    from
5        destinations a
6        left join origins b using (id)
```

In this case we have two tables, destinations with the table alias a, and origins with the alias b. Both tables have a column called id. By joining on this table we can use the geometry from a and b to create the line. We use a left join because we want to preserve all the points from our destinations table and join it to the source origin in b.

Nearest neighbor(s)

Finding the nearest neighbor to a feature is actually quite easy. In spatial SQL, this means that we want to compare a feature to another set of features and find the feature(s) that are nearest to it. So we can simply order those features by distance and limit the values that are returned, in this case the three nearest trees to an entrance to Grand Central Station:

Listing 4.32: Simple nearest neighbor

```
1    select
2        geom,
3        health,
4        spc_common
5    from
6        nyc_2015_tree_census
7    order by
8        st_distance(buildpoint(-73.977733, 40.752273, 4326), geom)
9    limit
10       3
```

However, we can use one of the shorthand functions to make this even shorter, in this case <-> which will is the same as ST_Distance.

Listing 4.33: Cleaning up the code

```
1    select
2        geom,
3        health,
4        spc_common
5    from
6        nyc_2015_tree_census
7    order by
8        buildpoint(-73.977733, 40.752273, 4326) <-> geom
9    limit
10       3
```

Performing a bulk nearest neighbor join, or from all values in one table to another requires some extra steps.

Bulk nearest neighbor

For this analysis, I must first credit Paul Ramsey who wrote a blog post on this method in 2016[105] which introduced me to the bulk nearest neighbor join as well as lateral joins. I have used the lateral join method to do a number of different analyses as we will see moving forward. But for now we will limit this to nearest neighbors. The post itself finds the distance from each property parcel to the nearest fire hydrant which we can repeat as well. To do so we can import another new dataset, NYC fire hydrants[106]:

```
ogr2ogr \
-f PostgreSQL PG:"host=localhost user=docker password=docker \
dbname=gis port=25432" \
NYCDEPCitywideHydrants.geojson \
-nln nyc_fire_hydrants -lco GEOMETRY_NAME=geom
```

With this we can sample buildings within 1 kilometer of John's of Bleeker Street, a famous New York City pizzeria, in the West Village of Manhattan.

Listing 4.34: Building our bulk nearest neighbor

```
1   -- Create a point at John's of Bleeker Street
2   with point as (
3       select
4           buildpoint(-74.003544, 40.7316243, 4326) :: geography as geog
5   ),
6
7   -- Find all the buildings that are within 1 kilometer of John's
8   buildings as (
9       select
10          geom,
11          name,
12          mpluto_bbl
13      from
14          nyc_building_footprints
15      where
16          st_dwithin(
17              geom::geography,
18              (
19                  select
20                      geog
21                  from
22                      point
23              ),
24              1000
25          )
26  )
27
28  -- Selects three columns from the "buildings" CTE
29  -- And one from the cross join lateral
30  select
31      geom,
32      name,
33      mpluto_bbl,
34      nearest.distance
35  from
36      buildings
37
38      -- This join selects the distance to the nearest fire hydrant laterally
39      -- or for each row in the "buildings" dataset. As you can see it uses
40      -- columns from the outside query, and limits the results to 1
41      cross join lateral (
42          select
43              unitid,
44              st_distance(geom :: geography, buildings.geom :: geography) as distance
45          from
```

---

[105]https://carto.com/blog/lateral-joins

[106]https://data.cityofnewyork.us/Environment/NYCDEP-Citywide-Hydrants/6pui-xhxz

```
46              nyc_fire_hydrants
47        order by
48              geom <-> buildings.geom
49        limit
50              1
51     ) nearest
```

First we create a CTE to make a point at the center of the John's and turn it into a geography, and a second CTE to grab all the buildings within 1 km of the John's, making sure to cast our geometries to geographies to make sure we have an accurate distance. From here we can write our query that runs the cross lateral join. Breaking this down:

```
select geom, name, mpluto_bbl, nearest.distance from buildings
```

We will select the geometry, name, and ID from our buildings table, and then the distance from "nearest" which is an alias for the result of our cross join.

```
cross join lateral (
```

This begins the cross lateral join and everything between the parentheses will be added to each row, sort of like the for/each loop we described earlier

```
select unitid,
st_distance(geom::geography, buildings.geom::geography) as distance
from nyc_fire_hydrants
order by geom <-> buildings.geom
limit 1
```

Here we are running the query that will return values that can be joined to each row. First we select the ID of the hydrant and the distance between the building and the hydrant using the geography from our fire hydrants table. Next we use the shorthand order by distance (<->) and limit the result to 1, or the first result, or the hydrant closest to the building.

```
) nearest
```

Closes the lateral join and gives the result an alias of "nearest". We can create a table from this query to visualize the results:

Listing 4.35: Creating our bulk nearest neighbor table

```
1   create table nearest_hydrant_pizza as with point as (
2        select
3               buildpoint(-74.003544, 40.7316243, 4326) :: geography as geog
4   ),
5   buildings as (
6        select
7               geom,
8               name,
9               mpluto_bbl
10       from
11              nyc_building_footprints
12       where
```

```
13                      st_dwithin(
14                              geom :: geography,
15                              (
16                                      select
17                                              geog
18                                      from
19                                              point
20                              ),
21                              1000
22                      )
23  )
24  select
25          geom,
26          name,
27          mpluto_bbl,
28          nearest.distance
29  from
30          buildings
31          cross join lateral (
32                  select
33                          unitid,
34                          st_distance(geom :: geography, buildings.geom :: geography) as distance
35                  from
36                          nyc_fire_hydrants
37                  order by
38                          geom <-> buildings.geom
39                  limit
40                          1
41          ) nearest
```

And here we can see the results with both the table we created and the fire hydrants layer (Figure 4.23).

Snap points to lines

As we will see with the NYC Taxi Data, often times with GPS generated data is not always ready to use in spatial analysis. New York City, and in fact any area with large buildings, are notorious for decreasing the accuracy of GPS data. Now of course roads, are in fact areas, not linestrings, but in many cases we do want to snap a set of points to road centerlines to prepare our data for analysis.

We will do that with the NYC Taxi Data and road centerlines in NYC. To do that we need to import another file into our database:

```
ogr2ogr \
 -f PostgreSQL PG:"host=localhost user=docker password=docker \
 dbname=gis port=25432" \
 street_centerlines.geojson \
 -nln nyc_street_centerlines -lco GEOMETRY_NAME=geom
```

To do this we need to:

- Determine the closest linestring to each point
- Find the location on the linestring closest to the point
- Move the point to that location

First let's pick a sample of points around Union Square (Figure 4.24, on the following page):

Listing 4.36: Finding sample points

```
1  select
```

Figure 4.23: Distance to the nearest fire hydrant

```
2        *
3    from
4        nyc_yellow_taxi_0601_0615_2016
5    where
6        st_dwithin(
7            pickup :: geography,
8            buildpoint(-73.987224, 40.733342, 4326) :: geography,
9            300
10       )
11       and pickup_datetime between '2016-06-02 9:00:00+00'
12       and '2016-06-02 18:00:00+00'
```

Our next task is to determine the closest road to each point. We can do this by using a bulk nearest neighbor join as we have seen above. We want to include the ID and street name from the centerlines table.

Listing 4.37: Closest road to each point

```
1    -- Select all pickups within 300 meters of Union Square
2    -- between 9am and 6pm on June 2nd, 2016
3    with pickups as (
4        select
5            pickup,
6            tip_amount,
7            total_amount
8        from
9            nyc_yellow_taxi_0601_0615_2016
10       where
```

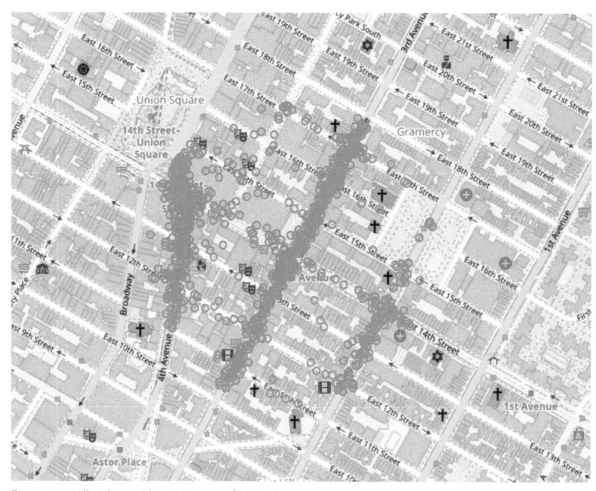

Figure 4.24: All pickups within 300 meters of Union Square

```
11          st_dwithin(
12              pickup :: geography,
13              buildpoint(-73.987224, 40.733342, 4326) :: geography,
14              300
15          )
16          and pickup_datetime between '2016-06-02 9:00:00+00'
17          and '2016-06-02 18:00:00+00'
18  )
19
20  -- Find the nearest road to each point using a
21  -- cross join lateral
22  select
23      a.*,
24      street.name,
25      street.ogc_fid,
26      street.geom
27  from
28      pickups a
29      cross join lateral (
30          select
31              ogc_fid,
32              full_stree as name,
33              geom
34          from
```

```
35              nyc_street_centerlines
36        order by
37            a.pickup <-> geom
38        limit
39            1
40    ) street
```

This will give us a table with our original pickup geometry, tip amount, total trip amount, the street name, and street ID.

In our final step we need to find the nearest point on the centerline to the pickup point, and then move (or interpolate) that point along the line. The function ST_InterpolatePoint should ring a bell here, which allows us to add a point along a linestring, not a multi-linestring, based on a number from 0 to 1, 0 being the starting point and 1 being the end point of the line.

To find the closest location on the linestring to our pickup point we can use another similarly named function: ST_LineLocatePoint. This takes two arguments, a linestring and a point geometry in that order, and returns the input we need for the proceeding function: a number from 0 to 1 which indicates the location of the nearest point on the line.

In summary, we first need to calculate the location of the point with ST_LineLocatePoint, then use the return value of that function to calculate ST_InterpolatePoint, which will return the final snapped point. In the query we will also make another geometry which is a line which will connect the location of the original point to the snapped point:

Listing 4.38: Snapping our points

```
1   with pickups as (
2     select
3         pickup,
4         tip_amount,
5         total_amount
6     from
7         nyc_yellow_taxi_0601_0615_2016
8     where
9         st_dwithin(
10            pickup :: geography,
11            buildpoint(-73.987224, 40.733342, 4326) :: geography,
12            300
13        )
14        and pickup_datetime between '2016-06-02 9:00:00+00'
15        and '2016-06-02 18:00:00+00'
16  ),
17  nearest as (
18    select
19        a.*,
20        street.name,
21        street.ogc_fid,
22        street.geom
23    from
24        pickups a
25        cross join lateral (
26            select
27                ogc_fid,
28                full_stree as name,
29                geom
30            from
31                nyc_street_centerlines
32            order by
33                a.pickup <-> geom
34            limit
35                1
```

```
36              ) street
37      )
38   select
39          a.*,
40
41          -- Create a line between the original point and the new snapped point
42          st_makeline(
43              pickup,
44              st_lineinterpolatepoint(
45                  st_linemerge(b.geom),
46                  st_linelocatepoint(st_linemerge(b.geom), pickup)
47              )
48          ) as line,
49
50          -- Add a column for the snapped point
51          st_lineinterpolatepoint(
52              st_linemerge(b.geom),
53              st_linelocatepoint(st_linemerge(b.geom), pickup)
54          ) as snapped
55   from
56          nearest a
57          join nyc_street_centerlines b using (ogc_fid)
```

This results in our snapped points and our lines (Figures 4.25 and 4.26, on the facing page):

Now we can also create table with each of the individual geometries to show in QGIS. First let's make a table of our full results:

Listing 4.39: Creating a table for QGIS

```
1    create
2    or replace view nyc_taxi_union_square as with pickups as (
3        select
4            pickup,
5            tip_amount,
6            total_amount
7        from
8            nyc_yellow_taxi_0601_0615_2016
9        where
10           st_dwithin(
11               pickup :: geography,
12               buildpoint(-73.987224, 40.733342, 4326) :: geography,
13               300
14           )
15           and pickup_datetime between '2016-06-02 9:00:00+00'
16           and '2016-06-02 18:00:00+00'
17   ),
18   nearest as (
19       select
20           a.*,
21           street.name,
22           street.ogc_fid,
23           street.geom
24       from
25           pickups a
26           cross join lateral (
27               select
28                   ogc_fid,
29                   full_stree as name,
30                   geom
31               from
32                   nyc_street_centerlines
33               order by
34                   a.pickup <-> geom
```

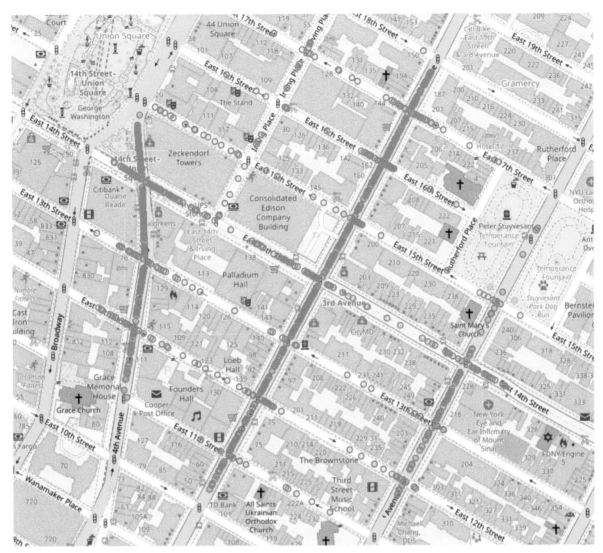

Figure 4.25: Points snapped to road centerlines

```
35              limit
36                 1
37          ) street
38  )
39  select
40      a.*,
41      st_makeline(
42          pickup,
43          st_lineinterpolatepoint(
44              st_linemerge(b.geom),
45              st_linelocatepoint(st_linemerge(b.geom), pickup)
46          )
47      ) as line,
48      st_lineinterpolatepoint(
49          st_linemerge(b.geom),
50          st_linelocatepoint(st_linemerge(b.geom), pickup)
51      ) as snapped
52  from
53      nearest a
```

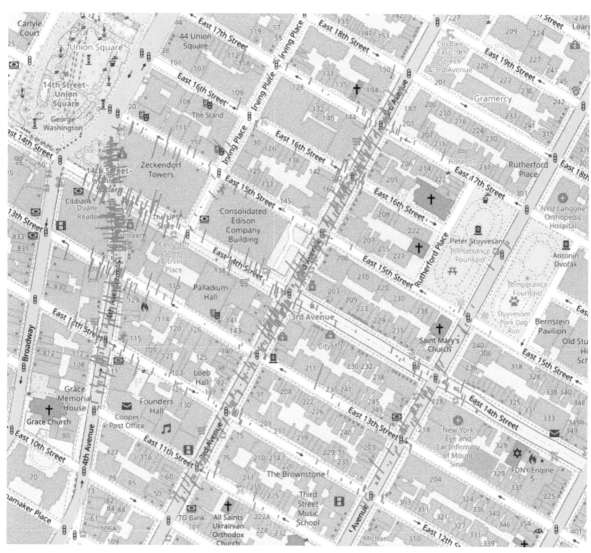

Figure 4.26: Visualizing the lines between the original point location and snapped point location

```
54    join nyc_street_centerlines b using (ogc_fid)
```

Then create several tables with each geometry:

Listing 4.40: Tables for each geometry type

```
1    create table nyc_taxi_union_square_snapped as
2    select
3        snapped,
4        name,
5        ogc_fid
6    from
7        nyc_taxi_union_square;
8
9    create table nyc_taxi_union_square_roads as
10   select
11       geom,
12       name,
13       ogc_fid
```

```
14  from
15      nyc_taxi_union_square;
16
17  create table nyc_taxi_union_square_points as
18  select
19      pickup,
20      name,
21      ogc_fid
22  from
23      nyc_taxi_union_square;
24
25  create table nyc_taxi_union_square_lines as
26  select
27      line,
28      name,
29      ogc_fid
30  from
31      nyc_taxi_union_square;
```

So in our output table from above we have the street segment unique ID, the tip amount, total trip amount. This is enough to group the point values by each unique ID. Keep in mind you will want to remove any trips where the total amount is 0 to avoid any division by 0 errors.

Listing 4.41: Aggregating by street segment

```
1   -- Calculate the tip percentage for each trip with a total over $0
2   with a as (
3       select
4           *,
5           tip_amount /(total_amount - tip_amount) as tip_percent
6       from
7           nyc_taxi_union_square
8       where
9           total_amount > 0
10  )
11
12
13  -- Get the average tip percentage for each road segment
14  select
15      avg(a.tip_percent),
16      b.geom,
17      b.ogc_fid
18  from
19      a
20      join nyc_street_centerlines b using (ogc_fid)
21  group by
22      b.geom,
23      b.ogc_fid
```

And that is it! You can create a table using this query so we can view it in QGIS.

Listing 4.42: Creating the table for QGIS

```
1   create table nyc_taxi_union_square_tips as with a as (
2       select
3           *,
4           tip_amount / total_amount as tip_percent
5       from
6           nyc_taxi_union_square
7       where
8           total_amount > 0
9   )
10  select
11      avg(a.tip_percent),
```

```
12       b.geom,
13       b.ogc_fid
14   from
15       a
16       join nyc_street_centerlines b using (ogc_fid)
17   group by
18       b.geom,
19       b.ogc_fid
```

And here is our resulting map:

Figure 4.27: Average tip by road segment

Basic statistics

Gathering basic statistics for a single polygon layer or for aggregated results for a points layer is as easy as using the aggregate functions in PostgreSQL that we have seen earlier such as COUNT, SUM, MIN, MAX, and AVG. We can also use other aggregate functions such as PERCENTILE_DISC, PERCENTILE_CONT, stddev_samp, and others.

One that we haven't seen yet is MODE which allows us to find the most repeated value in a set of data. To do this we can find the most common tree in a specific neighborhood:

Listing 4.43: Basic stats with MODE

```
1   select
2       mode() within group (
3           ORDER BY
4               a.spc_common
5       ) as most_common
6   from
7       nyc_2015_tree_census a
8       join nyc_neighborhoods b on st_intersects(a.geom, b.geom)
9   where
10      b.neighborhood = 'East Village'
```

In this case it is the Honey Locust tree. We can validate this by running this query:

Listing 4.44: Validating MODE

```
1   select
2       count(a.*),
3       a.spc_common
4   from
5       nyc_2015_tree_census a
```

```
 6      join nyc_neighborhoods b on st_intersects(a.geom, b.geom)
 7  where
 8      b.neighborhood = 'East Village'
 9  group by
10      a.spc_common
11  order by
12      count(a.*) desc
```

546	honeylocust
333	Callery pear
252	Sophora
203	ginkgo
139	London planetree

Shortest line between features

Using the same data as above we can illustrate how to find the shortest path between two features. There is a function to accomplish this in PostGIS so it is as easy as using this function, ST_ShortestLine. We will need two geometries to pass as arguments and one line will be returned. In this case we can illustrate this by showing the paths from the nearest 100 fire hydrants to the building footprint of the Empire State Building.

Listing 4.45: ST_ShortestLine

```
 1  with building as (
 2      select
 3          geom
 4      from
 5          nyc_building_footprints
 6      where
 7          name = 'Empire State Building'
 8  )
 9  select
10      st_shortestline(h.geom, b.geom)
11  from
12      nyc_fire_hydrants h,
13      building b
14  order by
15      h.geom <-> b.geom asc
16  limit
17      100
```

As you can see the lines will connect at any point around the building, so it will connect to a point that provides the shortest possible path (Figure 4.28).

Points to path

To turn a series of points into a line, we can use the function ST_MakeLine. If you only have two geometries you can pass those as two individual arguments, however if you have more than two, you will have to create an array. A quick way to do this is to wrap a select query in an array, which will create an array of the points.

Listing 4.46: Creating an array of random points

```
 1  select
 2      array(
 3          select
```

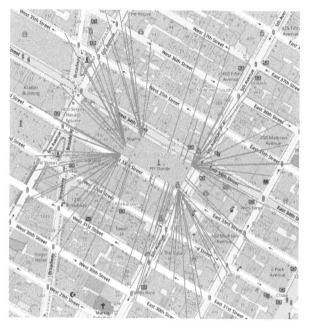

Figure 4.28: Shortest line between features

```
 4              geom
 5          from
 6              nyc_311
 7          where
 8              geom is not null
 9          limit
10              10
11      )
```

This also gives you the flexibility to order the points or, in our case, limit the results and filter out any null geometries. Let's try this with 10 rows (Figure 4.29, on the facing page):

Listing 4.47: Creating a line from those points

```
 1  select
 2      st_makeline(
 3          array(
 4              select
 5                  geom
 6              from
 7                  nyc_311
 8              where
 9                  geom is not null
10              order by
11                  id
12              limit
13                  10
14          )
15      )
```

And now 100 (Figure 4.30, on page 292):

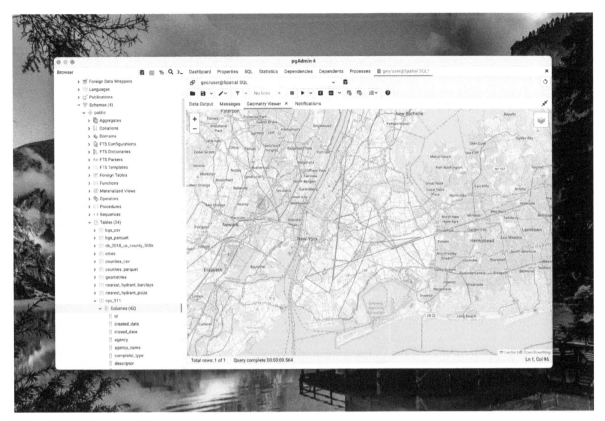

Figure 4.29: Points to path

Delete holes

If you need to delete holes from a polygon, there are a few steps to complete that process. First we need a polygon with a hole, which we can accomplish with this query by creating a 100 meter buffer around Penn Station and cutting that out of the zip code 10001 (Figure 4.31, on page 293):

Listing 4.48: Removing holes

```
1   select
2
3       -- Clips the 100 meter buffer out of the 10001 zip code
4       st_difference(
5           st_transform(geom, 4326),
6
7           -- Creates a 100 meter buffer
8           st_buffer(
9               buildpoint(-73.9936596, 40.7505483, 4326) :: geography,
10              100
11          ) :: geometry
12      )
13  from
14      nyc_zips
15  where
16      zipcode = '10001'
```

The best way to walk through this is by going through each step to eventually come to the result. So let's start by running our first step, which is to find the exterior ring of our geometry (Figure 4.32, on page 294):

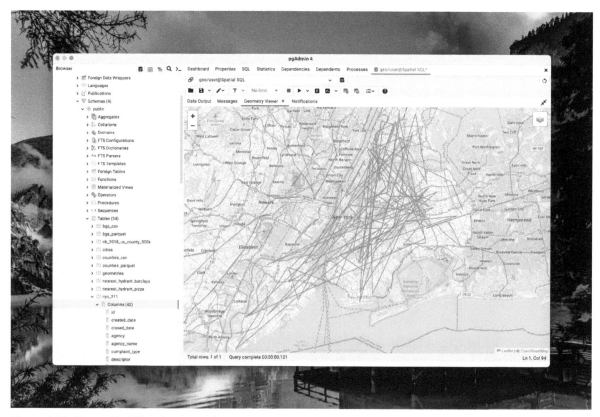

Figure 4.30: Now with 100 points to path

Listing 4.49: Finding the exterior ring

```
1   with a as (
2       select
3           10001 as id,
4           st_difference(
5               st_transform(geom, 4326),
6               st_buffer(
7                   buildpoint(-73.9936596, 40.7505483, 4326) :: geography,
8                   100
9               ) :: geometry
10          ) as geom
11      from
12          nyc_zips
13      where
14          zipcode = '10001'
15  )
16  select
17      id,
18
19      -- Takes only the exterior perimeter of the polygon
20      st_exteriorring(geom) as geom
21  from
22      a
```

And next we can make it back into a polygon using ST_MakePolygon (Figure 4.33, on page 295):

Listing 4.50: Converting back to a polygon

```
1   with a as (
```

Figure 4.31: Zip code 10001 with a hole inside it

```
 2    select
 3        10001 as id,
 4        st_difference(
 5            st_transform(geom, 4326),
 6            st_buffer(
 7                buildpoint(-73.9936596, 40.7505483, 4326) :: geography,
 8                100
 9            ) :: geometry
10        ) as geom
11    from
12        nyc_zips
13    where
14        zipcode = '10001'
15 )
16 select
17     id,
18
19     -- Creates a new polygon just from the exterior ring
20     -- which removes all holes
21     st_makepolygon(
22         st_exteriorring(geom)
23     ) as geom
24 from
25     a
```

Now this works for normal polygons but many times you will be dealing with multipolygons. We can test this out by first creating a multipolygon. We do this by creating a second query that does the

Figure 4.32: Finding the exterior ring of the polygon

same task as our first query, but this time in zip code 10017 and with a buffer around Grand Central
Station. And in a third CTE, we will union the two geometries together using ST_Union (Figure 4.34,
on page 296).

Listing 4.51: Handling multi-polygons

```
1    -- Creates a polygon with a hole in zip code 10001
2    with a as (
3        select
4            st_difference(
5                st_transform(geom, 4326),
6                st_buffer(
7                    buildpoint(-73.9936596, 40.7505483, 4326) :: geography,
8                    100
9                ) :: geometry
10           ) as geom
11       from
12           nyc_zips
13       where
14           zipcode = '10001'
15   ),
```

Figure 4.33: Turning it back into a full polygon

```
16
17    -- Creates a polygon with a hole in zip code 10017
18    b as (
19        select
20            st_difference(
21                st_transform(geom, 4326),
22                st_buffer(
23                    buildpoint(-73.9773136, 40.7526559, 4326) :: geography,
24                    100
25                ) :: geometry
26            ) as geom
27        from
28            nyc_zips
29        where
30            zipcode = '10017'
31    ),
32
33    -- Unions both polygons into a multi-polygon
34    c as (
35        select
36            1 as id,
```

```
37              st_union(a.geom, b.geom)
38      from
39          a,
40          b
41  )
42  select
43      *
44  from
45      c
```

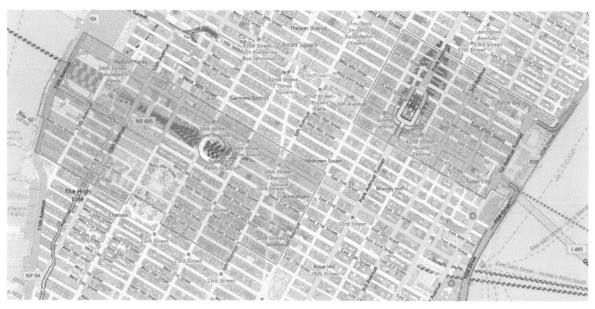

Figure 4.34: Holes in a multi-polygon

We cannot use the ST_ExteriorRing function since it only works with a polygon and we now have a multi-polygon. To create polygons we first have to dump our two polygons using ST_Dump (Figure 4.35, on page 297):

Listing 4.52: More polygon transformation

```
1   with a as (
2       select
3           st_difference(
4               st_transform(geom, 4326),
5               st_buffer(
6                   buildpoint(-73.9936596, 40.7505483, 4326) :: geography,
7                   100
8               ) :: geometry
9           ) as geom
10      from
11          nyc_zips
12      where
13          zipcode = '10001'
14  ),
15  b as (
16      select
17          st_difference(
18              st_transform(geom, 4326),
19              st_buffer(
20                  buildpoint(-73.9773136, 40.7526559, 4326) :: geography,
21                  100
22              ) :: geometry
```

```
23            ) as geom
24        from
25            nyc_zips
26        where
27            zipcode = '10017'
28    ),
29    c as (
30        select
31            1 as id,
32            st_union(a.geom, b.geom) as geom
33        from
34            a,
35            b
36    )
37    select
38        id,
39        (st_dump(geom)).geom
40    from
41        c
```

Figure 4.35: Finding the exterior ring of the multi-polygon

This will return two rows with to individual polygons which we can then use to capture the exterior rings:

Listing 4.53: More polygon transformation

```
1    with a as (
2        select
3            st_difference(
4                st_transform(geom, 4326),
```

```
 5                  st_buffer(
 6                      buildpoint(-73.9936596, 40.7505483, 4326) :: geography,
 7                      100
 8                  ) :: geometry
 9              ) as geom
10      from
11          nyc_zips
12      where
13          zipcode = '10001'
14  ),
15  b as (
16      select
17          st_difference(
18              st_transform(geom, 4326),
19              st_buffer(
20                  buildpoint(-73.9773136, 40.7526559, 4326) :: geography,
21                  100
22              ) :: geometry
23          ) as geom
24      from
25          nyc_zips
26      where
27          zipcode = '10017'
28  ),
29  c as (
30      select
31          1 as id,
32          st_union(a.geom, b.geom) as geom
33      from
34          a,
35          b
36  )
37  select
38      id,
39
40      -- Takes the exterior ring from the geometry dump
41      st_exteriorring(
42          (st_dump(geom)).geom
43      )
44  from
45      c
```

Now we have two final steps. First we want to make those geometries into polygons, and then collect them using ST_Collect back into the original multi-polygon. The issue is that since we want to aggregate our geometries back by using the id column, we need to use a specific variant of ST_Collect. You can see this at the bottom of the documentation for ST_Collect (Figure 4.36):

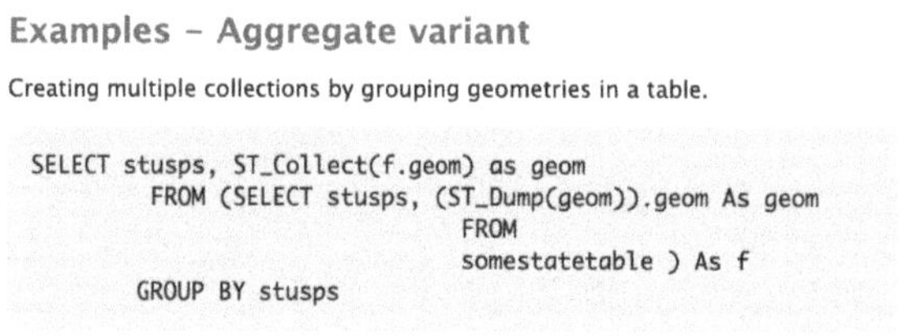

Examples – Aggregate variant

Creating multiple collections by grouping geometries in a table.

```
SELECT stusps, ST_Collect(f.geom) as geom
    FROM (SELECT stusps, (ST_Dump(geom)).geom As geom
                    FROM
                        somestatetable ) As f
    GROUP BY stusps
```

Figure 4.36: The specific variant of ST_Collect we need to use

So to do this we can use the same structure, but add in our exterior rings in the subquery following the FROM and then make our polygons within the collection function. In short, this means that in the subquery, we actually have multiple rows of geometries resulting from the ST_Dump result, which is known as a set result which is why we have to add the `.geom` to extract the actual geometries. This allows `ST_Collect` to find those groups of rows and group them based on the outer `GROUP BY` condition, and for our purposes we can create the polygons from the exterior rings here. There is a great post on this topic[107] at this link in the footnotes.

Listing 4.54: Our final query

```sql
1   with a as (
2       select
3           st_difference(
4               st_transform(geom, 4326),
5               st_buffer(
6                   buildpoint(-73.9936596, 40.7505483, 4326) :: geography,
7                   100
8               ) :: geometry
9           ) as geom
10      from
11          nyc_zips
12      where
13          zipcode = '10001'
14  ),
15  b as (
16      select
17          st_difference(
18              st_transform(geom, 4326),
19              st_buffer(
20                  buildpoint(-73.9773136, 40.7526559, 4326) :: geography,
21                  100
22              ) :: geometry
23          ) as geom
24      from
25          nyc_zips
26      where
27          zipcode = '10017'
28  ),
29  c as (
30      select
31          1 as id,
32          st_union(a.geom, b.geom) as geom
33      from
34          a,
35          b
36  )
37  select
38      id,
39
40      -- Collect the individual geometries to turn them back into
41      -- one polygon
42      st_collect(st_makepolygon(geom)) as geom
43  from
44      (
45          select
46              id,
47              st_exteriorring((st_dump(geom)).geom) as geom
48          from
49              c
50      ) s
51  group by
52      id;
```

And then we have our filled multi-polygon geometry (Figure 4.37, on the following page):

---

[107] https://loc8.cc/sql/cuny-postgis-holes

Figure 4.37: Our filled multi-polygons

Pole of inaccessibility

To calculate a pole of inaccessibility, or the most isolated point in a polygon, PostGIS has a function named ST_MaximumInscribedCircle, which acts a bit differently than many of the other functions we have used so far. The function signature is below:

```
(geometry, geometry, double precision) ST_MaximumInscribedCircle(geometry geom);
```

Description

Finds the largest circle that is contained within a (multi)polygon, or which does not overlap any lines and points. Returns a record with fields:

- center - center point of the circle
- nearest - a point on the geometry nearest to the center
- radius - radius of the circle

This actually returns a table structure, or a record, with three columns: center, nearest, and radius. You also need to call the function following the FROM argument in the query. Let's take a look at an example below:

Listing 4.55: ST_MaximumInscribedCircle

```
1   select
2       *
3   from
4       st_maximuminscribedcircle(
5           (
6               select
7                   st_transform(geom, 4326)
8               from
9                   nyc_zips
10              where
11                  zipcode = '10001'
```

```
12          )
13      )
```

If we want to see the actual pole of inaccessibility we can return one column:

Listing 4.56: Pole of inaccessibility

```
1   select
2       center
3   from
4       st_maximuminscribedcircle(
5           (
6               select
7                   st_transform(geom, 4326)
8               from
9                   nyc_zips
10              where
11                  zipcode = '10001'
12          )
13      )
```

And if we want to see the inscribed circle itself we can use the radius in combination with the center to create a buffer around it too:

Listing 4.57: Creating the maximum inscribed circle

```
1   select
2       st_buffer(center, radius)
3   from
4       st_maximuminscribedcircle(
5           (
6               select
7                   st_transform(geom, 4326)
8               from
9                   nyc_zips
10              where
11                  zipcode = '10001'
12          )
13      )
```

We can also compare the pole of inaccessibility with the centroid to see how those compare by creating a union with the inscribed circle query as well as the centroid (Figure 4.38, on the next page):

Listing 4.58: Pole of inaccessibility vs. centroid

```
1   select
2       st_transform(center, 4326) as geom
3   from
4       st_maximuminscribedcircle(
5           (
6               select
7                   st_transform(geom, 4326)
8               from
9                   nyc_zips
10              where
11                  zipcode = '10001'
12          )
13      )
14  union
15  select
16      st_centroid(st_transform(geom, 4326)) as geom
17  from
18      nyc_zips
19  where
```

```
20      zipcode = '10001'
```

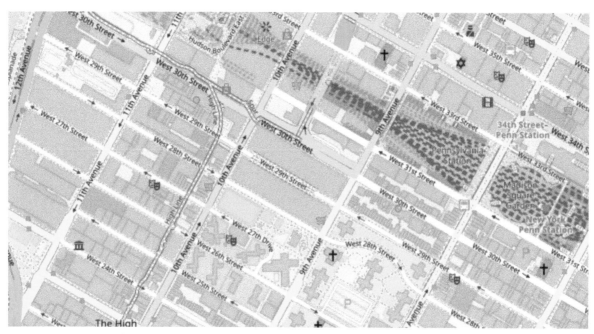

Figure 4.38: Pole of inaccesability compared to a centroid

4.3   Lines to polygons, and polygons to lines

Turning polygons into lines and vice versa is quite easy. To turn polygons into lines you can use ST_
Boundary to turn the outside of the polygon to linestrings:

Listing 4.59: Lines to polygons

```
1   select
2       st_boundary(st_transform(geom, 4326))
3   from
4       nyc_zips
5   where
6       zipcode = '10001'
```

Let's say you want to create individual linestrings from the full line. We can do this by using the cross
lateral join and generating a series of numbers from 1 to the number of points in the geometry with ST_
NPoints, minus 1. We will need to use the result of the ST_Boundary function since the ST_PointN only
works with linestrings. Once we have that we can create a line for each number in the series using ST_
PointN and the next point in the series by adding 1 to the number in the series. We subtract 1 in the
cross lateral join because if we add 1 to the max value of the total number of points we will see an error
since there won't be a point in the geometry greater than the max number of points.

Listing 4.60: Creating individual linestrings

```
1   select
2       st_makeline(
3           st_pointn(
4               st_boundary(st_transform(z.geom, 4326)),
5               numbers.num
6           ),
7           st_pointn(
```

```
8              st_boundary(st_transform(z.geom, 4326)),
9              numbers.num + 1
10         )
11     ),
12     numbers.num
13  from
14     nyc_zips z
15     cross join lateral generate_series(1, st_npoints(z.geom) - 1) as numbers(num)
16  where
17     z.zipcode = '10001'
```

This will return a table of individual lines. To turn it back into a polygon we can use ST_Polygonize. It accepts a set of linestrings or an array of linestrings. The set is simply the rows in the column that contains the linestrings so we can accomplish this by wrapping the set of lines in ST_Polygonize:

Listing 4.61: Back to a polygon

```
1  select
2     st_polygonize(
3         st_makeline(
4             st_pointn(
5                 st_boundary(st_transform(z.geom, 4326)),
6                 numbers.num
7             ),
8             st_pointn(
9                 st_boundary(st_transform(z.geom, 4326)),
10                numbers.num + 1
11            )
12        )
13     )
14  from
15     nyc_zips z
16     cross join lateral generate_series(1, st_npoints(z.geom) - 1) as numbers(num)
17  where
18     z.zipcode = '10001'
```

4.4   Snap points to grid

To snap points to a grid we can use the function ST_SnapToGrid which will snap points to an arbitrary grid defined in the units of the projection. In this case we can project our original points from the NYC 311 data. We first transform this to a projection that supports meters, in this case 3857, and then create a grid of 500 meters and 1000 meters. Then to show the points project it back to 4326. We will use a random sample of 100,000 points (Figure 4.39, on the following page):

Listing 4.62: ST_SnapToGrid

```
1  select
2     st_transform(
3         st_snaptogrid(st_transform(geom, 3857), 500, 1000),
4         4326
5     ) as geom
6  from
7     nyc_311
8  limit
9     100000
```

4.5   Tessellate triangles

To tessellate a polygon into triangles we can use the ST_DelaunayTriangles function which we have seen before which we can see in the below query (Figure 4.40, on page 305):

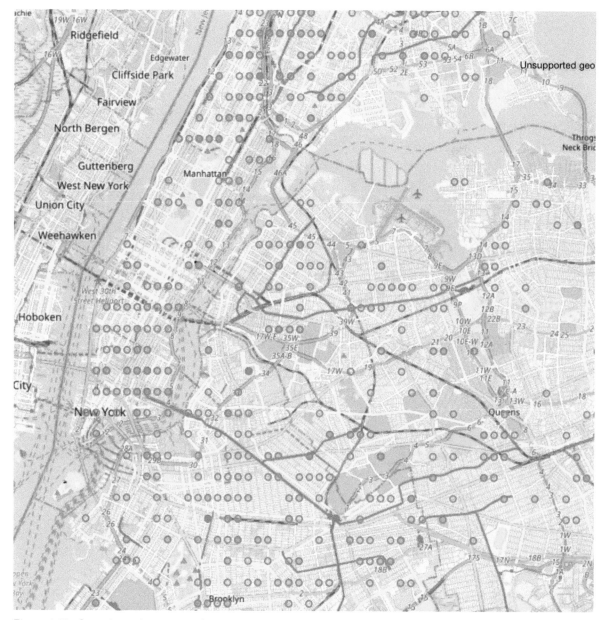

Figure 4.39: Snapping points to a grid

Listing 4.63: ST_DelaunayTriangles

```
1  select
2      st_delaunaytriangles(st_transform(geom, 4326))
3  from
4      nyc_zips
5  where
6      zipcode = '10009'
```

Figure 4.40: More Delaunay triangles

Of course this will create a geometry collection, and to turn this into rows we can use ST_Dump. We can also get the area of the individual geometries and return the top 10 largest triangles:

Listing 4.64: Dump to individual polygons

```
1  with a as (
```

```
2      select
3          (
4              -- Create a dump to return the individual triangles
5              st_dump(
6
7                  -- Create the triangles like above
8                  st_delaunaytriangles(st_transform(geom, 4326))
9              )
10         ).geom
11     from
12         nyc_zips
13     where
14         zipcode = '10009'
15     )
16
17  -- Select and order by areas
18  select
19      a.geom,
20      st_area(geom) as area
21  from
22      a
23  order by
24      st_area(geom) desc
25  limit
26      10
```

4.6 Tapered buffers

To create a variable width buffer around a linestring will require several steps. First we have to create
a single linestring geometry to use with our query. To do this we can grab the bike path along Hudson
Street in lower Manhattan and turn it from a `MultiLineString` into a `LineString` (Figure 4.41, on the
facing page).

Listing 4.65: Getting our path

```
1   -- Select all bike routes on Hudson Street
2   with lines as (
3       select
4           1 as id,
5           st_linemerge(st_union(geom)) as geom
6       from
7           nyc_bike_routes
8       where
9           street = 'HUDSON ST'
10  )
11  select
12      *
13  from
14      lines
```

Next, we will add a second CTE that will dump the points from the linestrings as well as the length of
the geometry, and the original geometry.

Listing 4.66: Extracting the points

```
1   with lines as (
2       select
3           1 as id,
4           ST_LineMerge(st_union(geom)) as geom
5       from
6           nyc_bike_routes
7       where
```

Figure 4.41: Our merged bike path

```
8                street = 'HUDSON ST'
9    ),
10
11   -- Dump all of the points and find the length of the geometry
12   first as (
13       select
14           id,
15           st_dumppoints(geom) as dump,
16           st_length(geom) as len,
17           geom
18       from
19           lines
20   )
21   select
22       *
23   from
24       first
```

You will recall that the geometry dump will return a set (also known as a set returning function or SRF) which means that it has two values in the set: the index of the point and the geometry.

Next, we will perform an operation over the rows. There are a few things we will break down here so let's take a look at the full query first with the new CTE starting on line 19:

Listing 4.67: Building out the query

```
1    with lines as (
2        select
3            1 as id,
4            ST_LineMerge(st_union(geom)) as geom
5        from
```

```
 6           nyc_bike_routes
 7       where
 8           street = 'HUDSON ST'
 9   ),
10   first as (
11       select
12           id,
13           st_dumppoints(geom) as dump,
14           st_length(geom) as len,
15           geom
16       from
17           lines
18   ),
19
20   -- For each path, select the id, path, and a buffer
21   -- around the path point. Using ST_LineLocatePoint
22   -- we use the line geometry and the point to find
23   -- the distance along the line, then make it smaller
24   -- using the log of the length
25   second as (
26       select
27           id,
28           (dump).path [1],
29           st_buffer(
30               (dump).geom,
31               ST_LineLocatePoint(geom, (dump).geom) * log(len)
32           ) as geom
33       from
34           first
35   )
36   select
37       *
38   from
39       second
```

First we select the id and then we can see this:

```
(dump).path[1]
```

If you recall with geometry dump functions, you need to wrap that value in parentheses and can access the geom with the .geom operator. The other value which is an integer contained between square brackets is the index of the point on the linestring. This value is accessed with the .path operator since it is an array data type. If we want to access the first value we need to use the array access method, or a number in square brackets, in this case [1]. That array can contain more than one value, in the case of multi-geometries you can see this in the examples in the PostGIS documentation[108].

Next we have this, formatted for readability:

```
st_buffer(
  (dump).geom,
  st_linelocatepoint(
    geom,
    (dump).geom
  ) * len / 10
) as geom
```

---

[108]https://postgis.net/docs/ST_DumpPoints.html

So we start with our buffer, which will take two arguments, first the point to build the buffer from, and then a numeric value which represents the distance in the unit of measurement of the projection to draw the buffer radius. The point geometry is pulled from the geometry dump using:

```
(dump).geom
```

To get the value for the radius, since we are creating a tapered buffer we will first want to get the scaled value. Here are the steps taking place in the code we are about to review:

1. We will use the `ST_LineLocatePoint` function which takes two arguments are returns a fractional value representing the fraction of the position of the point on the line (i.e. a 0.5 value represents a point on the line at the midway point). The two arguments are:

   1. The line geometry represented by geom
   2. A point geometry from the line, represented by `(dump).geom`

2. Then we multiply the fraction by the length value which is the same since it is one geometry. For example, if the length is 100 meters and the fraction returned is 0.5, we will get a value of 50.

3. Finally, we divide the length multiplier by 10 to decrease the buffer size otherwise it will be too large given the 4326 projection

```
st_linelocatepoint( geom, (dump).geom) * len / 10)
```

Finally, we union the buffer geometries together, which alone won't produce the result we want, which is why we will wrap it in the `ST_ConvexHull` function. Let's take a look.

```
third as (
 select
 id,
 st_convexhull(
   st_union(geom, lead(geom) over(partition by id order by id, path)
   )
 ) as geom from second)
```

First, we select the ID then we start to construct our geometry. Keep in mind this function is set up to work with multiple IDs, which we will get to in a minute. First we call `ST_ConvexHull`, then `ST_Union` as we stated above. Next is where we address the ordering of the geometries and the grouping by id. We use the `LEAD` function from PostgreSQL here which is a window function that allows us to access the geometry from the current row and other rows as well given a specific order and offset, in this case we use the `OVER` component of the window function to partition, or group, the functions by ID, and the order it first by ID and then the geometry order of the path from our geometry dump.

So this is our final query (Figure 4.42, on page 311):

Listing 4.68: Final tapered width buffer

```
1  with lines as (
2      select
3          1 as id,
4          st_linemerge(st_union(geom)) as geom
```

```
 5       from
 6           nyc_bike_routes
 7       where
 8           street = 'HUDSON ST'
 9   ),
10   first as (
11       select
12           id,
13           st_dumppoints(geom) as dump,
14           st_length(geom) as len,
15           geom
16       from
17           lines
18   ),
19   second as (
20       select
21           id,
22           (dump).path [1],
23           st_buffer(
24               (dump).geom,
25               ST_LineLocatePoint(geom, (dump).geom) * len / 10
26           ) as geom
27       from
28           first
29   ),
30
31   -- Create a convex hull around the buffers by union-ing
32   -- all the buffers together. These are ordered using the
33   -- LEAD window function and partition
34   third as (
35       select
36           id,
37           st_convexhull(
38               st_union(
39                   geom,
40                   lead(geom) over(
41                       partition by id
42                       order by
43                           id,
44                           path
45                   )
46               )
47           ) as geom
48       from
49           second
50   )
51   select
52       id,
53       st_union(geom) as geom
54   from
55       third
56   group by
57       id
```

Variable width buffer

In a similar case to above we can also use any numeric value to create a variable width buffer. We can use the same final query as above but swap out the length of a line for a numeric value. In this case I used a random number using the RANDOM() function in PostgreSQL which will return a random number between 1 and 0, and then multiplied that number by 100 which will return a buffer distance between 0 and 100. Of course, you need to transform the geometry to a coordinate system that accepts meters and then back to 4326 to visualize it (Figure 4.43, on page 313).

Figure 4.42: The complete tapered buffer

Listing 4.69: Variable width buffer

```
1   with lines as (
2       select
3           1 as id,
4           st_linemerge(st_union(geom)) as geom
5       from
6           nyc_bike_routes
7       where
8           street = 'HUDSON ST'
9   ),
10  first as (
11      select
12          id,
13          st_dumppoints(geom) as dump,
14          st_length(geom) as len,
15          geom
16      from
17          lines
18  ),
19  second as (
20      select
21          id,
22          (dump).path [1],
23          st_transform(
```

```
24              st_buffer(st_transform((dump).geom, 3857), random() * 100),
25              4326
26          ) as geom
27      from
28          first
29  ),
30  third as (
31      select
32          id,
33          st_convexhull(
34              st_union(
35                  geom,
36                  lead(geom) over(
37                      partition by id
38                      order by
39                          id,
40                          path
41                  )
42              )
43          ) as geom
44      from
45          second
46  )
47  select
48      id,
49      st_union(geom) as geom
50  from
51      third
52  group by
53      id
```

Your result will be different with the above query since the RANDOM() function will, true to its name, return random values.

Symmetrical difference

PostGIS has a built-in function for symmetrical difference aptly named ST_SymDifference. It takes two geometries and will return the portions of two geometries that do not intersect. We can test this with zip codes and neighborhoods (Figure 4.44, on page 314):

Listing 4.70: ST_SymDifference

```
1   select
2       st_symdifference(
3           (
4               select
5                   geom
6               from
7                   nyc_neighborhoods
8               where
9                   neighborhood = 'NoHo'
10          ),
11          (
12              select
13                  st_transform(geom, 4326)
14              from
15                  nyc_zips
16              where
17                  zipcode = '10012'
18          )
19      )
```

Figure 4.43: Variable width buffer

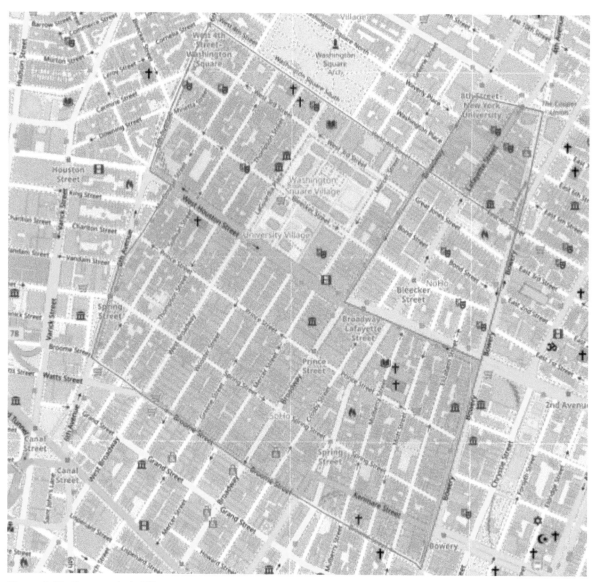

Figure 4.44: Symmetrical difference

5. Advanced Spatial Analytics

In the next chapters, we will start to take our spatial SQL skills and add complexity to the analyses we are performing. We will look at more advanced analysis patterns in this chapter, and topics such as raster data, spatial data science with Python (yes Python in a database), suitability analysis, H3 spatial indexes, and using pgRouting to perform analysis with routing. Let's begin with some more advanced analysis topics!

5.1   Spatial data enrichment or area weighted interpolation

A very common operation in spatial analytics is to perform spatial interpolation between two polygon layers that do not share the same boundaries. A common example of this would be analyzing population data from one set of boundaries, such as Census Block Groups, and interpreting how many people live in another set of boundaries that do not match to those boundaries, such as zip codes. This is known as enrichment or area weighed interpolation.

The easiest way to think about this is if you have a polygon you want to enrich with an dataset that contains polygons that overlap the target polygon. For simplicity, we can think of each underlying polygon as having 100 people living in each. For each polygon that is entirely contained by the target polygon, we can count all 100 people as living in that polygon. However, for the polygons that overlap, we need to adjust that based on the overlap.

If we had underlying data such as the distribution of the population, land cover, buildings, or roads, we could use a method known as dasymetric interpolation[109], which is described in the documentation for the `tobler` Python library, which is a part of the Python Spatial Analysis Library or PySAL.

For argument's sake, let's assume that we have several polygons that are overlapping the target polygon by exactly 50%, with the remaining 50% outside it. In this case we would count 50% of the population, or 50 people as living in the target polygon. So to describe this analysis in pseudocode:

- Select target polygons to be enriched
- Find the polygons that contain the data to enrich with that intersect the target polygons
- Calculate the percentage overlap of the data containing polygons to the target polygon
- Divide the data by the overlap percentage

Our first task is to find the area of the overlap between the target polygon (our NYC neighborhoods data) and the polygons we are using to enrich it, in this case the US Census Block Groups that we are going to import shortly, and the total area the block groups. So first let's import our new block group data.

This data has the Census Block Groups from all of New York State and three data points from the 2021 American Community Survey, which is a dataset that samples the US population to make estimations about population over a 5-year rolling time window, meaning this data was collected between 2017 and 2021. The data was downloaded from the US Census website[110] and comes in a Geopackage. The problem however is that the data contains 8,319 columns. While PostgreSQL supports 1600 columns, in most cases this is highly inefficient and it makes more sense to extract the data you need rather than

---

[109]https://github.com/pysal/tobler#dasymetric

pull it all into one table. If you were to try (like I did before reviewing the metadata) you will cause some errors in the logs that will consume the memory of your database.

For this we can actually use our ogr2ogr import to filter the data we want to import. Using the flag for SQL we can write a query that selects and renames the columns we want to use, in this case they are columns representing income, median age, and total population. You can find the full metadata at this link[111], and it is also saved in the book files in case the link breaks. Below are the columns of the data we want to import:

- B01001e1 - Total population (*SEX BY AGE: Total: Total population -- (Estimate)*)
- B19001e1 - Median income (*HOUSEHOLD INCOME IN THE PAST 12 MONTHS (IN 2021 INFLATION-ADJUSTED DOLLARS): Total: Households -- (Estimate)*)
- B01002e1 - Median age (*MEDIAN AGE BY SEX: Total: Total population -- (Estimate)*)

To do this we just need to modify our ogr2ogr command line to add the SQL commands in Spatialite and SQLite.

First we need to find the column names within the layers of the geodatabase using the ogrinfo command:

Listing 5.1: Reading the GeoPackage

```
1    ogrinfo ACS_2021_5YR_BG_36_NEW_YORK.gdb ACS_2021_5YR_BG_36_NEW_YORK -geom=YES -so
```

What this will show us is a list of column names within each layer. We will be using three ogr2ogr statements to import our data into our database, which may seem odd because we are running a SQL statement in the command to filter the data, why couldn't we just perform a join between the tables? Well, I thought the same thing, but the results were not great. I tried a number of options and settings to see if this would work but to no avail. I couldn't find great documentation on this specific issue but overall I believe that instead of spending time to do this, using an ELT (or extract load transform) workflow would be more valuable instead of spending time to make the ETL (extract transform load) process work.

In an ELT scenario the goal is to simply extract the data, load it into the target (in this case our Post-GIS database), and then transform it in the target location. While we are not performing a pure ELT workflow since we are selecting a few columns of data to cut down on what we load into our database, the concept is roughly the same since we still have to join our data in the database. So with that let's finish up the data imports. As you will see each layer inside the GeoDataBase acts as its own layer in the query:

```
1    ogr2ogr \
2    -f PostgreSQL PG:"host=localhost user=docker password=docker
3    dbname=gis port=25432" ACS_2021_5YR_BG_36_NEW_YORK.gdb \
4    -dialect sqlite -sql "select GEOID as geoid, b01001e1 as population, B01002e1 as age from X01_AGE_AND_SEX" \
5    -nln nys_2021_census_block_groups_pop -lco GEOMETRY_NAME=geom
```

```
1    ogr2ogr \
2    -f PostgreSQL PG:"host=localhost user=docker password=docker \
3    dbname=gis port=25432" ACS_2021_5YR_BG_36_NEW_YORK.gdb \
4    -dialect sqlite -sql "select GEOID as geoid, B19001e1 as income from X19_INCOME" \
5    -nln nys_2021_census_block_groups_income -lco GEOMETRY_NAME=geom
```

```
1    ogr2ogr \
2    -f PostgreSQL PG:"host=localhost user=docker password=docker \
3    dbname=gis port=25432" ACS_2021_5YR_BG_36_NEW_YORK.gdb \
```

---

[110]https://loc8.cc/sql/census-tiger-time-series

[111]https://loc8.cc/sql/census-tiger-metadata

```
4    -dialect sqlite -sql "select SHAPE as geom, GEOID as geoid from ACS_2021_5YR_BG_36_NEW_YORK" \
5    -nln nys_2021_census_block_groups_geom -lco GEOMETRY_NAME=geom
```

Now that we have our table in our database we can simply join them together:

Listing 5.2: Creating our block group data

```
1    create table nys_2021_census_block_groups as
2    select
3        a.geoid,
4        st_makevalid(st_transform(a.geom, 4326)) as geom,
5        b.income,
6        c.population,
7        c.age
8    from
9        nys_2021_census_block_groups_geom a
10       join nys_2021_census_block_groups_income b on a.geoid = right(b.geoid, 12)
11       join nys_2021_census_block_groups_pop c on a.geoid = right(c.geoid, 12)
```

Here we select the block groups that fall within the New York City counties which can be found by using the first five characters of the geoid column. The first two characters correspond to the state (36 for New York) and the next 3 characters correspond to the county. In the case of New York City those are Bronx, Kings (Brooklyn), New York (Manhattan) Queens, and Richmond (Staten Island) (Figure 1.3, on page 372).

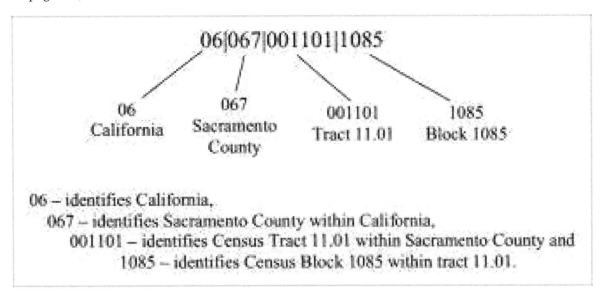

Figure 5.1: US Census FIPS Code breakdown (US Census)

Once we have the Block Group data, we need to find the overlapping area and divide that by the total area. The equation will look like this:

```
Population of Block Group *
(Area of
  (Intersection of
      (Block Group polygon, Neighborhood polygon)
  )
  / Area of block group polygon)
```

Which translated into spatial SQL will look like this:

```
population *
(st_area(
  st_intersection(
    block_groups.geom, nyc_hoods.geom)
  ) / st_area(block_groups.geom)
)
```

The best way to accomplish this is, once again, with a cross lateral join, but before that you may need to update your neighborhoods table. I encountered an issue with an invalid geometry which you can fix with this query:

Listing 5.3: Fix invalid geometries

```
1   update nyc_neighborhoods set geom = st_makevalid(geom) where st_isvalid(geom) is false
```

Then run this query:

Listing 5.4: Enrichment query

```
1   select
2       neighborhood,
3
4       -- These are the values from the cross join lateral
5       a.pop,
6       a.count,
7       a.avg
8   from
9       nyc_neighborhoods
10      cross join lateral (
11          select
12
13              -- This selects the sum of all the intersecting areas
14              -- populations using the proportional overlap calculation
15              sum(
16                  population * (
17                      st_area(st_intersection(geom, nyc_neighborhoods.geom)) / st_area(geom)
18                  )
19              ) as pop,
20              count(*) as count,
21
22              -- This selects the average area overlapping area
23              -- of all the intersecting areas
24              avg(
25                  (
26                      st_area(st_intersection(nyc_neighborhoods.geom, geom)) / st_area(geom)
27                  )
28              ) as avg
29          from
30              nys_2021_census_block_groups
31          where
32              left(geoid, 5) in ('36061', '36005', '36047', '36081', '36085')
33              and st_intersects(nyc_neighborhoods.geom, geom)
34      ) a
35  order by
36      a.pop desc
```

This will show us the enriched population, number of polygons intersecting each neighborhood, and average overlap of each block group intersecting the neighborhood.

neighborhood	pop	count	avg
Upper West Side	220359.46205455554	168	0.9291097182876799
Flushing	209420.50417090932	196	0.8162379074456494
Upper East Side	205153.28976399385	193	0.8914866436674864
Bedford-Stuyvesant	200572.77136294966	179	0.8462737532512835
Jamaica	163046.50931758404	125	0.8034214281877039

5.2   Nearest neighbor in report format

Imagine a scenario where the City of New York wants us to find the nearest 5 trees to all subway entrances in the city. The catch is that for each subway station they want each tree listed as well as the station, meaning that the station data will be repeated five times and then the five nearest trees will be listed, for example:

entrance	tree
14th St	Tree 1
14th St	Tree 2
14th St	Tree 3
14th St	Tree 4
14th St	Tree 5

So how can we define this? Let's use pseudo-code to define what we want to do.

Given two tables:

- Join the first table (subway entrances)
- To five nearest locations from the other table

If this sounds familiar, you are right. We did this in our bulk nearest neighbor join before but only with one row. And luckily we only need to make one small change. We just need to change our limit to the number of rows we want to return. First, let's import the subway entrances data into our new database:

Listing 5.5: Importing subway enterances data

```
1   ogr2ogr \
2       - f PostgreSQL PG :"host=localhost user=docker password=docker \
3       dbname=gis port=25432" Subway_Entrances.geojson \
4       - nln nyc_subway_enterances - lco GEOMETRY_NAME = geom
```

And then as we said, all we have to do is just rewrite our bulk nearest neighbor query:

Listing 5.6: Bulk nearest neighbor query

```
1   select
2       sw.name,
3       sw.objectid,
4       near.tree_id,
5       near.spc_common,
6       near.distance
7   from
8       nyc_subway_enterances sw
9
10      -- Since this is a cross join it will join to every possible combination
```

```
11      -- Since we have a limit of 5 below, it will join it to each row in the
12      -- main subway entrances table 5 times
13      cross join lateral (
14          select
15              tree_id,
16              spc_common,
17              st_distance(sw.geom :: geography, geom :: geography) as distance
18          from
19              nyc_2015_tree_census
20          order by
21              sw.geom <-> geom
22          limit
23              5
24      ) near
```

As an extra challenge, can you add a ranking column to the data ? ROW_NUMBER() OVER() will do the trick here:

Listing 5.7: Adding a row number

```
1   select
2       sw.name,
3       sw.objectid,
4       near.tree_id,
5       near.spc_common,
6       near.distance,
7       near.ranking
8   from
9       nyc_subway_enterances sw
10      cross join lateral (
11          select
12              tree_id,
13              spc_common,
14              st_distance(sw.geom :: geography, geom :: geography) as distance,
15              row_number() over() as ranking
16          from
17              nyc_2015_tree_census
18          order by
19              sw.geom <-> geom
20          limit
21              5
22      ) near
23  limit
24      50
```

However, in the rare event that there are two trees at the same exact distance, we can use rank and partition by the station ID and order it by the distance in our outer query:

Listing 5.8: Adding rankings

```
1   select
2       sw.name,
3       sw.objectid,
4       near.tree_id,
5       near.spc_common,
6       near.distance,
7       rank() over(
8
9           -- The partition will perform the ranking for each
10          -- subway entrance ID for the 5 matching trees linked
11          -- to that station ID
12          partition by sw.objectid
13
14          -- The ranking will be ordered by the distance
```

```
15          order by
16              distance desc
17          )
18  from
19      nyc_subway_enterances sw
20      cross join lateral (
21          select
22              tree_id,
23              spc_common,
24              st_distance(sw.geom :: geography, geom :: geography) as distance
25          from
26              nyc_2015_tree_census
27          order by
28              sw.geom <-> geom
29          limit
30              5
31      ) near
32  limit
33      50
```

And that will cover any odd edge cases that may occur:

15th St & Kings Hwy at SE corner	1	298572	pin oak	61.95273918	1
15th St & Kings Hwy at SE corner	1	298456	red maple	41.03466717	2
15th St & Kings Hwy at SE corner	1	298455		40.93255304	3
15th St & Kings Hwy at SE corner	1	299014	pin oak	29.28572605	4
15th St & Kings Hwy at SE corner	1	298964	pin oak	24.72797621	5

Before we proceed I want to point out that you can use the CROSS JOIN LATERAL using pretty much any spatial function you want to help scale it to go row by row. Just some ideas:

- Objects within a distance
- Objects by category
- Distance to cluster
- Average distance to neighbors
- Polygons that share a border
- Raster data within a distance
- Overlap percentage

And pretty much anything that you can think up. The goal of this book is to help lay out as many potential use cases as possible, but here is a perfect example of how you can take it forward to perform any number of combinations that you can think up!

5.3 Flat line of sight

A common analysis that is used in many fields such as planning, real estate, construction, and telecommunications is understanding direct line of sight, or if you can directly view a location from another location and what obstacles might be in the way. There are actually a few methods of accomplishing this task:

- If we have elevation or obstruction data in a vector file we can simply draw a line between our two points and see if any of the values intersecting that line are greater than any one of the end points. However, this looses accuracy since the line between the points may rise or fall in elevation across the duration of the line if the heights between the two points are different, which in most cases they are likely to be. Using geometry (the mathematical field in this case not the GEOMETRY that we have been discussing so far), you could calculate the two legs of the triangle that forms between the two points to find the angle of the base and the hypotenuse, then use those measurements to calculate the height along the path using the distance of the measurement you want to take from the start or end point.

- Another approach is using 3D geometries. Earlier in the book we covered that you can use a third dimension on your geometries to store a Z-value, or height, in meters. PostGIS and any other database or data warehouse that supports 3D geometries will then allow you to do a 3D intersection of a 3D line between your two points.
- Finally, in a combination approach you can use an elevation file to add to the height of your building 3D polygons to get an accurate height, assuming that your building polygon heights are measured from the base of the structure.

Before we get started we are going to add some new data from the Denver Regional Council of Governments Regional Data Catalog, in this case their 2018 roofprints data which contains building roofprints but also their height and the elevation the building sits at too.

Listing 5.9: Import Denver buildings

```
1  ogr2ogr \
2  -f PostgreSQL PG:"host=localhost user=docker password=docker \
3  dbname=gis port=25432" planimetrics_2018_roofprints.json \
4  -nln denver_buildings -lco GEOMETRY_NAME=geom
```

So our first step when creating a flat line of sight analysis is to find the line between the two points. In this case we will select two random points from the dataset by ordering our data using the RANDOM function:

Listing 5.10: Selecting two random buildings

```
1   select
2       geom,
3       bldg_heigh,
4       ground_ele,
5       gid
6   from
7       denver_buildings
8   order by
9       random()
10  limit
11      2
```

Next we will aggregate our data into arrays, so we can save keystrokes and use one column name and reference using the array position for the two buildings:

Listing 5.11: Adding arrays

```
1   with a as (
2       select
3           geom,
4           bldg_heigh,
5           ground_ele,
6           gid
7       from
8           denver_buildings
9       order by
10          random()
11      limit
12          2
13  )
14  select
15
```

```
16      -- This will create an array for the two buildings above.
17      -- One below for the centroid
18      array_agg(st_centroid(st_transform(geom, 4326))) as geom,
19
20      -- One for the building height + ground height
21      array_agg(bldg_heigh + ground_ele) as height,
22
23      -- One for the building IDs
24      array_agg(gid) as id
25  from
26      a
```

Now in this step we will simply create the line we will use to calculate our line of sight, so we can see it on the map. To do this we will use the ST_MakeLine function to build a line between our two geometries. We can access the two points using subqueries and the array position, [1] for the first geometry and [2] for the second (Figure 5.2, on the next page).

Listing 5.12: Creating the line of sight

```
1   with a as (
2       select
3           geom,
4           bldg_heigh,
5           ground_ele,
6           gid
7       from
8           denver_buildings
9       order by
10          random()
11      limit
12          2
13  ), bldgs as (
14      select
15          array_agg(st_centroid(st_transform(geom, 4326))) as geom,
16          array_agg(bldg_heigh + ground_ele) as height,
17          array_agg(gid) as id
18      from
19          a
20  ),
21  line as (
22      select
23
24          -- Here we create a line between the two centroids
25          -- using both the geometries in individual sub-queries
26          st_makeline(
27              (
28                  select
29                      geom [1]
30                  from
31                      bldgs
32              ),
33              (
34                  select
35                      geom [2]
36                  from
37                      bldgs
38              )
39          )
40  )
41  select
42      *
43  from
44      line
```

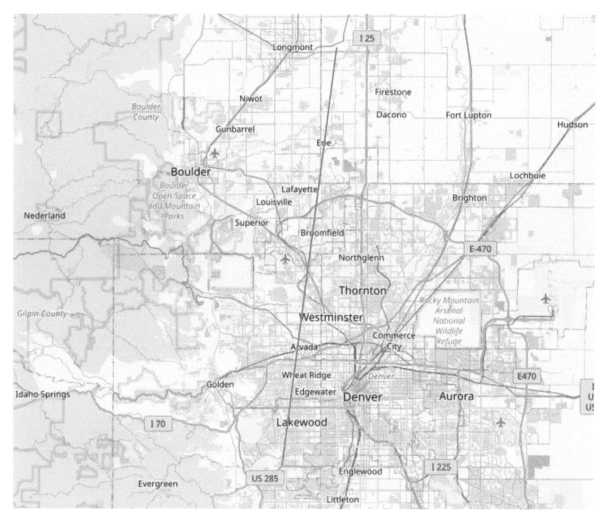

Figure 5.2: Line between our two random points

From here, we are going to run a simply query that will find all the buildings that intersect the line we just created that have a height greater than either of the two buildings creating the line. We can use the array from the previous query to access the heights of the two buildings. Below is the complete query:

Listing 5.13: Complete query

```
1   with a as (
2       select
3           geom,
4           bldg_heigh,
5           ground_ele,
6           gid
7       from
8           denver_buildings
9       order by
10          random()
11      limit
12          2
13  ), bldgs as (
14      select
15          array_agg(st_centroid(st_transform(geom, 4326))) as geom,
16          array_agg(bldg_heigh + ground_ele) as height,
```

```
17              array_agg(gid) as id
18      from
19              a
20  ),
21  line as (
22
23      -- Here we use a simple select statement rather tha sub-queries
24      -- like the previous step to grab the height column too
25      select
26          st_makeline(geom [1], geom [2]) as geom,
27          height
28      from
29          bldgs
30  )
31  select
32
33      -- This will return all the buildings higher than the line
34      b.gid,
35      b.bldg_heigh + b.ground_ele as height,
36      st_transform(b.geom, 4326),
37      line.height
38  from
39      denver_buildings b
40      join line on st_intersects(line.geom, st_transform(b.geom, 4326))
41  where
42
43      -- This finds any building taller than either of our two buildings
44      b.bldg_heigh + b.ground_ele < line.height [1]
45      or b.bldg_heigh + b.ground_ele < line.height [2]
```

Below are the results with one image of the complete results and one zoomed into one area (Figures 5.3, on the following page and 5.4, on page 327):

5.4 3D line of sight

Now to create a much more accurate line of sight analysis we need to turn our buildings into 3D geometries. While this is also not completely accurate since these are only building roofprints, some datasets will include building parts which will form a much more accurate 3-dimensional picture of a building. For our purposes we are simply going to calculate the height of the building and the elevation where the building is located. First we need to add a new geometry to our table:

Listing 5.14: Updating the buildings table

```
1  alter table
2      denver_buildings
3  add
4      column geom_z geometry
```

Once we have done that we can update our table and use the 2-dimensional geometry and a function called ST_Force3D to force a third dimension onto the geometry, in this case the building height plus the ground elevation.

Listing 5.15: Creating 3D geometries

```
1  update
2      denver_buildings
3  set
4      geom_z = st_force3d(
5
6          -- First value is the building geometry in EPSG 4326
7          st_transform(geom, 4326),
```

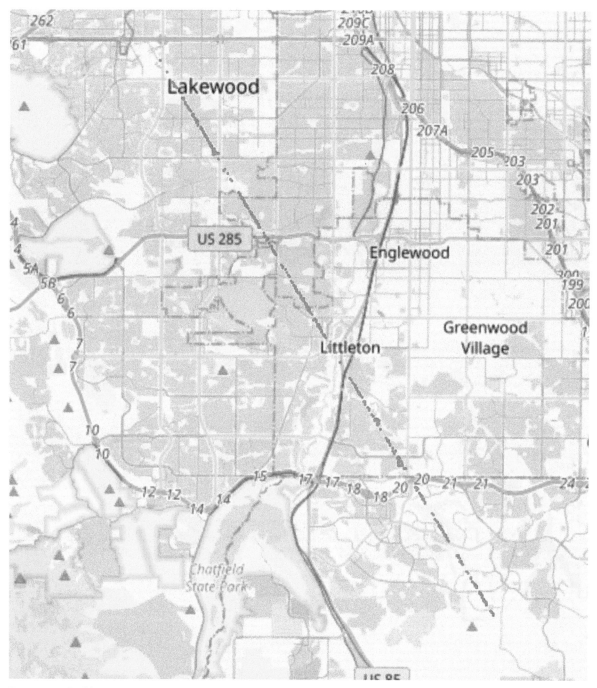

Figure 5.3: Buildings intersecting our 2D line of sight

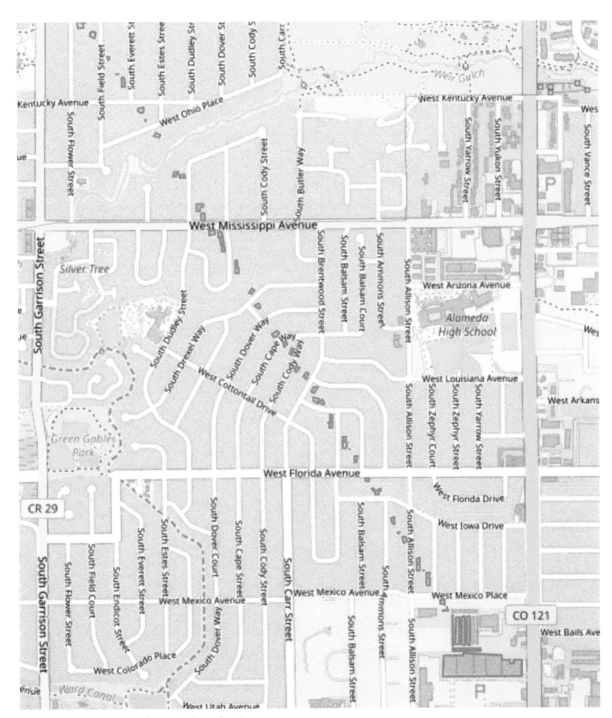

Figure 5.4: Detail view of our 2D line of sight

```
 8
 9              -- This is our Z or height value, the building height
10              -- plus the ground elevation
11              bldg_heigh + ground_ele
12          )
```

Now we have a 3D geometry that we can use. The process from this point out is quite similar to the previous query with a few differences (Results in figure 5.5).

- First we select two buildings, which is the same as before, however we will search for one building then search for a second within 2 kilometers of the first building to reduce a potentially long-running query.
- Next we union those two tables together, so the first three steps equate to the first step from the previous query
- After that we select the centroids of the two source buildings. In the following step we create a single geometry consisting of the two points, scale the geometries back to 2-dimensional using ST_Force2D, and find all the buildings within 3 kilometers of those two points

Figure 5.5: Sample of buildings within 3 km

- Finally, we find all the buildings that intersect a line we create in the final query using ST_MakeLine and then find the crossing buildings using ST_3DIntersects, which is the same as ST_Intersects but in a 3-dimensional space (Figure 5.6, on page 331).

Listing 5.16: Full 3D query

```
1   -- Find our first building
2   with a as (
```

```
 3      select
 4          geom_z,
 5          gid
 6      from
 7          denver_buildings
 8      limit
 9          1 offset 100
10  ),
11
12  -- Find a building with its ID and GeometryZ
13  -- within 2 kilometers
14  b as (
15      select
16          geom_z,
17          gid
18      from
19          denver_buildings
20      where
21          st_dwithin(
22              st_transform(geom, 3857),
23              (
24                  select
25                      st_transform(geom, 3857)
26                  from
27                      a
28              ),
29              2000
30          )
31      limit
32          1
33  ),
34
35  -- Use UNION to create a single table with matching columns
36  c as (
37      select
38          *
39      from
40          a
41      union
42      select
43          *
44      from
45          b
46  ),
47
48  -- Store the geometries and and IDs in arrays
49  bldgs as (
50      select
51          array_agg(st_centroid(geom_z)) as geom,
52          array_agg(gid) as id
53      from
54          c
55  ),
56
57  -- This query finds all the buildings within 3 kilometers of each building
58  denver as (
59      select
60          st_transform(geom, 3857) as geom,
61          geom_z,
62          gid
63      from
64          denver_buildings
65      where
66          st_dwithin(
67
```

```
68              -- We union the two points and turn them back into 2D
69              -- Geometries so we can run the query to find all
70              -- buildings with 3 kilometers one time
71              st_union(
72                  (
73                      select
74                          st_force2d(st_transform(geom [1], 3857))
75                      from
76                          bldgs
77                  ),
78                  (
79                      select
80                          st_force2d(st_transform(geom [2], 3857))
81                      from
82                          bldgs
83                  )
84              ),
85              st_transform(geom, 3857),
86              3000
87          )
88  )
89  select
90      d.gid,
91      st_transform(d.geom, 4326) as geom
92  from
93      denver d
94
95      -- Now we can use our ST_3DIntersects function to find
96      -- all the buildings crossing our path
97      join bldgs on st_3dintersects(
98
99          -- The path can be built using the same ST_MakeLine
100         -- function we have been using
101         st_makeline(bldgs.geom [1], bldgs.geom [2]),
102         d.geom_z
103     )
```

5.5   Calculate polygons that share a border

In all the spatial relationships we have explored so far, there is one that we haven't used yet because it doesn't exist out of the box with PostGIS. This one finds polygons that share portions of borders with other polygons, defined by simply sharing more than one point, a percentage of the border, or a specific length. This can be useful when you want to find more direct relationships between polygons, or features that may have a more direct relationship than simply sharing a point. Let's review each of the scenarios for a single polygon. If you want to expand this to every row you can still do this with a join or cross join, and aggregate the IDs into an array.

Before we start, we will create a table that contains the census block groups just for New York City that also excludes block groups with no population:

Listing 5.17: Building a table to use with our new function

```
1  create table nyc_2021_census_block_groups_morans_i as
2  select
3      *
4  from
5      nys_2021_census_block_groups
6  where
7      left(geoid, 5) in ('36061', '36005', '36047', '36081', '36085')
8      and population > 0
```

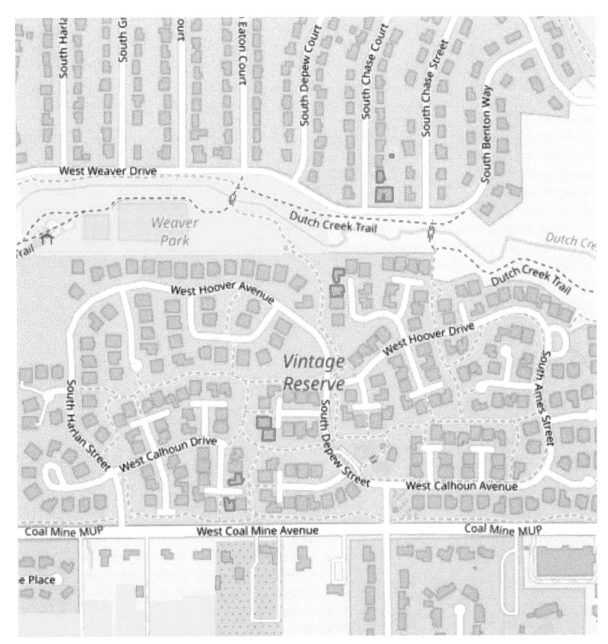

Figure 5.6: The final 3D line of sight

Next, let's find all polygons that intersect with our source block group (Figure 5.7, on the facing page):

Listing 5.18: All intersecting polygons

```
 1  with a as (
 2      select
 3          *
 4      from
 5          nyc_2021_census_block_groups
 6      where
 7          geoid = '360470201002'
 8  )
 9  select
10      bgs.geoid,
11
12      -- Finds the number of points of the
13      -- portion of the border that intersects
14      st_npoints(
15          st_intersection(
16              bgs.geom,
17              (
18                  select
19                      geom
20                  from
21                      a
22              )
23          )
24      ) as intersected_points,
25
26      -- Finds the length of the
27      -- portion of the border that intersects
28      st_length(
29          st_intersection(
30              bgs.geom,
31              (
32                  select
33                      geom
34                  from
35                      a
36              )
37          ) :: geography
38      ) as length,
39      geom
40  from
41      nyc_2021_census_block_groups bgs
42  where
43      st_intersects(
44          (
45              select
46                  geom
47              from
48                  a
49          ),
50          bgs.geom
51      )
52      and bgs.geoid != (
53          select
54              geoid
55          from
56              a
57      )
```

geoid	intersected_points	length
360470199003	2	214.424014004512
360470201001	2	87.75447723840115
360470227004	4	214.7015855236718
360470305001	1	0
360470199002	1	0
360470201003	4	190.0550311628189
360470203001	4	275.8191358756717
360470203002	1	0

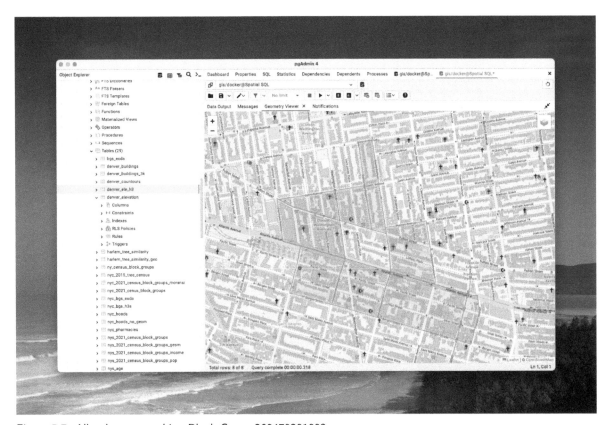

Figure 5.7: All polygons touching Block Group 360470201002

As you can see there are three polygons that only share one point. Let's get rid of those first by using ST_Intersection to find the shared geometry and then use ST_NPoints to find the number of points, then filter out those that have 1 point (Figure 5.8, on page 335):

Listing 5.19: Polygons that share more than one point

```
1  with a as (
2      select
3          *
4      from
5          nyc_2021_census_block_groups
6      where
7          geoid = '360470201002'
8  )
```

```
 9   select
10       bgs.*,
11       st_npoints(
12           st_intersection(
13               bgs.geom,
14               (
15                   select
16                       geom
17                   from
18                       a
19               )
20           )
21       ) as intersected_points,
22       st_length(
23           st_intersection(
24               bgs.geom,
25               (
26                   select
27                       geom
28                   from
29                       a
30               )
31           ) :: geography
32       ) as length,
33       geom
34   from
35       nyc_2021_census_block_groups bgs
36   where
37
38       -- Only select polygons that have a border overlap
39       -- of 2 points or more
40       st_npoints(
41           st_intersection(
42               bgs.geom,
43               (
44                   select
45                       geom
46                   from
47                       a
48               )
49           )
50       ) > 1
51       and bgs.geoid != (
52           select
53               geoid
54           from
55               a
56       )
```

geoid	intersected_points	length
360470199003	2	214.424014004512
360470201001	2	87.75447723840115
360470227004	4	214.7015855236718
360470201003	4	190.0550311628189
360470203001	4	275.8191358756717

Now let's find the polygons that share a border of at least 100 meters (Figure 5.9, on page 337):

Listing 5.20: Polygons that share more than 100 meters

Figure 5.8: All polygons touching Block Group 360470201002 with 2 or more points in common

```
1   with a as (
2       select
3           *
4       from
5           nyc_2021_census_block_groups
6       where
7           geoid = '360470201002'
8   )
9   select
10      bgs.*,
11      st_npoints(
12          st_intersection(
13              bgs.geom,
14              (
15                  select
16                      geom
17                  from
18                      a
19              )
20          )
21      ) as intersected_points,
22      st_length(
23          st_intersection(
24              bgs.geom,
25              (
26                  select
27                      geom
28                  from
29                      a
30              )
```

```
31              ) :: geography
32          ) as length,
33          geom
34  from
35          nyc_2021_census_block_groups bgs
36  where
37
38          -- Only select polygons that have a border overlap
39          -- of 100 meters or more
40          st_length(
41              st_intersection(
42                  bgs.geom,
43                  (
44                      select
45                          geom
46                      from
47                          a
48                  )
49              ) :: geography
50          ) > 100
51          and bgs.geoid != (
52              select
53                  geoid
54              from
55                  a
56          )
```

geoid	intersected_points	length
360470199003	2	214.424014004512
360470227004	4	214.7015855236718
360470201003	4	190.0550311628189
360470203001	4	275.8191358756717

Finally, what about polygons that share a percentage of the total perimeter of the source polygon. We can use ST_Perimeter to do so after casting our source polygon to a GEOGRAPHY data type, then divide the length of the intersected polygons by the perimeter value (Figure 5.10, on page 339):

Listing 5.21: Polygons that share more than 25 percent of the perimeter of the source polygon

```
1   with a as (
2       select
3           *
4       from
5           nyc_2021_census_block_groups
6       where
7           geoid = '360470201002'
8   )
9   select
10      bgs.geoid,
11      geom,
12      st_npoints(
13          st_intersection(
14              bgs.geom,
15              (
16                  select
17                      geom
18                  from
19                      a
20              )
21          )
```

Figure 5.9: All polygons touching Block Group 360470201002 that share a border of 100 meters

```
22        ) as intersected_points,
23        st_length(
24            st_intersection(
25                bgs.geom,
26                (
27                    select
28                        geom
29                    from
30                        a
31                )
32            ) :: geography
33        ) as length,
34        (
35            -- Finding the length of the shared border
36            st_length(
37                st_intersection(
38                    bgs.geom,
39                    (
40                        select
41                            geom
42                        from
43                            a
44                    )
45                ) :: geography
46
47            -- Dividing that by the perimeter of the source polygon
48            ) / st_perimeter(
49                (
50                    select
51                        geom :: geography
```

```
52              from
53                   a
54              )
55         )
56    ) as percent_of_source
57 from
58    nyc_2021_census_block_groups bgs
59 where
60    -- Finding touching polygons that share more than 25% of
61    -- the source polygon's border
62    (
63        st_length(
64            st_intersection(
65                bgs.geom,
66                (
67                    select
68                        geom
69                    from
70                        a
71                )
72            ) :: geography
73        ) / st_perimeter(
74            (
75                select
76                    geom :: geography
77                from
78                    a
79            )
80        )
81    ) >.25
82    and bgs.geoid != (
83        select
84            geoid
85        from
86            a
87    )
```

geoid	intersected_points	length	percent_of_source
360470203001	4	275.8191358756717	0.28065931804857114

And then there was one. With that let's move on to our next exercise.

5.6   Finding the most isolated feature

As you have seen so far there are a lot of ways we can perform spatial analysis with spatial SQL, but not all analyses are built the same, especially when we increase the amount of data needed in our analysis. One of the most important skills you can learn as your data scale increases is to find different ways to minimize the problem at hand to increase the analysis speed. One way we can look at this is by trying to find the most isolated building in New York City.

The brute force method for this would be to measure the distance from each building to the nearest building. But with just over 1.2 million buildings in our dataset this would be quite inefficient. Below is an example of the code we could run, but **I do not recommend running it** since when I ran it on my computer, I ended up stopping the query after 10 minutes.

Listing 5.22: The brute force method

```
1  -- This follows the same structure as our nearest neighbor query
2  select
```

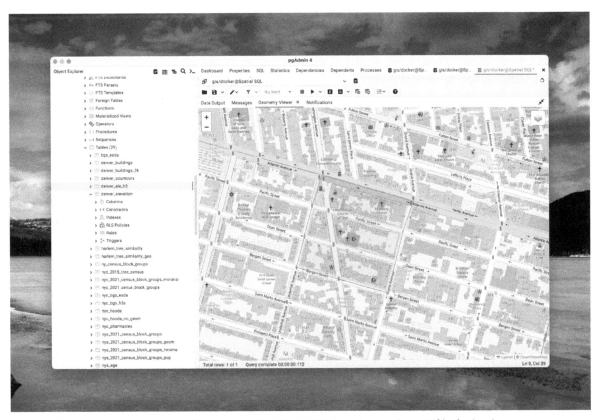

Figure 5.10: All polygons touching Block Group 360470201002 that share at least 25% of a border

```
3      ogc_fid,
4      st_transform(geom, 4326) as geom,
5      closest.distance
6  from
7      building_footprints b
8      cross join lateral (
9          select
10             st_distance(geom, b.geom) as distance
11         from
12             building_footprints
13         order by
14             geom <-> b.geom
15         limit
16             1
17     ) closest
18 order by
19     closest.distance desc
```

This is where the creativity comes in, and by creativity I mean finding methods to limit the amount of data you actually need to analyze. Some other potential examples of this are:

- Imagine you have millions of points that you want to create drive time isochrones around. Instead of running for each point, approximate the drive times by using a grid and creating the isochrones from each.
- In our raster use case you can use H3 cells to aggregate and approximate your raster data for faster analysis (an analysis we will perform later in the book).

For our use case, we need to limit the number of buildings we are evaluating in our distance measurements, and we can do this using H3 cells. However, this is not an original idea. Simon Wrigley put together a great tutorial using a similar process in PostGIS to find the most remote building in Great Britain[112].

Since we have already installed the two H3 libraries we need in our Docker container, we can simply install then in our database using two queries:

```
create extension h3
create extension h3_postgis
```

Our first step is to add a column in our building footprints dataset to store our H3 index:

Listing 5.23: Add an H3 column

```
1   alter table
2       nyc_building_footprints
3   add
4       column h3 text
```

Next we update the table to add an H3 index from the centroid of the building footprint polygon at H3 level 10. The H3 indexes run from level 1 to 15, 1 being the largest (at roughly 600 to 700 billion square meters per cell) and 15 being the smallest (at just under 1 square meter). You can see this in this web app[113] that allows you to view H3 cells at various levels. To create the cells we will first turn the buildings into centroids, then use the function h3_lat_lng_to_cell to create the cell ID:

Listing 5.24: Add the H3 index

```
1   update
2       nyc_building_footprints
3   set
4       h3 = h3_lat_lng_to_cell(
5           st_centroid(
6               st_transform(geom, 4326)
7           ), 10)
```

This only takes about 29 seconds to complete (in case you were keeping track) on my computer. From here the next logical step is to look at all the H3 cells that have the lowest number of buildings in them. In our case there are several H3 cells with only one building in them. If you replicate this analysis and you use a higher resolution cell you may need to select the cells under a certain threshold or go to a lower threshold until you get cells that only have one building.

The next logical step would be to group all the cells by the count of buildings within them and then visualize the H3 cells, but instead of adding another step we can actually select the building geometries that fall in a cell with a count of 1. This will be a refresher from one of our earlier chapters but what clause would allow us to filter by an aggregate?

———

This is one we haven't used much, but the correct answer is HAVING which acts just like a WHERE clause but with aggregated data. What we can do is select everything from our main buildings table, and using a subquery we can query all the H3 IDs that have a count of 1 using HAVING to filter the data (Figure 5.11, on page 342).

---

[112]https://loc8.cc/sql/simon-wrigley-geo-big-data

[113]https://wolf-h3-viewer.glitch.me/

Listing 5.25: H3 cells with under 1 building

```
1   select
2       bin,
3       st_transform(geom, 4326) as geom
4   from
5       nyc_building_footprints b
6   where
7
8       -- Returns all the H3 cells that meet the condition in the subquery
9       h3 in (
10          select
11              h3
12          from
13              nyc_building_footprints
14
15          -- First we group the H3 cells to use the aggregate function
16          group by
17              h3
18
19          -- This finds all the H3 cells that have an aggregate
20          -- count greater than 1
21          having
22              count(*) = 1
23      )
```

At this point we know the buildings that are potential candidates for the most remote and using this method we have narrowed our candidates down to 2,187 from over 1.2 million. With this significantly smaller amount we can find the distance for each of these buildings to its nearest building by combining the subquery with HAVING from our previous step and parts of the brute force query from the beginning of the section:

Listing 5.26: Final query

```
1   select
2       bin,
3       closest.distance,
4       st_transform(geom, 4326) as geom
5   from
6       nyc_building_footprints b
7       cross join lateral (
8           select
9
10              -- Finding the distance to the nearest building in meters
11              st_distance(
12                  st_transform(geom, 3857),
13                  st_transform(b.geom, 3857)
14              ) as distance
15          from
16              nyc_building_footprints
17
18              -- This removes the ID of the building we want to analyze
19          where
20              bin != b.bin
21          order by
22              geom <-> b.geom
23          limit
24              1
25      ) closest
26  where
27      h3 in (
28          select
29              h3
30          from
```

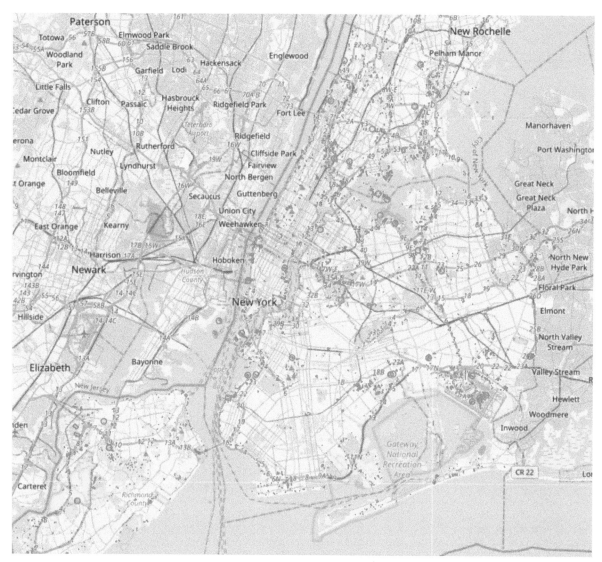

Figure 5.11: Candidate buildings for the most remote building

```
31              nyc_building_footprints
32          group by
33              h3
34          having
35              count(*) = 1
36      )
37  order by
38      closest.distance desc
```

bin	distance
2127308	1005.9038869674532
3397806	745.4296782710237
2128487	671.5739992682301

...continued on next page

bin	distance
2124071	490.094313204366
4540195	455.3490996545422

With that we can see that there is one building that is about 1,000 meters from the nearest building which appears to be the most remote building in New York City (Figure 5.12).

Listing 5.27: Finding the most isolated building

```
1  select
2     *
3  from
4     nyc_building_footprints
5  where
6     bin = '2127308'
```

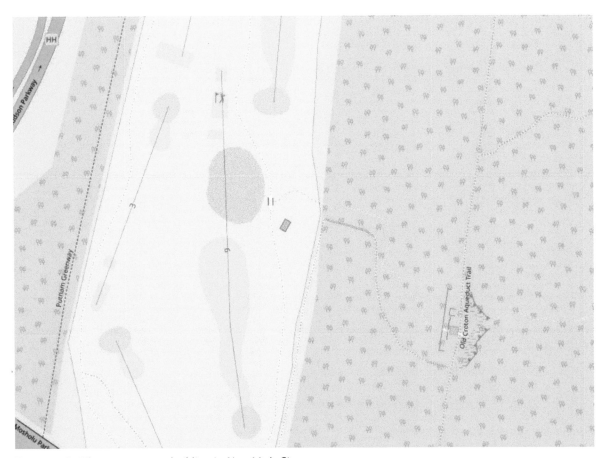

Figure 5.12: The most remote building in New York City

As you can see the most remote building in New York City by about 300 meters is this building near the 9th hole of the Van Cortlandt Park Golf Course in the northern part of the Bronx.

5.7 Kernel density estimation (KDE)

While seeing points on a map can give you some sense of how dense a layer of data might be, quantifying how densely compact those features are is another task all together. One popular approach is using kernel density estimation (KDE) which creates an estimate, or smoothed, view of the distribution of the data given the weighted distances of the data. As I am not a statistician I will refer you to this link[114] which provides a clear definition and visualization of how a KDE works with non-spatial data as well as this quote from the University Consortium of Geospatial Information Science.

"The kernel density estimate at a location will be the sum of the fractions of all observations at that location. In a GIS environment, kernel density estimation usually results in a density surface where each cell is rendered based on the kernel density estimated at the cell center."

Fortunately for us, a former colleague of mine, Abel Vázquez Montoro, implemented this as a function in PostGIS which we can use since it is publicly available as a Gist[115] on his GitHub. With that let's take a look at the function and break apart what is happening.

First the function is declared with the arguments:

- **ids** - an array of integers
- **geoms** - an array of geometries

We can see that the function returns a table with the following structure:

- **id** - integer or bigint
- **geom** - geometry
- **kdensity** - integer

Listing 5.28: Creating our function

```
1   CREATE OR REPLACE FUNCTION ST_KDensity(
2       ids bigint [],
3
4       -- Note that the function takes all geometries as an array
5       geoms geometry [])
6
7       -- This will return a table with an ID, geometry,
8       -- and integer representing the density
9       RETURNS TABLE (id bigint, geom geometry, kdensity integer)
10  AS $$
```

In this next section we are declaring some variables using *DECLARE* which only needs to be used once. Then we start the function after the *BEGIN* keyword. The first three steps assign values to the variables. The := is the same as an equals sign but just the PL/SQL compliant version[116]. The variable assignments include (in order)

- The centroid of all the geometries (mc)
- The length of the ids array (c)
- The square root of the factorial of the natural logarithm of 2

Listing 5.29: Function variable declarations

```
1   declare mc geometry;
2
3   -- Stores two values for later use
4   c integer;
5
6   k numeric;
7
```

---

[114]https://mathisonian.github.io/kde/

[115]https://gist.github.com/AbelVM/dc86f01fbda7ba24b5091a7f9b48d2ee

[116]https://www.postgresql.org/docs/current/plpgsql-statements.html#PLPGSQL-STATEMENTS-ASSIGNMENT

```
 8   -- This will find the center of mass of all geometries
 9   -- by collecting all geometries and finding the centroid
10   begin mc := st_centroid(st_collect(geoms));
11
12   -- This will set the variable "c" above to the
13   -- length of the array containing the IDs
14   c := array_length(ids, 1);
15
16   -- Stores the value for "k"
17   k := sqrt(1 / ln(2));
```

Now we construct the query which will be run by the function. In our first CTE the query contains the point ID, geometry, and the distance to the centroid of all geometries. In the FROM statement, the query un-nests the array which contains the IDs and geometries and gives it a shorthand alias of gid for the ID, and g for the geom.

Listing 5.30: Set up query return

```
 1   return query with dist as (
 2       select
 3           t.gid,
 4           t.g,
 5
 6           -- Finds the distance for each geometry
 7           -- to the center of mass for all geometries
 8           st_distance(t.g, mc) as distance
 9       from
10
11           -- This allows us to unnest the arrays from the original query
12           -- which values are stored in t(gid, g)
13           unnest(ids, geoms) as t(gid, g)
14   ),
```

Our next CTE finds the median value using the PERCENTILE_CONT function which is a window function to find the value at median (or 0.5):

Listing 5.31: Finding the median

```
 1   md as (
 2       select
 3
 4           -- Finds the median distance value within
 5           -- the data created in the last step.
 6           -- Note that this is a window query and
 7           -- how the data is ordered by distance
 8           percentile_cont(0.5) within group (
 9               order by
10                   distance
11           ) as median
12       from
13           dist
14   ),
```

The next CTE performs the KDE equation which finds the square root of:

- The sum of the X coordinate minus the X coordinate of the centroid to the 2nd power
- Divided by the array length plus the sum of the Y coordinate minus the Y coordinate of the centroid to the 2nd power
- All divided by the array length again

Listing 5.32: KDE equation

```
1  sd as ( SELECT sqrt( sum((ST_X(g) - ST_X(mc)) ^ 2) / c + sum((ST_Y(g) - ST_Y(mc)) ^ 2) / c )
2    as standard_distance FROM dist ),
```

The next CTE creates a standard search radius based on the documentation here[117]. This takes a constant of 0.9 multiplied by the smallest value from the previous CTE, which the LEAST performs which finds the smallest value from a set of data, as well as the constant "k" multiplied by the median, which is then multiplied by length of the array to the power of -0.2. That is a lot, but effectively it is just an expression of the equation listed in the documentation link in the footnotes.

Listing 5.33: Search radius

```
1  sr as (
2      select
3
4          -- Establishes the search radius for the KDE function using the data just created
5          0.9 * least(sd.standard_distance, k * md.median) * c ^(-0.2) as search_radius
6      from
7          sd,
8          md
9  )
```

Next we assemble the final query. Here we are performing a cross join between the data in the CTE dist and the search radius CTE, sr. To find the number of features in the cluster for each point, we perform a pure LATERAL join that finds the count of points within the length of the search radius from the center of mass to the specific location under evaluation.

Listing 5.34: Final parts of the function

```
1
2  select
3
4      -- Note that this mirrors the final table structure
5      -- defined at the beginning of the function
6      gid as id,
7      g as geom,
8      kd :: int as kdensity
9  from
10
11      -- This is a three way cross join, first
12      -- from the search radius CTE, "sr"
13      sr,
14
15      -- Then the distance CTE, "dist"
16      dist as a,
17
18      -- Then a lateral join to get the count of nearby features
19      -- as "kd", determined by the values that are within the distance from the
20      -- geometry to the center of mass, all within the search radius
21      lateral(
22          select
23              count(*) as kd
24          from
25              dist _b
26          where
27              st_dwithin(a.g, _b.g, sr.search_radius)
28      ) b;
29
30  end;
31
32  $$
```

---

[117]https://loc8.cc/sql/arcgis-kernel-density

```
33  language plpgsql immutable parallel safe;
```

And with that we have our complete function:

Listing 5.35: Final KDE function

```
 1  create
 2  or replace function st_kdensity(ids bigint [], geoms geometry [])
 3  returns table(id bigint, geom geometry, kdensity integer) as $$ declare mc geometry;
 4
 5  c integer;
 6
 7  k numeric;
 8
 9  begin mc := st_centroid(st_collect(geoms));
10
11  c := array_length(ids, 1);
12
13  k := sqrt(1 / ln(2));
14
15  return query with dist as (
16      select
17          t.gid,
18          t.g,
19          st_distance(t.g, mc) as distance
20      from
21          unnest(ids, geoms) as t(gid, g)
22  ),
23  md as (
24      select
25          percentile_cont(0.5) within group (
26              order by
27                  distance
28          ) as median
29      from
30          dist
31  ),
32  sd as (
33      select
34          sqrt(
35              sum((st_x(g) - st_x(mc)) ^ 2) / c + sum((st_y(g) - st_y(mc)) ^ 2) / c
36          ) as standard_distance
37      from
38          dist
39  ),
40  sr as (
41      select
42          0.9 * least(sd.standard_distance, k * md.median) * c ^(-0.2) as search_radius
43      from
44          sd,
45          md
46  )
47  select
48      gid as id,
49      g as geom,
50      kd :: int as kdensity
51  from
52      sr,
53      dist as a,
54      lateral(
55          select
56              count(*) as kd
57          from
58              dist _b
59          where
```

```
60              st_dwithin(a.g, _b.g, sr.search_radius)
61      ) b;
62
63  end;
64
65  $$ language plpgsql immutable parallel safe;
```

Now we can run our query and create a new table for all the trees in the East Village:

Listing 5.36: Testing the new function

```
1   create table east_village_kde as WITH a AS(
2       SELECT
3           array_agg(ogc_fid) as ids,
4           array_agg(geom) as geoms
5       FROM
6           nyc_2015_tree_census
7       where
8           st_intersects(
9               geom,
10              (
11                  select
12                      geom
13                  from
14                      nyc_neighborhoods
15                  where
16                      neighborhood = 'East Village'
17              )
18          )
19  )
20  SELECT
21      b.*
22  FROM
23      a,
24      ST_KDensity(a.ids, a.geoms) b
```

And here is our final map (Figure 5.13, on the facing page):

5.8 Isovist

We have already covered line of sight analyses and later we will introduce isochrones or drive times. An isovist is a unique analysis that creates the visible area from a specific point is another possible analysis using spatial SQL. This specific analysis and function was once again developed by Abel Vázquez Montoro, and you can see the original code here[118].

For this example we will find the isovist for the center of Times Square, one of the most well known areas in New York City and also the one that likely has the highest density of billboards in the city, if not the world. First we will show the analysis results step by step and then show the entire function. To run the example functions in the next steps you can add each section by replacing the outermost query from the previous code snippet (such as `select * from step_1`) with the code from the next code snippet.

In the first three steps we will select our buildings from our NYC Buildings dataset. The function itself takes in an array of geometries, so our first step will be to unnest that array. From there we find all the buildings within 630 meters, which is roughly the distance that I was able to see from the selected point to another point on Google Street View in Times Square. The last step is to create a buffer and add that as a geometry to the data (Figure 5.14, on page 351):

---

[118]https://abelvm.github.io/sql/isovists/

Figure 5.13: KDE analysis with East Village trees

Listing 5.37: Selecting the buildings

```
 1  with buildings_0 as(
 2      select
 3          t.geom
 4      from
 5
 6          -- Find all the buildings within 2 kilometers of Times Square where
 7          -- geometries are stored in an array
 8          unnest(
 9            (
10              select
11                  array_agg(geom)
12              from
13                  nyc_building_footprints
14              where
15                  st_dwithin(
16                      geom :: geography,
17                      st_setsrid(st_makepoint(-73.985136, 40.758786), 4326) :: geography,
18                      2000
19                  )
20            )
21          ) as t(geom)
22  ),
23  buildings_crop as(
24
25      -- Now only the buildings within 630 meters of Times Square
26      select
27          geom
28      from
29          buildings_0
```

```
30      where
31          st_dwithin(
32              st_setsrid(st_makepoint(-73.985136, 40.758786), 4326) :: geography,
33              geom :: geography,
34              630
35          )
36  ),
37  buildings as(
38
39      -- Union these two tables together
40      select
41          geom
42      from
43          buildings_crop
44      union
45      all
46      select
47          st_buffer(
48              st_setsrid(st_makepoint(-73.985136, 40.758786), 4326) :: geography,
49              630
50          ) :: geometry as geom
51  )
52  select
53      *
54  from
55      buildings
```

The next step creates a set of rays around the center point. This uses a set of functions to create lines using ST_MakeLine between the center point and points generated from a function called ST_Project[119] which creates a set of points around a point (in this case our center point), at a certain distance, and based on a specific radius. What we end up with is a shape that looks like a ray burst around our center point (Figure 5.15, on page 352):

Note that instead of adding the same code we will just show the next parts that are added in. Make sure to combine the CTEs using commas.

Listing 5.38: Creating the rays

```
1   rays as(
2       select
3           t.n as id,
4           st_setsrid(
5
6               -- Creates teh lines or rays
7               st_makeline(
8                   st_setsrid(st_makepoint(-73.985136, 40.758786), 4326),
9
10                  -- ST_Project creates a points 630 meters from the center of Times Square
11                  st_project(
12                      st_setsrid(st_makepoint(-73.985136, 40.758786), 4326) :: geography,
13
14                      -- Sets the distance to 631 meters
15                      630 + 1,
16
17                      -- This sets the azimuth, or angle of the point from the centroid
18                      -- to 0 plus the number from the series generated on line 29 which
19                      -- contains the integers 0 to 100, then multiples it by 3.6
20                      -- or 1/100th of 360, the degrees in a circle
21                      radians(0 + t.n :: numeric * 3.6)
22                  ) :: geometry
23              ),
```

---

[119]https://postgis.net/docs/en/ST_Project.html

Figure 5.14: Buildings within 630 meters of Times Square

```
24                4326
25          ) as geom
26
27          -- Builds the series of integers used in ST_Project
28      from
29          generate_series(0, 100) as t(n)
30  )
31  select
32      *
33  from
34      rays
```

The next step is to find the:

- Points of the buildings that intersect the rays that we just created
- Rank those points in order of distance
- Then in the CTE `intersection_closest` find the closest point on each ray and union those results to the original center point (Results in figure 5.16, on page 354)

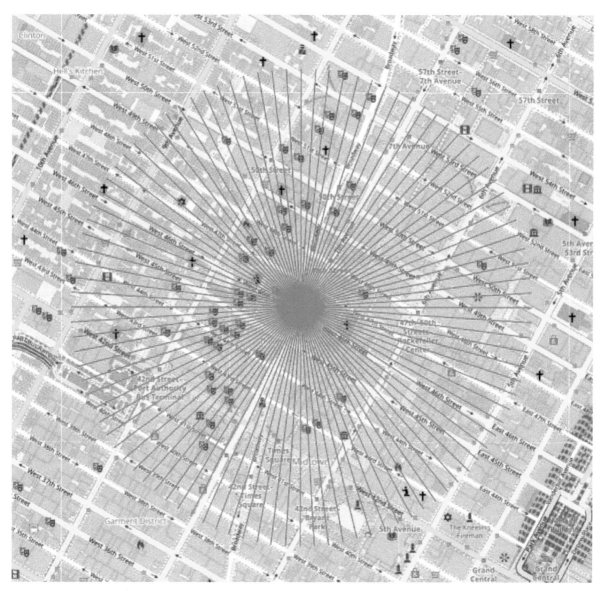

Figure 5.15: Our ray of lines

Listing 5.39: Finding the buildings that intersect

```
1   -- Finds all the building boundaries that touch a ray
2   intersections as(
3       select
4           r.id,
5           (
6               st_dump(st_intersection(st_boundary(b.geom), r.geom))
7           ).geom as point
8       from
9           rays r
10          left join buildings b on st_intersects(b.geom, r.geom)
11  ),
12
13  -- Finds and orders the touching buildings by distance
14  intersections_distances as(
15      select
16          id,
17          point as geom,
18          row_number() over(
19              partition by id
20              order by
21                  st_setsrid(st_makepoint(-73.985136, 40.758786), 4326) <-> point
22          ) as ranking
23      from
24          intersections
25  ),
26  intersection_closest as(
27      -- For the first building touching a ray, sets that point of intersection
28      -- as the end point on the ray
29      select
30          -1 as id,
31          case
32              when 360 = 360 then null :: geometry
33              else st_setsrid(st_makepoint(-73.985136, 40.758786), 4326)
34          end as geom
35      union
36      all (
37
38          -- Unions the building IDs that are closest using the
39          -- ranking by distance
40          select
41              id,
42              geom
43          from
44              intersections_distances
45          where
46              ranking = 1
47          order by
48              id
49      )
50      union
51      all
52
53      -- This adds the center point a second time
54      -- in case the field of view is less than 360 degrees
55      select
56          999999 as id,
57          case
58              when 360 = 360 then null :: geometry
59              else st_setsrid(st_makepoint(-73.985136, 40.758786), 4326)
60          end as geom
61  )
62  select
63      *
```

```
64   from
65      intersection_closest
```

Figure 5.16: Buildings that intersect the isovist

Finally, we have a set of queries that build a polygon around those points:

Listing 5.40: Creating the isovist

```
1   -- Creates a line from the geometries and then a polygon from the line
2   -- of the closest intersecting points
3   isovist_0 as(
4       select
5           st_makepolygon(st_makeline(geom)) as geom
6       from
7           intersection_closest
8   ),
9
10  -- Selects the polygons that actually intersect the building
11  isovist_buildings as(
12      select
13          st_collectionextract(st_union(b.geom), 3) as geom
14      from
15          isovist_0 i,
16          buildings_crop b
17      where
18          st_intersects(b.geom, i.geom)
19  )
20
21  -- This clips the building footprints from the isovist
22  -- created above to give the most accurate view.
23  -- We use the COALESCE function to return the first non
24  -- NULL result so we can ignore any non-intersecting buildings
25  select
26      coalesce(st_difference(i.geom, b.geom), i.geom)
27  from
28      isovist_0 i,
29      isovist_buildings b;
```

And this returns our final isovist (Figure 5.17, on the following page):

The complete function is as follows that also has some additional arguments that have default values which means that you don't have to include them unless you want to modify the default values:

Listing 5.41: The final isovist function

```
1   create
2   or replace function isovist(
3
4       -- Sets up the arguments for our function
5       in center geometry,
6       in polygons geometry [],
7       in radius numeric default 150,
8       in rays integer default 36,
9       in heading integer default -999,
10      in fov integer default 360
11  ) returns geometry as $$ declare arc numeric;
12
13  -- Creates static variables for angle and geometry
14  angle_0 numeric;
15
16  geomout geometry;
17
18  -- Calculates the arc distance using the field of view (fov)
19  -- degrees and the number of rays
20  begin arc := fov :: numeric / rays :: numeric;
21
22  if fov = 360 then angle_0 := 0;
23
24  else angle_0 := heading - 0.5 * fov;
25
26  end if;
27
```

Figure 5.17: The final isovist

```
28  with buildings_0 as(
29      select
30          t.geom
31      from
32          unnest(polygons) as t(geom)
33  ),
34  buildings_crop as(
35      select
36          geom
37      from
38          buildings_0
39      where
40          st_dwithin(center :: geography, geom :: geography, radius)
41  ),
42  buildings as(
43      select
44          geom
45      from
46          buildings_crop
47      union
48      all
49      select
50          st_buffer(center :: geography, radius) :: geometry as geom
51  ),
```

```
52  rays as(
53      select
54          t.n as id,
55          st_setsrid(
56              st_makeline(
57                  center,
58                  st_project(
59                      center :: geography,
60                      radius + 1,
61                      radians(angle_0 + t.n :: numeric * arc)
62                  ) :: geometry
63              ),
64              4326
65          ) as geom
66      from
67          generate_series(0, rays) as t(n)
68  ),
69  intersections as(
70      select
71          r.id,
72          (
73              st_dump(st_intersection(st_boundary(b.geom), r.geom))
74          ).geom as point
75      from
76          rays r
77          left join buildings b on st_intersects(b.geom, r.geom)
78  ),
79  intersections_distances as(
80      select
81          id,
82          point as geom,
83          row_number() over(
84              partition by id
85              order by
86                  center <-> point
87          ) as ranking
88      from
89          intersections
90  ),
91  intersection_closest as(
92      select
93          -1 as id,
94          case
95              when fov = 360 then null :: geometry
96              else center
97          end as geom
98      union
99      all (
100         select
101             id,
102             geom
103         from
104             intersections_distances
105         where
106             ranking = 1
107         order by
108             id
109     )
110     union
111     all
112     select
113         999999 as id,
114         case
115             when fov = 360 then null :: geometry
116             else center
```

```
117            end as geom
118    ),
119    isovist_0 as(
120        select
121            st_makepolygon(st_makeline(geom)) as geom
122        from
123            intersection_closest
124    ),
125    isovist_buildings as(
126        select
127            st_collectionextract(st_union(b.geom), 3) as geom
128        from
129            isovist_0 i,
130            buildings_crop b
131        where
132            st_intersects(b.geom, i.geom)
133    )
134    select
135        coalesce(st_difference(i.geom, b.geom), i.geom) into geomout
136    from
137        isovist_0 i,
138        isovist_buildings b;
139
140    return geomout;
141
142    end;
143
144    $$ language plpgsql immutable;
```

And to use the function with some different values for our radius and number of rays (Figure 5.18, on the next page):

Listing 5.42: Using the new function

```
1    select
2        *
3    from
4        isovist(
5
6            -- This is our center point in Times Square
7            st_setsrid(st_makepoint(-73.985136, 40.758786), 4326),
8            (
9                -- Selects all the geometries
10               select
11                   array_agg(geom)
12               from
13                   nyc_building_footprints
14               where
15                   st_dwithin(
16                       geom :: geography,
17                       st_setsrid(st_makepoint(-73.985136, 40.758786), 4326) :: geography,
18                       2000
19                   )
20           ),
21           300,
22           36
23       )
```

5.9   Expert Voices: Danny Sheehan

Name: Danny Sheehan **Title**: Solutions Architect - AWS

Figure 5.18: Isovist within 300 meters

How/where did you learn spatial SQL?

I first learned spatial SQL in the CartoDB Editor web mapping tool.

Why do you enjoy using spatial SQL?

I enjoy using spatial SQL for querying in a database or data lake.

Can you share an interesting way or use case that you are using spatial SQL for today?

For a lot of use cases I use Amazon Athena and store data as Parquet-this is an easy and low cost way to run spatial queries on cloud native file formats. I'm eager to see developments and support for GeoParquet along with other formats like netCDF, etc.

Part 3

Spatial SQL Use Cases

1. Suitability Analysis

One area that I have done a good amount of work in during the course of my career is suitability analysis, or analyzing which areas might be best to locate a specific feature using many spatial attributes. For example this could be a new retail store that wants to be in an area that reaches their target market. Using demographic data we can use many variables to find suitable locations for this new store location. This is a simple example but we will see more as we dive into this chapter.

1.1 Market expansion potential

A common suitability analysis is analyzing the potential fit of areas for expansion based on suitability and other factors. This could be for any type of site such as a retail location, government offices or service centers, distribution centers, or any type of site that requires a certain set of conditions to thrive. In this case we will be using pharmacies in New York City which can be located close together in some areas and farther apart in others, but overall there are many pharmacies in the city competing for space and business.

The data we will be using was extracted from OpenStreetMap using the Overpass API via Overpass Turbo[120], a user interface wrapped around the Overpass API. To import this data we can use this command:

Listing 1.1: Load pharmacy data

```
1  ogr2ogr \
2  -f PostgreSQL PG:"host=localhost user=docker password=docker dbname=gis port=25432" nyc_pharmacies.geojson \
3  -nln nyc_pharmacies -lco GEOMETRY_NAME=geom
```

For this analysis we are going to analyze the potential within neighborhoods in New York City for new Duane Reade locations, which is a specific franchise of pharmacy, for another theoretical competing pharmacy that wants to co-locate with Duane Reade locations to directly compete with their business. Once again this will have many CTEs to highlight each step of the analysis. First we will select all the pharmacies that match the name Duane Reade:

Listing 1.2: Duane Reade locations

```
1   with a as (
2       select
3           id,
4           amenity,
5           brand,
6           name,
7           geom
8       from
9           nyc_pharmacies
10      where
11          name ilike '%duane%'
12  )
```

---

[120]https://overpass-turbo.eu/

Next we are going to add the name of each neighborhood that each store resides in to the stores data using ST_Intersects:

Listing 1.3: Adding neighborhood names

```
1  b as (
2      select
3          a.*,
4          b.neighborhood
5      from
6          a
7          join nyc_hoods b on st_intersects(a.geom, b.geom)
8  )
```

In the third step, we will create a buffer of 800 meters around each store which will require us to transform the geometry to EPSG 3857 to make sure our geometry uses meters rather than decimal degrees:

Listing 1.4: 800 meter buffer

```
1  c as (
2      select
3          id,
4          st_buffer(st_transform(geom, 3857), 800) as buffer,
5          neighborhood
6      from
7          b
8  )
```

In the fourth step, we will transform our geometry back to EPSG 4326 and union those geometries, grouped by neighborhood which will result in one or more buffers as single geometries for each neighborhood (Figure 1.1, on the facing page):

Listing 1.5: Group by neighborhood

```
1  d as (
2      select
3          st_transform(st_union(buffer), 4326) as geom,
4          neighborhood
5      from
6          c
7      group by
8          neighborhood
9  )
```

In our fifth step, we will enrich each of the group buffers with total population while also calculating the area of the combined buffers. This will allow us to calculate the population density for each of the grouped buffers. In this case we are simply analyzing the population density for these areas, you can continue to add variables into the analysis as you see fit including points of interest, transportation stops/stations, other types of stores, and more.

Listing 1.6: Group and union

```
1  e as (
2      select
3          d.*,
4
5          -- Finds the population of each overlapping block group
6          -- proportional to the area overlap
7          sum(
8              bgs.population * (
9                  st_area(st_intersection(d.geom, bgs.geom)) / st_area(bgs.geom)
```

Figure 1.1: Buffers around store locations grouped and unioned by neighborhood

```
10              )
11          ) as pop,
12          st_area(st_transform(d.geom, 3857)) as area
13      from
14          d
15          join nys_2021_census_block_groups bgs on st_intersects(bgs.geom, d.geom)
16      group by
17          d.geom,
18          d.neighborhood
19  )
```

In our final step we will simply calculate the population density for each of these areas:

Listing 1.7: Calculate population density

```
1  select
2      *,
3      pop / area as potential
4  from
5      e
```

And our final query:

Listing 1.8: Final query

```
1  -- Selects necessary data for Duane Reade locations
```

```
 2  with a as (
 3      select
 4          id,
 5          amenity,
 6          brand,
 7          name,
 8          geom
 9      from
10          nyc_pharmacies
11      where
12          name ilike '%duane%'
13  ),
14
15  -- Spatially join the Duane Reade stores to neighborhoods and adds neighborhood names
16  b as (
17      select
18          a.*,
19          b.neighborhood
20      from
21          a
22          join nyc_neighborhoods b on st_intersects(a.geom, b.geom)
23  ),
24
25  -- Creates a buffer for each store
26  c as (
27      select
28          id,
29          st_buffer(st_transform(geom, 3857), 800) as buffer,
30          neighborhood
31      from
32          b
33  ),
34
35  -- Union the buffers together by neighborhood
36  d as (
37      select
38          st_transform(st_union(buffer), 4326) as geom,
39          neighborhood
40      from
41          c
42      group by
43          neighborhood
44  ),
45
46  -- Calculates the proportional population for each group of buffers
47  -- and also the area of the grouped buffers
48  e as (
49      select
50          d.*,
51          sum(
52              bgs.population * (
53                  st_area(st_intersection(d.geom, bgs.geom)) / st_area(bgs.geom)
54              )
55          ) as pop,
56          st_area(st_transform(d.geom, 3857)) as area
57      from
58          d
59          join nys_2021_census_block_groups bgs on st_intersects(bgs.geom, d.geom)
60      group by
61          d.geom,
62          d.neighborhood
63  )
64
65  -- Calculates the population density
66  select
```

```
67      neighborhood,
68      pop / area as potential
69  from
70      e
71  order by
72      pop / area desc
```

And we can see the top five neighborhoods for the competitor to focus their search:

neighborhood	potential
Kips Bay	0.02320599976630974
Inwood	0.023181512204697885
Fordham	0.022357258309427155
Gramercy	0.021964586699969726
East Village	0.021819711504376737

While this is a simple example you can take this base and add more variables, expand areas, and perform multiple different ways to analyze market potential. Another great example of this is an analysis looking at a new distribution center location of a company that focuses on small towns. When the company located their site for a new location using a radius of 500 miles, it is possible to count the number of towns that have a store already and towns that do not, representing the potential footprint expansion for that company.

1.2 Similarity search or twin areas

Calculating twin areas, or performing a similarity search, is another analysis we can perform to find similarity between one target area and multiple areas that contain the same data points. We can do this with our neighborhoods and trees to find the neighborhood that has the most similar tree makeup as Harlem in Manhattan. To do this we first need to create a new table with columns that contain various tree types as well as their percentage of the total trees in the neighborhood:

Listing 1.9: Neighborhood similarity based on tree type

```
1   create table tree_similarity as
2
3   -- Finds the count of all trees in each neighborhood
4   with a as (
5       select
6           count(t.*) as total_trees,
7           n.neighborhood
8       from
9           nyc_2015_tree_census t
10          join nyc_neighborhoods n on st_intersects(t.geom, n.geom)
11      group by
12          n.neighborhood
13  )
14
15  -- Finds the count of each type of tree in each neighborhood
16  select
17      n.neighborhood,
18      (
19          count(t.*) filter (
20              where
21                  t.spc_common ilike '%pine%'
22          ) :: numeric / a.total_trees
23      ) as pine,
```

```
24      (
25          count(t.*) filter (
26              where
27                  t.spc_common ilike '%maple%'
28          ) :: numeric / a.total_trees
29      ) as maple,
30      (
31          count(t.*) filter (
32              where
33                  t.spc_common ilike '%linden%'
34          ) :: numeric / a.total_trees
35      ) as linden,
36      (
37          count(t.*) filter (
38              where
39                  t.spc_common ilike '%honeylocust%'
40          ) :: numeric / a.total_trees
41      ) as honeylocust,
42      (
43          count(t.*) filter (
44              where
45                  t.spc_common ilike '%oak%'
46          ) :: numeric / a.total_trees
47      ) as oak
48
49  -- Joins the above data with data from the original CTE
50  from
51      nyc_2015_tree_census t
52      join nyc_neighborhoods n on st_intersects(t.geom, n.geom)
53      join a using (neighborhood)
54  group by
55      n.neighborhood,
56      a.total_trees
```

First we calculate the count of the total trees in our subquery, so we don't have to do that each time going forward. Then we use FILTER to do a conditional count and then cast it to the numeric data type. From here we can turn this into a table to perform our queries on the table, rather than a query each time. Then we perform a JOIN with our normal ST_Intersects pattern. We can make this into a table, so we can use it later on as needed.

Now while there are far more structured ways to find similarity from one are to others such as using Principal Component analysis outlined in this blog post[121], for our purposes we will use a simple, yet effective, technique to create a composite score that measures how different the tree count by species is from Harlem. You could change this to density of trees by area or any other measure that you see fit. But for the first step let's calculate the difference from the original dataset.

Listing 1.10: Difference compared to our target neighborhood

```
1   with a as (
2       select
3           *
4       from
5           tree_similarity
6       where
7           neighborhood = 'Harlem'
8   )
9   select
10      t.neighborhood,
11
12      -- Here we subtract the values from our target neighborhood in table "t"
```

---

[121]https://carto.com/blog/spatial-data-science-site-planning

```
13        -- which is Harlem, from the average values across the city
14        t.pine - a.pine as pine_dif,
15        t.maple - a.maple as maple_dif,
16        t.oak - a.oak as oak_dif,
17        t.linden - a.linden as linden_dif,
18        t.honeylocust - a.honeylocust as honeylocust_dif
19    from
20        tree_similarity t,
21        a
22    where
23        t.neighborhood != 'Harlem'
```

Here we end up with data that will show us the difference in each tree category from Harlem which will be either a negative or positive number, so the closer to 0 the more similar it is to that specific tree species in Harlem. Now of course the numbers can vary quite a bit between the neighborhoods so in this case we will normalize our data from 0 to 1. The way to do this is to take the value in the row and subtract the minimum from that column of data, and then divide it by the difference between the maximum and minimum values in the column. In equation form:

```
zi = (xi - min(x)) / (max(x) - min(x))
```

As you will see below this will become quite a long query, so it will be annotated with comments that correspond to the detailed notes in the list below:

- A: This is the first step of finding the difference between the tree species count in Harlem compared to ever other neighborhood
- B: Here we will find the minimum and maximum values for every column and store those values in an array, so we can save some keystrokes in this query and the next
- C: Here we are doing three things
    - First we find the absolute value of the difference, which will make all the results positive numbers. This means that the closer to 0, the more similar to the tree makeup in Harlem
    - Then we will calculate the 0 to 1 scaled index. This will seem backwards most would interpret 1 as a better score, but in our case 0 is in fact a score closer to the tree composition in Harlem
    - Which means we will subtract the 0 to 1 value from 1 to reverse the index so now the closer to 1, the closer to the tree counts in Harlem
- D: Here we add the values for each tree species for each row and then divide it by 5 so we can return the index from 1 to 0

Listing 1.11: Final query

```
1   create table harlem_tree_similarity as with a as (
2       select
3           *
4       from
5           tree_similarity
6       where
7           neighborhood = 'Harlem'
8   ),
9
10  -- A: Find the difference between Harlem and all other neighborhoods
11  b as (
12      select
13          t.neighborhood,
14          t.pine - a.pine as pine_dif,
15          t.maple - a.maple as maple_dif,
16          t.oak - a.oak as oak_dif,
```

```
17          t.linden - a.linden as linden_dif,
18          t.honeylocust - a.honeylocust as honeylocust_dif
19      from
20          tree_similarity t,
21          a
22      where
23          t.neighborhood != 'Harlem'
24  ),
25
26  -- B: Find the min and max values in each column and store it as an array
27  c as (
28      select
29          array [min(pine_dif), max(pine_dif)] as pine,
30          array [min(maple_dif), max(maple_dif)] as maple,
31          array [min(oak_dif), max(oak_dif)] as oak,
32          array [min(linden_dif), max(linden_dif)] as linden,
33          array [min(honeylocust_dif), max(honeylocust_dif)] as honeylocust
34      from
35          b
36  ),
37
38  -- C: Find the absolute value of each difference value, normalize the data, and subtract that value from 1
39  d as (
40      select
41          b.neighborhood,
42          1 - (abs(b.pine_dif) - c.pine [1]) / (c.pine [2] - c.pine [1]) as pine_norm,
43          1 - (b.maple_dif - c.maple [1]) / (c.maple [2] - c.maple [1]) as maple_norm,
44          1 - (b.oak_dif - c.oak [1]) / (c.oak [2] - c.oak [1]) as oak_norm,
45          1 - (b.linden_dif - c.linden [1]) / (c.linden [2] - c.linden [1]) as linden_norm,
46          1 - (b.honeylocust_dif - c.honeylocust [1]) / (c.honeylocust [2] - c.honeylocust [1]) as honeylocust_norm
47      from
48          b,
49          c
50  )
51
52  -- D: Add up and divide the values
53  select
54      neighborhood,
55      (
56          pine_norm + maple_norm + oak_norm + linden_norm + honeylocust_norm
57      ) / 5 as final
58  from
59      d
60  order by
61      2 desc
```

And with our new table we can check the results and style them in QGIS to see which neighborhoods are the most similar after we create a new table joining the neighborhoods to the geometries (Figure 1.2, on the next page):

Listing 1.12: Create a new table for QGIS

```
1  create table harlem_tree_similarity_geo as
2  select
3      s.*,
4      h.geom
5  from
6      harlem_tree_similarity s
7      join nyc_hoods h using (neighborhood)
```

Figure 1.2: Similarity score in QGIS compared to Harlem

1.3   Suitability or composite score

An analysis that has proved highly effective and useful for combining datasets and creating analysis outputs that can be easily understood by many audiences is using composite scoring. Once again, there are more advanced methods to performing this analysis such as using residuals from machine learning analysis. This analysis only uses the data in a normalized form along with other data. You can also weight variables by multiplying them by a fraction, for example if you want to weight a variable half as much as the other variables you can multiply the final output by 0.5.

While you can use geometries to do this analysis I recommend using a spatial index since it creates areas of equal area and spotting trends that might be hidden inside polygons that vary by size and extent. For this example we will be using four datasets to find a suitable area in New York City using three demographic variables and tree counts in each H3 cell grid using the H3 functions in PostGIS. We will try and find areas with the highest number of trees, areas with median annual household incomes closest to $70,000, areas with a median age closest to 35, and areas with the highest population.

Again we will use our US Census Block Group data for New York City to create our H3 layer. We need to perform two additional steps before writing our query. First is that we need to assign an H3 index to our trees, which we can do by using the h3_lat_lng_to_cell function from the H3 library. First we need to create a new column on our dataset:

Listing 1.13: Add H3 column

```
1   alter table
2       nyc_2015_tree_census
3   add
```

```
4       column h3 text
```

And then update that column with our new H3 index, at level 10:

Listing 1.14: Update the table
```
1   update
2       nyc_2015_tree_census
3   set
4       h3 = h3_lat_lng_to_cell(geom, 10)
```

Next we need to add H3 cells to fill in our polygons of the census block groups and for this we can use a function called `h3_polygon_to_cells`. This function will not produce any overlapping H3 cells since it uses the centroids of the cells to determine if it falls in or out of the target polygon. As described in the source H3 documentation[122]:

Containment is determined by the cells' centroids. A partitioning using the GeoJSON-like data structure, where polygons cover an area without overlap, will result in a partitioning in the H3 grid, where cells cover the same area without overlap.

To do this we will create a new table with the resulting H3 cells by selecting the block groups that fall within the New York City counties (Figure 1.3).

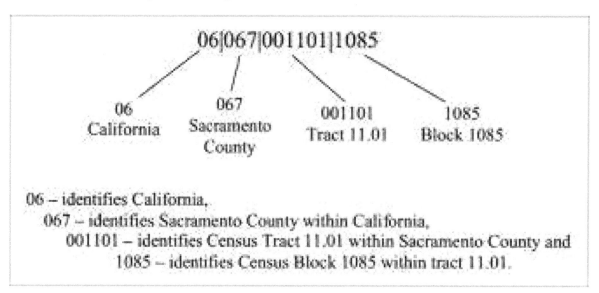

Figure 1.3: US Census FIPS Code breakdown (US Census)

Listing 1.15: Create our H3 polygon table
```
1   create table nyc_bgs_h3s as
2   select
3       geoid,
4       h3_polygon_to_cells(geom, 10)
5   from
6       nys_2021_census_block_groups
7   where
8       left(geoid, 5) in ('36061', '36005', '36047', '36081', '36085')
```

Which we can now see our data from our new table showing the first 5 rows:

---
[122]https://h3geo.org/docs/api/regions#polygontocells

geoid	h3_polygon_to_cells
360050001000	8a2a100f406ffff
360050001000	8a2a100f46a7fff
360050001000	8a2a100f4047fff
360050001000	8a2a100f5db7fff
360050001000	8a2a100f478ffff

As you can see there are multiple indexes for each block group ID, and we can also see how many H3 cells exist for each block group:

Listing 1.16: Count H3 cells by Block Group ID

```
1   select
2       geoid,
3       count(*)
4   from
5       nyc_bgs_h3s
6   group by
7       geoid
8   order by
9       count(*) desc
10  limit
11      5
```

geoid	count
360819901000	8663
360859901000	5419
360810716001	1270
360470702030	1200
360479901000	1177

So now we can proceed to creating our suitability scores. While many of the steps in this analysis could be combined for potential performance gains, this will show each step in more detail contained within its own CTE. We will go step by step and then show the complete query at the end. For our first step we simply need to find the number of trees within each H3 cell:

Listing 1.17: Building our suitability scores

```
1   with a as (
2       select
3           geoid,
4           count(*) as count
5       from
6           nyc_bgs_h3s_11
7       group by
8           geoid
9       order by
10          count(*) desc
11  )
```

Next we will join our table with our H3 values with the total population. This will be inaccurate since we are joining the total population for each block group to each occurrence of an H3 cell for that block group. We will divide the total population into each cell in the next step.

Listing 1.18: Join with population data

```
1  b as (
2      select
3          h3.geoid,
4          h3.h3_polygon_to_cells as h3,
5          c.population as pop
6      from
7          nyc_bgs_h3s h3
8          join nys_2021_census_block_groups c on h3.geoid = c.geoid
9  )
```

Next we will divide the population evenly among each H3 cell within each block group using the count from our first CTE table with the alias a:

Listing 1.19: Dividing population among H3 cells

```
1  c as (
2      select
3          b.pop :: numeric / a.count :: numeric as pop,
4          b.h3,
5          b.geoid
6      from
7          b
8          join a using (geoid)
9  )
```

In our fourth step we will build our calculations to find areas that are closest to our target values of $70,000 of median household income and median age of 35. To do this we will use the same process as the Harlem tree similarity analysis:

- Subtract the value for each row from the target values
- Turn the negative values into positive values resulting in a value of 0 being the best match

Listing 1.20: Finding the closest values

```
1  d as (
2      select
3          c.*,
4          abs(70000 - bgs.income) as income,
5          abs(35 - bgs.age) as age
6      from
7          c
8          join nys_2021_census_block_groups bgs using (geoid)
9  )
```

This will return data that looks like this:

pop	h3	geoid	income	age
179.25000000	8a2a100d688ffff	360610114011	180001	11.600000
1346.0000000	8a2a100882a7fff	360610175004	180001	24
164.50000000	8a2a1072536ffff	360610103002	180001	1.6000000
164.50000000	8a2a1072534ffff	360610103002	180001	1.6000000
164.50000000	8a2a100d2cb7fff	360610103002	180001	1.6000000

Our fifth step will simply join the H3 index of the previous CTE to the count of trees in each H3 cell from our trees dataset:

Listing 1.21: Joining the index to the tree counts

```
1   e as (
2       select
3           d.h3,
4           count(t.ogc_fid) as trees
5       from
6           d
7           join nyc_2015_tree_census t on d.h3 :: text = t.h3
8       group by
9           d.h3
10  )
```

The sixth step will look similar to the code we wrote in our similarity search query to calculate the minimum and maximum values across each column, so we can use those to normalize our data in the next step. Once again we will use arrays to cut down on keystrokes:

Listing 1.22: Mix/max as arrays

```
1   f as (
2       select
3           array [min(trees), max(trees)] as trees_s,
4           array [min(pop), max(pop)] as pop_s,
5           array [min(income), max(income)] as income_s,
6           array [min(age), max(age)] as age_s
7       from
8           e
9           join d on d.h3 = e.h3
10  )
```

Resulting in one row of data:

trees_s	pop_s	income_s	age_s
{1,86}	{0,3481}	{0,180001}	{0,51}

The seventh step is to simply join the results we need from the data stored in the CTEs with the aliases d and e:

Listing 1.23: Joining our data

```
1   g as (
2       select
3           e.trees,
4           d.age,
5           d.income,
6           d.pop,
7           d.h3
8       from
9           d
10          join e on d.h3 = e.h3
11  )
```

Resulting data will look like this:

trees	age	income	pop	h3
30	12.5		219.8333333	8a2a1001aa57fff
22	12.5		219.8333333	8a2a1001aacfff
4	12.5		219.8333333	8a2a1001aaefff

...continued on next page

trees	age	income	pop	h3
15	12.5		219.8333333	8a2a1001aac7fff
17	12.5		219.8333333	8a2a1001aae7fff

And our eighth and final CTE is to calculate the normalized values for each feature from 1 to 0. For the population and age values we will reverse these by subtracting the normalized data from 1, since in the base data 0 represents the best fit just as we did in the previous analysis.

Listing 1.24: Calculating normalized values

```
1   h as (
2     select
3       g.h3,
4
5       -- For each step we calculate the target value and subtract the minimum, then
6       -- divide it by the result of the difference of the largest and smallest value
7       (
8         (g.trees :: numeric - f.trees_s [1]) /(f.trees_s [2] - f.trees_s [1])
9       ) as trees_i,
10
11      -- Here we subtract the result from 1 to invert it
12      1 - ((g.age - f.age_s [1]) /(f.age_s [2] - f.age_s [1])) as age_i,
13      1 - (
14        (g.income - f.income_s [1]) /(f.income_s [2] - f.income_s [1])
15      ) as income_i,
16      ((g.pop - f.pop_s [1]) /(f.pop_s [2] - f.pop_s [1])) as pop_i
17    from
18      g,
19      f
20  )
```

h3	trees_i	age_i	income_i	pop_i
8a2a1001aa57fff	0.341176470	0.754901960		0.063152350
8a2a1001aacffff	0.247058823	0.754901960		0.063152350
8a2a1001aaefff	0.035294117	0.754901960		0.063152350
8a2a1001aac7fff	0.164705882	0.754901960		0.063152350
8a2a1001aae7fff	0.188235294	0.754901960	0.063152350	

And the last step is to query all our results and create one final index column by adding each individual index together. We can divide this by 4 if we want otherwise we can leave it which means a perfect fit will have a value of 4.

Listing 1.25: Final query

```
1   select
2     *,
3     trees_i + age_i + income_i + pop_i
4   from
5     h
```

h3	trees_i	age_i	income_i	pop_i	final_index
8a2a1001bd97fff	0.1764705	0.89803	0.98760006	0.04356	2.1056797282

…continued on next page

h3	trees_i	age_i	income_i	pop_i	final_index
8a2a1001bda7fff	0.2352941	0.89803	0.98760006	0.04356	2.1645032576
8a2a1001aadffff	0.0705882	0.89803	0.98760006	0.04356	1.9997973752
8a2a1001bd87fff	0.1647058	0.89803	0.98760006	0.04356	2.0939150223
8a2a1001bd9ffff	0.0000000	0.89803	0.98760006	0.04356	1.9292091399

And here is the complete query all together:

Listing 1.26: Full query

```
1   -- Get the count of cells in each block group
2   with a as (
3       select
4           geoid,
5           count(*) as count
6       from
7           nyc_bgs_h3s
8       group by
9           geoid
10      order by
11          count(*) desc
12  ),
13
14  -- Join the total population to each H3 cell
15  b as (
16      select
17          h3.geoid,
18          h3.h3_polygon_to_cells as h3,
19          c.population as pop
20      from
21          nyc_bgs_h3s h3
22          join nys_2021_census_block_groups c on h3.geoid = c.geoid
23  ),
24
25  -- Find the proportional population by dividing the total
26  -- population by the H3 cell count per block group
27  c as (
28      select
29          b.pop :: numeric / a.count :: numeric as pop,
30          b.h3,
31          b.geoid
32      from
33          b
34          join a using (geoid)
35  ),
36
37  -- Find the scaled values for each target data point
38  d as (
39      select
40          c.*,
41          abs(70000 - bgs.income) as income,
42          abs(35 - bgs.age) as age
43      from
44          c
45          join nys_2021_census_block_groups bgs using (geoid)
46  ),
47
48  -- Get the tree count in each cell
49  e as (
50      select
51          d.h3,
52          count(t.ogc_fid) as trees
```

```
53    from
54        d
55        join nyc_2015_tree_census t on d.h3 :: text = t.h3
56    group by
57        d.h3
58  ),
59
60  -- Add the min and max values for each data point to an array
61  f as (
62    select
63        array [min(trees), max(trees)] as trees_s,
64        array [min(pop), max(pop)] as pop_s,
65        array [min(income), max(income)] as income_s,
66        array [min(age), max(age)] as age_s
67    from
68        e
69        join d on d.h3 = e.h3
70  ),
71
72  -- Join the two previous CTEs together
73  g as (
74    select
75        e.trees,
76        d.age,
77        d.income,
78        d.pop,
79        d.h3
80    from
81        d
82        join e on d.h3 = e.h3
83  ),
84
85  -- Calculate the 0 to 1 index
86  h as (
87    select
88        g.h3,
89        (
90            (g.trees :: numeric - f.trees_s [1]) /(f.trees_s [2] - f.trees_s [1])
91        ) as trees_i,
92        1 - ((g.age - f.age_s [1]) /(f.age_s [2] - f.age_s [1])) as age_i,
93        1 - (
94            (g.income - f.income_s [1]) /(f.income_s [2] - f.income_s [1])
95        ) as income_i,
96        ((g.pop - f.pop_s [1]) /(f.pop_s [2] - f.pop_s [1])) as pop_i
97    from
98        g,
99        f
100 )
101
102 -- Add up to find the final index value
103 select
104     *,
105     trees_i + age_i + income_i + pop_i
106 from
107     h
```

If you want to visualize this data in QGIS or another tool you will need to use the function h3_cell_to_boundary to turn the H3 cell into a geometry. However, if we use KeplerGL, an open source tool originally developed by Uber (which was also where H3 originated) can read the H3 index as a string without a geometry.

To do this we first need to download our results as a CSV file, which we can do with a click inside of pgAdmin. Once the query has completed, you should see a download button (Figure 1.4, on the next page).

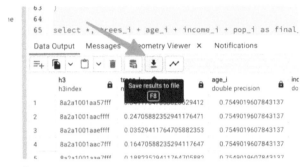

Figure 1.4: Exporting our CSV file

You will then be prompted to give the file a name (Figure 1.5).

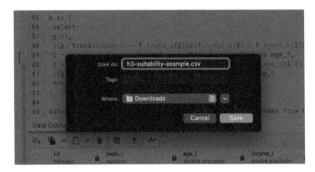

Figure 1.5: Saving the CSV file

Once you have completed these steps you can navigate to the Kepler website[123] and click the "GET STARTED" button on the homepage (Figure 1.6, on the next page).

The first thing you should see after clicking this button is a prompt to upload data, in this case the CSV which we just created. Go ahead and either navigate to the file on your computer by clicking the "browse your files" link or drag it onto the upload area (Figure 1.7, on the following page):

The map will open, and it should automatically recognize that you have an H3 index in your data and style it for you too (Figure 1.8, on page 381):

Personally, I think it is awesome that we just created a map visualization without a geometry. It is one of the things I greatly appreciate about spatial indexes is it is visually easy to approach and also creates compelling visualizations. We can also add a filter to answer our question of what are the most suitable areas for our study. To do so first navigate to the filter icon at the top of the left-hand menu (Figure 1.9, on page 381):

Once you have clicked that button, then click "+ **Add Filter**" (Figure 1.10, on page 382):

In the next menu click on the dropdown menu and then select the value for "**final_index**" (Figure 1.11, on page 382):

Now you can select the filter to see the areas with the best results. First the most suitable areas (Figure 1.12, on page 383):

---

[123]https://kepler.gl/

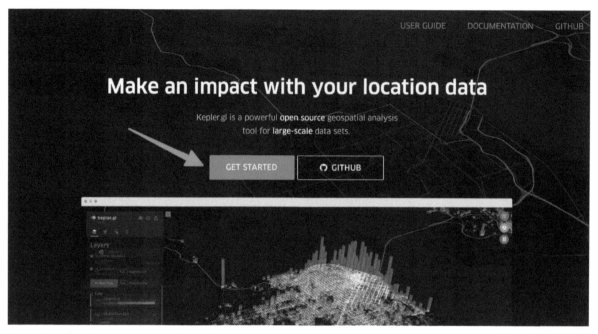

Figure 1.6: Starting your map in Kepler GL

Figure 1.7: Loading data into Kepler GL

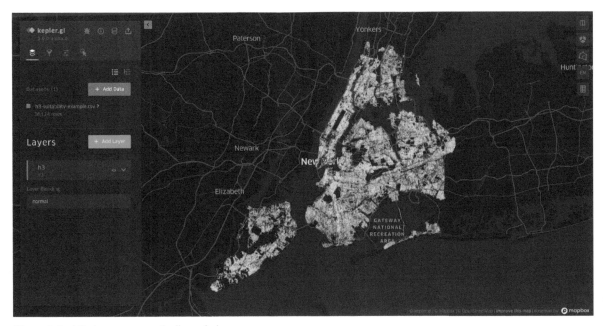

Figure 1.8: H3 data, automatically styled

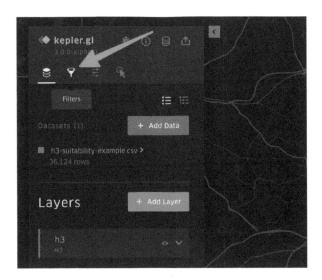

Figure 1.9: Adding a filter

Figure 1.10: Adding a filter

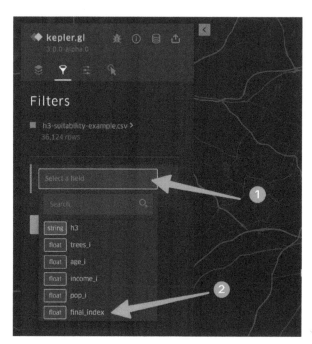

Figure 1.11: Selecting your filter field

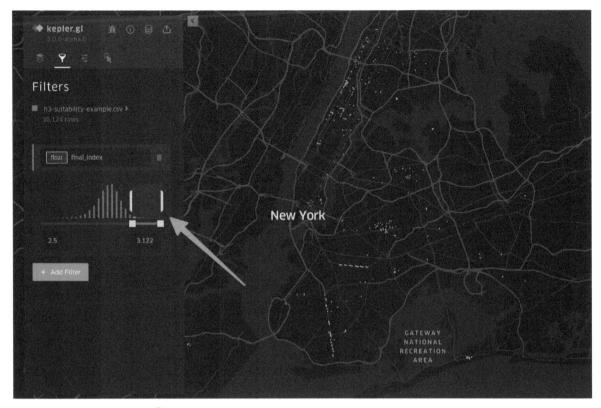

Figure 1.12: Adjusting your filter

It looks like there are some suitable areas in Brooklyn along to well known tree-line parkways (the pattern of straight lines): Eastern Parkway in the north and Ocean Parkway in the south. There are also several pockets in Queens and upper Manhattan. We can also see the least suitable areas (Figure 1.13, on page 384):

Several areas stand out here in Manhattan in SoHo and very clearly in the Upper East Side, as well as neighborhoods on the far eastern edge of Queens bordering Nassau County: Douglaston, Little Neck, and Glen Oaks.

1.4   Mergers and acquisitions

In our final suitability analysis we will analyze a common scenario where two entities, be it retail stores, bank branches, grocery stores, or any type of physical location that has a spatial market overlap, want to merge in the most effective way to combine their footprint. The goal is to do this in a way that finds the locations that make the most sense to stop operating or convert to a new model without reducing trade area coverage.

There are several ways to address this, including weighting the locations by their trade area coverage, proximity to competitor locations, or proximity to access points like public transportation, highways, etc. All of those features can be easily added to the trade areas once they are created using some of the techniques we have already discussed so far in this book, so this query will simply show how to accomplish the spatial aspects of the problem. In this example we will use two pharmacy chains, Duane Reade and CVS, and find the most optimal solution to consolidate their physical footprint. Our first step is to calculate the population within 800 meters of each store location. We will use the overlap method to only count the population that falls inside the buffer and turn this into a new table:

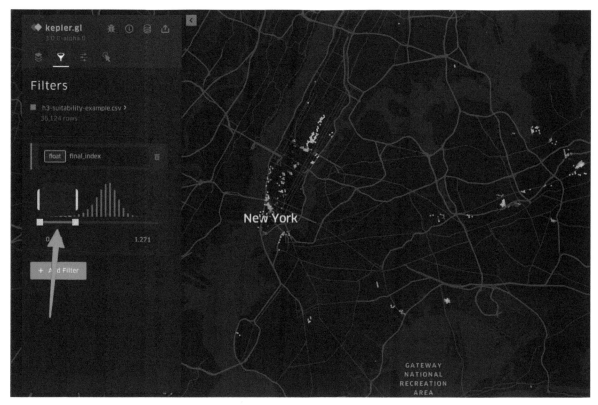

Figure 1.13: Finding the least suitable matches

Listing 1.27: Create our pharmacies enriched table

```
1   create table pharmacy_stats as
2   select
3       p.id,
4       p.amenity,
5       p.brand,
6       p.name,
7       p.geom,
8
9       -- Add a buffer of 800 meters for later use
10      st_transform(st_buffer(st_transform(p.geom, 3857), 800), 4326) as buffer,
11
12      -- Get the total proportional population for each buffer
13      sum(
14          bgs.population * (
15              st_area(
16                  st_intersection(
17                      st_transform(st_buffer(st_transform(p.geom, 3857), 800), 4326),
18                      bgs.geom
19                  )
20              ) / st_area(bgs.geom)
21          )
22      ) as pop
23  from
24      nyc_pharmacies p
25      join nyc_2021_census_block_groups bgs on st_intersects(p.geom, st_transform(bgs.geom, 4326))
26
27  -- Get just the stores for CVS and Duane Reade
28  where
29      p.name ilike '%duane%'
```

```
30      or p.name ilike '%cvs%'
31   group by
32      p.id,
33      p.amenity,
34      p.brand,
35      p.name,
36      p.geom
```

Now we will start to find the stores we want to exclude from the final count. For that, let's see how many stores there are to begin (Figure 1.14):

Listing 1.28: Count Duane Reade and CVS locations

```
1   select
2       *
3   from
4       nyc_pharmacies
5   where
6       name ilike '%duane%'
7       or name ilike '%cvs%'
```

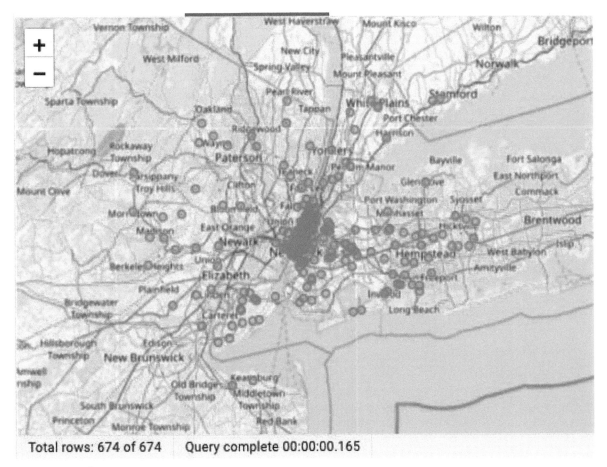

Total rows: 674 of 674   Query complete 00:00:00.165

Figure 1.14: All starting stores

At the beginning we have 674 total stores between the two brands in the greater New York City region, although we will limit the results to those just in New York City. Our first step will be to exclude any Duane Reade store that is within 200 meters of a CVS store. Our query begins with two CTEs to get our store data for each brand while also cresting a new column transforming the geometry to 3857. In the final CTE we use that new column to find the stores that fall within 200 meters, then see how many stores fall into that category, in this case 72 locations (keep in mind this is the number for the entire New York City metro area and in the final analysis we will only focus on the stores inside the New York City boundaries):

Listing 1.29: Remove Duane Reade locations within 200 meters

```
1   -- CTE with all Duane Reade locations
2   with dr as (
3       select
4           id,
5           amenity,
6           brand,
7           name,
8           geom,
9           st_transform(geom, 3857) as geom_3857
10      from
11          nyc_pharmacies
12      where
13          name ilike '%duane%'
14  ),
15
16  -- CTE with all CVS locations
17  cvs as (
18      select
19          id,
20          amenity,
21          brand,
22          name,
23          geom,
24          st_transform(geom, 3857) as geom_3857
25      from
26          nyc_pharmacies
27      where
28          name ilike '%cvs%'
29  ),
30
31  -- Find all Duane Reade locations within 200 meters of a CVS
32  remove_nearest as (
33      select
34          dr.*
35      from
36          dr,
37          cvs
38      where
39          st_dwithin(dr.geom_3857, cvs.geom_3857, 200)
40  )
41  select
42      count(*)
43  from
44      remove_nearest
```

We can also find the number of locations that have a 75% overlap of their buffer areas. To calculate the overlapping area of the Duane Reade buffers with the CVS buffers, divide by the area of the Duane Reade buffer in the WHERE clause and filter our the results where the area is greater than 0.75, which results in 31 total locations:

Listing 1.30: Remove locations with a 75 percent buffer overlap

```
1   with dr as (
2       select
3           *
4       from
5           pharmacy_stats
```

```
6      where
7          name ilike '%duane%'
8  )
9  select
10     dr.*,
11
12     -- Find the area of overlap between the two buffer groups
13     st_area(
14         st_intersection(pharmacy_stats.buffer, dr.buffer)
15     ) / st_area(dr.buffer)
16 from
17     dr
18     join pharmacy_stats on st_intersects(dr.buffer, pharmacy_stats.buffer)
19 where
20
21     -- Find the number of pharmacies that have an overlap greater than 75%
22     st_area(
23         st_intersection(pharmacy_stats.buffer, dr.buffer)
24     ) / st_area(dr.buffer) >.75
25     and pharmacy_stats.name ilike '%cvs%'
```

Since we did these analyses independently we have a few more steps to finish our analysis. First we want to see what our "before" scenario looks like which is the total combined trade area of the two brand's stores and the total population covered by that combined trade area. This means we want to union the 800 meter buffers of both locations so there is no double counting. In the CTE, we will create the unioned buffers followed by the area of all the buffers. Then we will intersect the unioned buffers with the block groups in the final query, which we need to do otherwise the intersection would go over each buffer which would account for counting population multiple times (Figure 1.15, on the following page):

Listing 1.31: Calculating our before scenario

```
1  with a as (
2      select
3
4          -- Union all buffers to find the "before" scenario total area
5          st_union(
6              st_transform(st_buffer(st_transform(p.geom, 3857), 800), 4326)
7          ) as buffer,
8          st_area(
9              st_union(st_buffer(st_transform(p.geom, 3857), 800))
10         ) as area
11     from
12         nyc_pharmacies p
13         join nyc_2021_census_block_groups bgs on st_intersects(
14             st_transform(st_buffer(st_transform(p.geom, 3857), 800), 4326),
15             st_transform(bgs.geom, 4326)
16         )
17     where
18         p.name ilike '%duane%'
19         or p.name ilike '%cvs%'
20 )
21 select
22     a.*,
23
24     -- Find the total population of all combined buffers
25     sum(
26         bgs.population * (
27             st_area(st_intersection(a.buffer, bgs.geom)) / st_area(bgs.geom)
28         )
29     ) as pop
30 from
31     a
```

```
32       join nyc_2021_census_block_groups bgs on st_intersects(a.buffer, st_transform(bgs.geom, 4326))
33    group by
34       1,
35       2
```

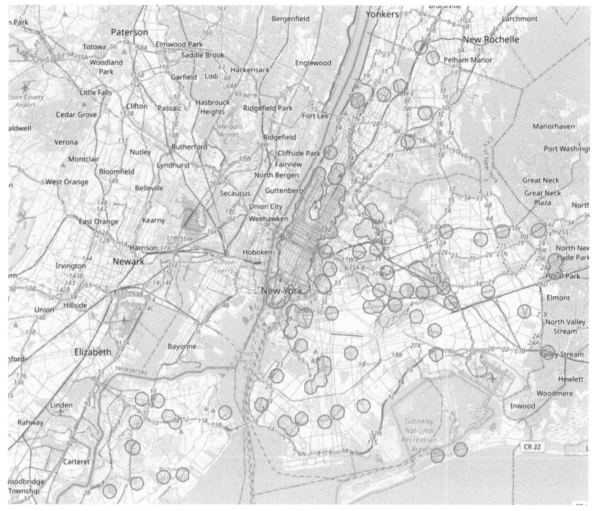

Figure 1.15: All unioned buffers in a before scenario

area	pop
224669913.8932964	2527400.3703658446
223115112.9693205	2512136.967491225

Here you can see that the combined coverage area covers about 224.7 square kilometers and about 2,527,400 people. To find out how our before and after scenarios look we first need to find the IDs of the stores we need to remove. The steps of the query are outlined below:

- First we have our *overlap* CTE which contains:
    - A CTE named dr to find the Duane Reade locations
    - A query that finds the locations that have a greater than 75% overlap with the buffers of CVS locations

- Then we perform our proximity analysis, with our first CTE named `dr` that finds all the Duane Reade locations while also creating a geometry with EPSG 3857
- We do the same for a CTE named `cvss`
- Then we have a CTE named `removed_nearest` that removes all the Duane Reade locations within 200 meters of a CVS
- We then UNION the two tables together to create a table with one column that contains the IDs of the Duane Reade locations that are to be removed

Listing 1.32: Final mergers query

```
 1   create table duane_reade_ids as with overlap as (
 2       with dr as (
 3           select
 4               *
 5           from
 6               pharmacy_stats
 7           where
 8               name ilike '%duane%'
 9       )
10
11       -- Find all the Duane Reade locations that have an overlap of over 75%
12       select
13           dr.id
14       from
15           dr
16           join pharmacy_stats on st_intersects(dr.buffer, pharmacy_stats.buffer)
17       where
18           st_area(
19               st_intersection(pharmacy_stats.buffer, dr.buffer)
20           ) / st_area(dr.buffer) >.75
21           and pharmacy_stats.name ilike '%cvs%'
22   ),
23
24   -- Select all Duane Reade stores
25   dr as (
26       select
27           id,
28           amenity,
29           brand,
30           name,
31           geom,
32           st_transform(geom, 3857) as geom_3857
33       from
34           nyc_pharmacies
35       where
36           name ilike '%duane%'
37   ),
38
39   -- Select all CVS stores
40   cvs as (
41       select
42           id,
43           amenity,
44           brand,
45           name,
46           geom,
47           st_transform(geom, 3857) as geom_3857
48       from
49           nyc_pharmacies
50       where
51           name ilike '%cvs%'
52   ),
53
54   -- Remove all the Duane Reade locations within 200 meters of a CVS
```

```
55  remove_nearest as (
56      select
57          dr.id
58      from
59          dr,
60          cvs
61      where
62          st_dwithin(dr.geom_3857, cvs.geom_3857, 200)
63  )
64  select
65      id
66  from
67      remove_nearest
68  union
69  select
70      id
71  from
72      overlap
```

From this we get 31 total Duane Reade locations that are to be removed. With that we can use the same query as before to calculate the combined area and population, with one extra CTE at the beginning that removes the stores that match the IDs that we plan to remove from consideration and change the nyc_pharmacies table name for the new CTE alias p otherwise the query remains unchanged (Figure 1.16, on the next page):

Listing 1.33: Putting it all together

```
1   -- We run the same query but we remove IDs not in the table we just created
2   with p as (
3       select
4           *
5       from
6           nyc_pharmacies
7       where
8           id not in (
9               select
10                  id
11              from
12                  duane_reade_ids
13          )
14  ),
15  a as (
16      select
17          st_union(
18              st_transform(st_buffer(st_transform(p.geom, 3857), 800), 4326)
19          ) as buffer,
20          st_area(
21              st_union(st_buffer(st_transform(p.geom, 3857), 800))
22          ) as area
23      from
24          nyc_pharmacies p
25          join nyc_2021_census_block_groups bgs on st_intersects(
26              st_transform(st_buffer(st_transform(p.geom, 3857), 800), 4326),
27              st_transform(bgs.geom, 4326)
28          )
29      where
30          p.name ilike '%duane%'
31          or p.name ilike '%cvs%'
32  )
33  select
34      a.*,
35      sum(
36          bgs.population * (
37              st_area(st_intersection(a.buffer, bgs.geom)) / st_area(bgs.geom)
```

```
38            )
39        ) as pop
40    from
41        a
42        join nyc_2021_census_block_groups bgs on st_intersects(a.buffer, st_transform(bgs.geom, 4326))
43    group by
44        1,
45        2
```

Figure 1.16: Our final output

area	pop
223115112.9693205	2512136.967491225

As you can see our new area is 223.1 and population covered is 2,512,136, a difference of 1.6 square kilometers and 15,264. Overall this allows the new operations to continue to function efficiently!

2. Working With Raster Data in PostGIS

Up until this point we have only worked with vector data and for most of the history of spatial SQL, the databases that utilized it only supported vector data. Of course, raster data plays an important role in spatial analytics. At some point, from what I can gather (it was not exactly clear from paging through 16 pages of PostGIS release notes), PostGIS added support for raster data somewhere between PostGIS 1.5 and 2.1. As of PostGIS 3.0 all the raster functionality has been rolled into its own extension.

2.1   Raster Ingest

We will use the raster extension to perform a variety of different analyses, but first we need to import some data into our database. To do so we will use a tool called raster2pgsql which will generate an SQL file to ingest our raster data into PostGIS. To do this, we need to create a second Docker image of PostGIS to access this functionality. We cannot use our existing image since it won't work, and generally running those commands in the same location as our data is not a best practice.

Luckily for us, the main PostGIS Docker instance has a version of PostGIS that we can use just for this purpose. To get started we can pull the image using the docker pull command in our terminal. Open a new terminal and run this command:

```
docker pull postgis/postgis:15-master
```

Alternatively you can also do this in the Docker desktop app. Go to the top search bar and search for **postgis**. Look for the container named "**postgis/postgis**". If you don't see it, you can search for **postgis/postgis** directly (Figure 2.1, on the following page).

Once you have found it you can hover over that item and open the menu labeled "Tag". You can select any image you want, but to match the instructions and version we are using in the book search for the version with the tag 15-master and click on it and then click "Pull".

You can validate that the image was pulled via either process by clicking on the "Images" tab on the left-hand side of Docker desktop, and you should see the image listed there (Figure 2.2, on the next page):

To run the image we can also use the terminal or Docker desktop. To use the terminal you can enter this command. Note there is one change we need to make which is highlighted in the code:

Listing 2.1: Run an additional Docker container

```
1   docker run --name mini-postgis -p 35432:5432 --network="host"
2   -v /Users/mattforrest/Documents/spatial-sql-book/raster:/mnt/mydata
3   -e POSTGRES_USER=admin -e POSTGRES_PASSWORD=password -d postgis/postgis:15-master
```

The -v flag creates a volume within the Docker container that connects to a folder on your computer. In this case we will create a folder named "raster" which will store all the data that we want to import into our main PostGIS database. You will need to replace this section with the folder location on your computer where that is stored. On my computer my data is stored at this location:

```
/Users/mattforrest/Documents/spatial-sql-book/raster
```

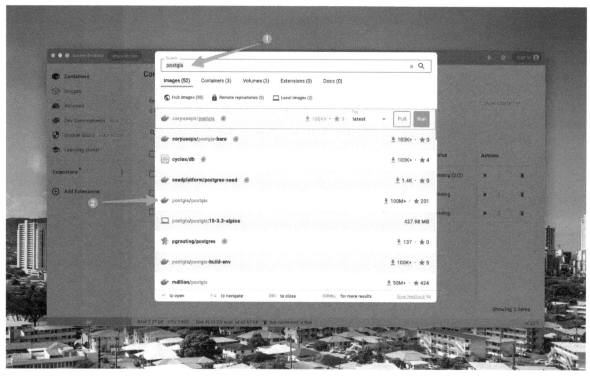

Figure 2.1: Creating a second PostGIS Docker instance

Name	Tag	Status
postgis/postgis 5c31842a05f0 ⚠ AMD64	15-3.3-alpine	Unused
kartoza/postgis		

Figure 2.2: Our second instance in Docker Desktop

Once you have done that you can go ahead and run the command in the terminal (Figure 2.3, on page 395):

Note that you may or may not see a second warning about an image platform issue (*linux/arm64/v8r*). This is because my computer has an Apple Silicon CPU not an Intel CPU, but this will work all the same. To validate that the container is running after using either method, click on "Containers" and you should see something like this (Figure 2.4, on the next page):

Now that we have our container running we are going to enable the `postgis_raster` extension in our main database. To do so we can run this command inside pgAdmin:

```
CREATE EXTENSION postgis_raster
```

Once complete we are going to open a new terminal session to run the command to import raster data into our main database. Once again you can open the terminal session by command line or use the terminal tied to the container within Docker desktop. In this case we will use our local terminal.

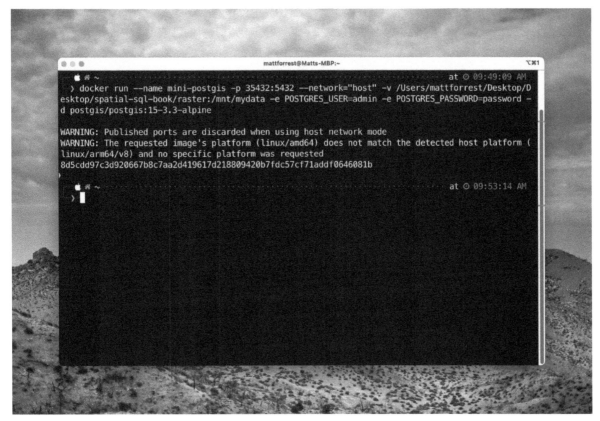

Figure 2.3: Running our instance in the command line

Figure 2.4: You will see the new instance in your Docker Desktop

The first command will connect our terminal to our Docker container. This will work if you also used the name *"mini-postgis"* otherwise you will need to change it to the name you used (Figure 2.5, on page 396):

```
docker container exec -it mini-postgis bash
```

Next we can confirm that we have access to the `raster2pgsql` library by simply running that command in the terminal (Figure 2.6, on page 397):

Make sure to double check that you placed the file `denver-elevation.tif` into the `/raster` folder.

And finally we will run our command to ingest our data. It is actually two commands strung together that will complete the process in one step rather than two:

Listing 2.2: Running raster2pgsql

Figure 2.5: Running shell commands inside your Docker container

```
1   raster2pgsql -s 4269 -I -C -M mnt/mydata/denver-elevation.tif -t 128x128 \
2   -F denver_elevation | psql -d gis -h 127.0.0.1 -p 25432 -U docker -W
```

- **raster2pgsql** - Initiates the command
- **-s 4269** - This flags the source projection EPSG ID of the raster, in this case 4269
- **-I** - Creates a GIST index on ingest
- **-C** - Creates a standard set of constraints on the raster column
- **-M** - This will run a VACUUM ANALYZE statement on the table to ensure optimal performance when using the raster
- **mnt/mydata/denver-elevation.tif** - This tells the command to import our raster file from our mounted volume, which in effect is an alias to the location on your computer
- **-t 128x128** - Splits the raster up into tiles of 128 by 128 pixels for faster calculations
- **-F denver_elevation_full** - This will add a column name of the raster name on to the raster
- **|** - This joins the first command with the second which will use the code generated by the first command to import the file into our database via the psql library
- **psql** - Starts the second command
- **-d gis** - Tells the command which database in our original PostGIS database to import the data into
- **-h 127.0.0.1** - Tells the command which host URL to use. 127.0.0.1 is just an alias for localhost, but we can't use localhost in the context of a container since localhost is in the container itself
- **-p 25432** - The port for our database
- **-U docker** - Username for our database
- **-W** - tells the command to skip the password prompt

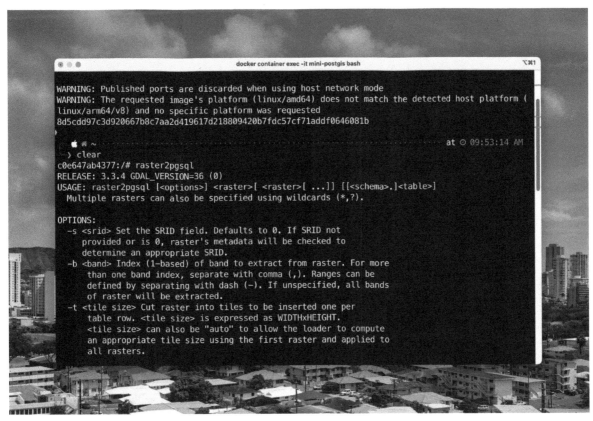

Figure 2.6: Making sure you have access to raster2pgsql

Go ahead and run the command in your terminal. It will stay open during the import process. Once the command ends you should see an output like this in your terminal (Figure 2.7, on page 398):

This process may take a long time as the raster is large, but once it is complete you can confirm that the raster has imported by selecting it from pgAdmin:

Listing 2.3: Querying raster data in PostGIS

```
1  select
2      *
3  from
4      denver_elevation_full
```

You will see that there are three columns: rid, rast, and filename. Each row represents a raster tile of 128 by 128 pixels. We can also confirm that this imported correctly by opening the raster with QGIS (Figure 2.8, on page 399):

And that is it we have imported our raster data into PostGIS. There are many other options and ways to pull your data in including from storage sources like Amazon Web Services S3, so there are many options for you to use. But for now we can take a look at some ways to use the raster functions with PostGIS.

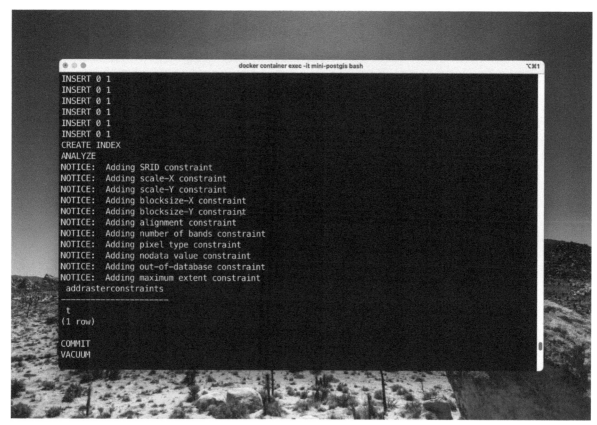

Figure 2.7: A complete ingest sequence

Raster contours

Seeing as we imported just imported elevation data into our database, a logical next step would be to create contour lines from our elevation raster. PostGIS has several functions[124] that allow you to perform analysis on rasters such as DEM analysis, map algebra, raster outputs, and more.

The specific function we will be using is ST_Contour which has the following signature:

```
setof record ST_Contour(raster rast, integer bandnumber, double precision level_
interval, double precision level_base, double precision[] fixed_
levels, boolean polygonize);
```

A few things to note:

1. First is that this function will return a set of records which means we will need to select the records out of the return value similar to when we have used ST_Dump.

2. Next is that since we imported our raster file as tiles, we will need to join those into one massive raster otherwise it would only run on one raster tile.

---

[124]https://postgis.net/docs/en/RT_reference.html

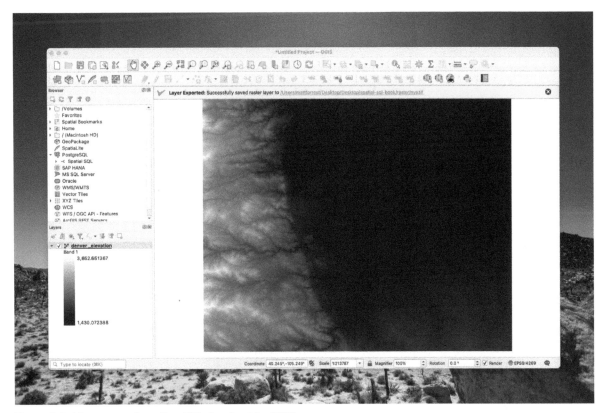

Figure 2.8: Your raster from PostGIS visualized in QGIS

3. The geometry that we are used to using is now replaced with the column rast and we need to designate a band (as there is only one in our raster it is 1).

Below is our query, and we can break apart each step:

Listing 2.4: Raster contours

```
1   with c as (
2       select
3           (st_contour(rast, 1, 200.00)).*
4       from
5           denver_elevation
6       where
7           filename = 'denver-elevation.tif'
8   )
9   select
10      st_transform(geom, 4326),
11      id,
12      value
13  from
14      c
```

- with c as (... - First we create a CTE to capture our values
- SELECT (ST_Contour(rast, 1, 500.00, 1430)).* - We have to select out all values from the ST_ Contour function. The arguments in order are:
    - raster - The raster column which is synonymous to geom
    - 1 - The band we want to build the contours on

- – 200.00 - The interval of the contours in meters
- FROM denver_elevation WHERE filename = 'denver-elevation.tif' - We select all the rasters that have the filename 'denver-elevation.tif' and close our CTE
- SELECT st_transform(geom, 4326), id, value FROM c - We select the id and value from the CTE and the geometry, transforming it to 4326 in the process

Go ahead and run the query and once it is complete you can check out the result (Figure 2.9, on the following page):

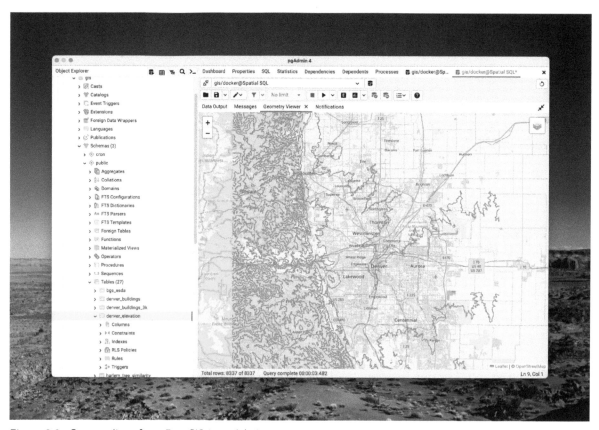

Figure 2.9: Contour lines from PostGIS in pgAdmin

If you create a table you can check it out in QGIS too and style it by the value (Figures 2.10, on page 401 and 2.11, on page 402):

2.2 Interpolation

Spatial interpolation, or the process of interpolating data over space where observations are unknown from known observation points, is a common analysis supported by tools like QGIS and workflows in Python. There are two primary methods for performing this analysis: inverse distance weighted (IDW) and krigging. Krigging would require some extra work to implement, although it is possible. PostGIS has already implemented a function for IDW which returns a raster with the interpolation. To do this we will import weather station data from the New York State Mesonet at the University of Albany which collects weather observations at stations across the state.

First let's import our data:

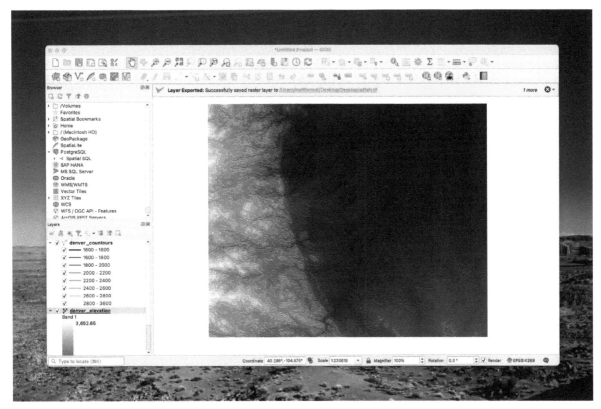

Figure 2.10: Contour lines overlayed with the original raster data

Listing 2.5: Importing NYS Mesonet data

```
1  ogr2ogr \
2  -f PostgreSQL PG:"host=localhost user=docker password=docker dbname=gis port=25432" nys_mesonet_202307.csv \
3  -dialect sqlite -sql 'select makepoint(cast("longitude [degrees_east]" as numeric), cast("latitude [degrees_north]" as numeric),
      AS geom, * from nys_mesonet_202307' \
4  -nln nys_mesonet_202307 -lco GEOMETRY_NAME=geom
```

Next there are three queries we need to run to generate our raster which we will walk through in detail.

These examples are from a blog post by Paul Ramsey from Crunchy Data[125] which walks through the process with a similar dataset. Let's take a look at our first query:

Listing 2.6: Interpolation Part 1

```
1  create table nys_mesonet_raster as with inputs as (
2     select
3         -- Sets the pixel size to 0.01 decimal degrees since
4         -- we are using EPSG 4326
5         0.01 :: float8 as pixelsize,
6
7         -- Sets the smoothing algorithm from "gdal_grid"
8         'invdist:power:5.5:smoothing:2.0' as algorithm,
9         st_collect(
10
11            -- Creates a geometry collection of our data and forces
12            -- a Z coodrinate of the max temparature
13            st_force3dz(
14                geom,
```

[125]https://www.crunchydata.com/blog/waiting-for-postgis-3.2-st_interpolateraster

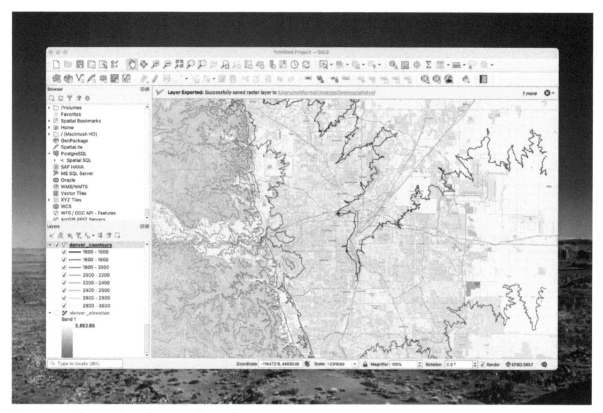

Figure 2.11: Contour lines from PostGIS in QGIS

```
15                   case
16                       when "apparent_temperature_max [degc]" = '' then null
17                       else "apparent_temperature_max [degc]" :: numeric
18                   end
19               )
20           ) as geom,
21
22           -- Expands the grid to add room around the edges
23           st_expand(st_collect(geom), 0.5) as ext
24       from
25           nys_mesonet_202307
26       where
27           time_end = '2023-07-23 12:00:00 EDT'
28   ),
```

First we are creating an input table from our Mesonet data. Below are the parameters we are passing into the query:

- `0.01::float8 AS pixelsize`
    - This defines the pixel size of the output raster in the unit of measurement of the projection (4326 in this case)
- `'invdist:power:5.5:smoothing:2.0' AS algorithm`
    - These are the options of the algorithm used to perform the interpolation which are pulled from the GDAL in the **gdal_grid** tool[126]

---

[126]https://gdal.org/programs/gdal_grid.html#interpolation-algorithms

- ST_Collect(ST_Force3DZ(geom, case when "apparent_temperature_max [degc]" = " then null else "apparent_temperature_max [degc]"::numeric end)) AS geom

    - This first collected the geometry into a geometry collection, forces the 3D or Z value which in this case will hold the value of the raster, and then adds the value onto the geometry. We use the CAST function since there are null values in the dataset.

- ST_Expand(ST_Collect(geom), 0.5) AS ext

    - This function expands the geometry bounding box and adds a buffer of 0.5 decimal degrees onto the bounding box

Next we will calculate the size of our raster using some calculation functions along with some PostgreSQL math functions:

Listing 2.7: Interpolation Part 2

```
1   sizes AS (
2     SELECT
3       ceil((ST_XMax(ext) - ST_XMin(ext)) / pixelsize) :: integer AS width,
4       ceil((ST_YMax(ext) - ST_YMin(ext)) / pixelsize) :: integer AS height,
5       ST_XMin(ext) AS upperleftx,
6       ST_YMax(ext) AS upperlefty
7     FROM
8       inputs
9   )
```

- ceil((ST_XMax(ext) - ST_XMin(ext))/pixelsize)::integer AS width
- ceil((ST_YMax(ext) - ST_YMin(ext))/pixelsize)::integer AS height

    - The two functions above find the width and height of the area of interest by subtracting the maximum and minimum X values, and the same for the Y values

- ST_XMin(ext) AS upperleftx
- ST_YMax(ext) AS upperlefty

    - These two functions find the upper corners of the area of interest

Finally, we pass the two tables we created onto the final function, ST_InterpolateRaster

Listing 2.8: Interpolation Part 3

```
1   SELECT
2
3       -- Sets 1 as the raster ID since we only have one raster
4       1 AS rid,
5       ST_InterpolateRaster(
6
7           -- The geometry collection that will be used to interpolate to the raster
8           geom,
9
10          -- The algorithm we defined
11          algorithm,
12          ST_SetSRID(
13
14              -- This creates the band
15              ST_AddBand(
16
17                  -- Creates the empty raster with our arguments from the previous CTEs
18                  ST_MakeEmptyRaster(width, height, upperleftx, upperlefty, pixelsize),
19
20                  -- Sets the default values as a 32 bit float
21                  '32BF'
22              ),
23
```

```
24              -- The SRID the raster will use
25              ST_SRID(geom)
26          )
27      ) AS rast
28  FROM
29      sizes,
30      inputs;
```

First we select 1 as our ID as there is only one raster being created. Then we pass in the geom column and algorithm column from the inputs. Then we have a long series of functions:

- First, in the innermost function we create an empty raster:

  - ST_MakeEmptyRaster(width, height, upperleftx, upperlefty, pixelsize)

- Next we add the band type which can be any number of combinations of bit sizes and options for integers or floats as shown in the documentation page for the function ST_BandPixelType.

  - ST_AddBand(INNERMOST_FUNCTION), '32BF')

- Finally we retrieve the SRID from the geometry and pass it to the function ST_SetSRID

  - ST_SetSRID(INNER_TWO_FUNCTIONS), ST_SRID(geom))

And here is the complete query:

Listing 2.9: Final interpolation query

```
1   create table nys_mesonet_raster as with inputs as (
2       select
3           -- Sets the pixel size to 0.01 decimal degrees since
4           -- we are using EPSG 4326
5           0.01 :: float8 as pixelsize,
6
7           -- Sets the smoothing algorithm from "gdal_grid"
8           'invdist:power:5.5:smoothing:2.0' as algorithm,
9           st_collect(
10
11              -- Creates a geometry collection of our data and forces
12              -- a Z coordinate of the max temperature
13              st_force3dz(
14                  geom,
15                  case
16                      when "apparent_temperature_max [degc]" = '' then null
17                      else "apparent_temperature_max [degc]" :: numeric
18                  end
19              )
20          ) as geom,
21
22          -- Expands the grid to add room around the edges
23          st_expand(st_collect(geom), 0.5) as ext
24      from
25          nys_mesonet_202307
26      where
27          time_end = '2023-07-23 12:00:00 EDT'
28  ),
29  sizes AS (
30    SELECT
31      ceil((ST_XMax(ext) - ST_XMin(ext)) / pixelsize) :: integer AS width,
32      ceil((ST_YMax(ext) - ST_YMin(ext)) / pixelsize) :: integer AS height,
33      ST_XMin(ext) AS upperleftx,
34      ST_YMax(ext) AS upperlefty
35    FROM
36      inputs
37  )
38  SELECT
```

```
39
40     -- Sets 1 as the raster ID since we only have one raster
41     1 AS rid,
42     ST_InterpolateRaster(
43
44         -- The geometry collection that will be used to interpolate to the raster
45         geom,
46
47         -- The algorithm we defined
48         algorithm,
49         ST_SetSRID(
50
51             -- This creates the band
52             ST_AddBand(
53
54                 -- Creates the empty raster with our arguments from the previous CTEs
55                 ST_MakeEmptyRaster(width, height, upperleftx, upperlefty, pixelsize),
56
57                 -- Sets the default values as a 32 bit float
58                 '32BF'
59             ),
60
61             -- The SRID the raster will use
62             ST_SRID(geom)
63         )
64     ) AS rast
65 FROM
66     sizes,
67     inputs;
```

With that we have created a new raster that we can visualize in QGIS. Simply find the new table that you have created in the DB Manager section of QGIS and double click it to add it to the map (Figure 2.12):

Below are two examples of the outputs, one using an integer and one using a float in that order (Figures 2.13, on the following page and 2.14, on page 407).

Of course there are a lot more variables that go into temperature interpolation, so this is a very over-simplified example, but it shows us two things. First is the ability to perform fast analysis on raster data with spatial SQL. Second is the ability to structure input parameters using only SQL to make your analysis highly repeatable.

2.3   Raster to H3

Another way that I have seen spatial indexes being used in the field is to aggregate raster data to an H3 grid. While you can certainly perform map algebra on the raw raster data, H3 data has a few advantages in a database setting. You can:

- Map H3 cells to parents or children, or higher or lower levels of cells
- Find distances between cells
- Find neighbors of cells
- Calculate rings of cells around a cell

Since the H3 cells are strings they are also highly performant for joins to other data and for visualization in tools that support visualizing based on the strings. As for joining the H3 cells to raster data, the query is quite simple, one of the things I love about using H3 and raster data together. Below is our complete query:

Listing 2.10: Raster to H3

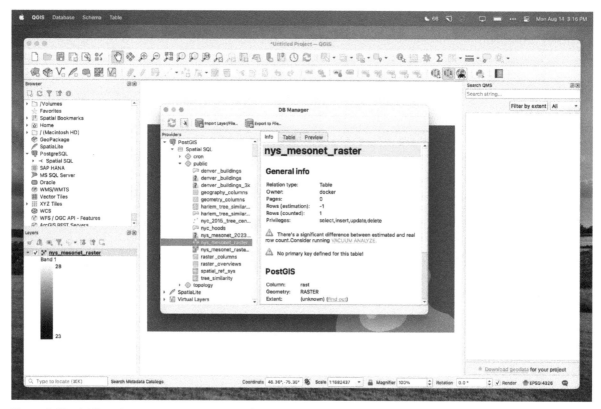

Figure 2.12: Adding the output mesonet raster data

```
1   create table denver_ele_h3 as
2   select
3       h3_lat_lng_to_cell(a.geom, 11) as h3,
4       avg(val) as avg_ele
5   from
6       (
7           select
8               r.*
9           from
10              denver_elevation,
11              lateral ST_PixelAsCentroids(rast, 1) as r
12      ) a
13  group by
14      1
```

As you can see there are only a few lines here. In our SELECT statement, we get the H3 cell from a POINT geometry at level 12, and the average elevation in the cell from all the centroids that call in the H3 cell. In our FROM statement we select from a subquery which contains this query:

Listing 2.11: Using ST_PixelAsCentroid

```
1   select
2       r.*
3   from
4       denver_elevation,
5       lateral ST_PixelAsCentroids(rast, 1) as r
```

Here we are selecting the values from a function called ST_PixelAsCentroids which is a set returning function. We use a lateral join (note not a cross lateral join) to join the values across the denver_

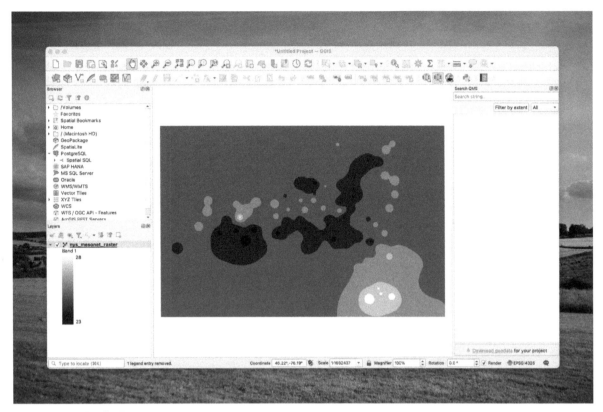

Figure 2.13: The final mesonet raster

elevation table. It returns four values: the x and y values for the raster, the band value, and the geometry which represents the raster centroid. With that we can run our query and create our table (this took about 3 ½ minutes on my computer). After that you can export your table to a CSV and import it into Kepler GL to see the visualization (Figure 2.15, on the following page):

While the resolution is not as granular as it would be with the pure raster it is still quite small and appropriate for approximate analysis with other vector or H3 datasets (Figure 2.16, on the next page):

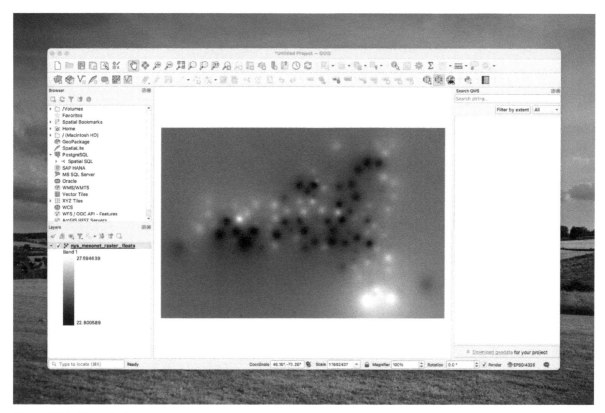

Figure 2.14: Smoothed mesonet raster

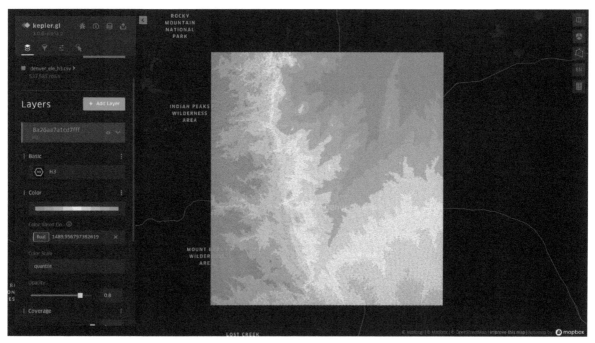

Figure 2.15: Raster to H3 output in Kepler GL

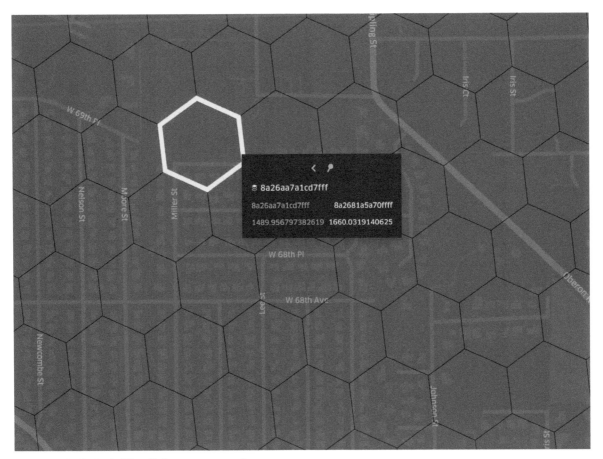

Figure 2.16: A single H3 cell from our raster data

3. Routing and Networks With pgRouting

There are a few challenges in geospatial that have created complete industries around them. Broadly labeled as location data services, these are tools that can perform geocoding, routing, and other complex routing problems. These services are generally exposed via API, and this works great if you are in need of a few routes or trade areas, but what if you want to create custom routes or run large batches of routes? These same location data services are not meant for this scale of batch analysis, rather for one time calls.

If you ever had this issue then I have good news for you. PostGIS has a great extension called pgRouting that allows you to import your own network data, which in most cases can be any dataset with connected lines that can be traversed in some way such as hiking/biking paths, roads and highways, boat routes, public transportation, and more. It also has tools that we will be using to import data from OpenStreetMap which gives you access to all the network data in OSM. We will use several tools and queries inside pgRouting to create simple routes, create routes for car and bike travel, build a custom cost solution for bike travel to prioritize safe travel for cyclists, build isochrones or trade areas, and solve a simple traveling salesman problem. Our first step however is to import the data we are going to use for our routes.

3.1 Prepare data to use in pgRouting

One of the first tasks we need to perform is to create a separate database to load our data into. Up to this point we have used the default database which in our case is "*gis*". You can do this in the same database if you choose, but I prefer to keep it separate just to keep things nice and tidy. To add the new database, in pgAdmin right-click on the connection, in this case the connection called "*Spatial SQL*" if you used the steps outlined in the book. Once the menu opens, select "*Create*" then click on "*Database*" (Figure 3.1, on the following page).

This will open a new window where you can give your database a new name, in this case we will call it "*routing*" (Figure 3.2, on page 411).

You can also see the code that you would need to do the comparable operation in SQL (Figure 3.3, on page 412):

Once you add the database name, you can go ahead and click save, and your new database should be created. Go ahead and click on the new database and open a new connection window to that database where we can run the CREATE EXTENSION command to add pgRouting:

```
CREATE EXTENSION pgrouting;
```

If this for some reason doesn't work (you may get an error that you need to install PostGIS as well), simply add the word CASCADE at the end and run it again. Next we are going to use our extra PostGIS instance we used in the raster section to run additional commands. If you do not have it running make sure to restart it either in the Docker Desktop application or using this command:

Listing 3.1: Running the extra Docker container

```
1  docker run --name mini-postgis -p 35432:5432 --network="host"
2   -v /Users/mattforrest/Desktop/Desktop/spatial-sql-book/raster:/mnt/mydata
```

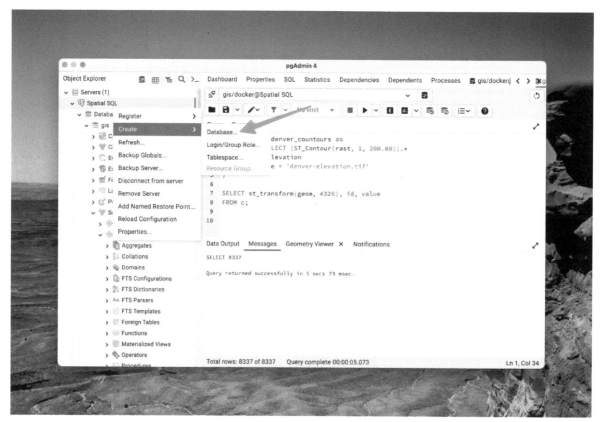

Figure 3.1: Creating a new database in pgAdmin

```
3   -e POSTGRES_USER=admin -e POSTGRES_PASSWORD=password -d postgis/postgis:15-master
```

Once again we will start a new terminal session in our local terminal using this command:

Listing 3.2: Accessing the Docker container terminal

```
1   docker container exec -it mini-postgis bash
```

Our first step is to install a library called osm2pgrouting which will allow us to import OSM data that we have downloaded into our routing database. The process will generate tables that will be needed by pgRouting to perform routing analysis. Go ahead and run these command in the Docker terminal session:

Listing 3.3: Installing libraries

```
1   apt update
2   apt install osm2pgrouting
```

You will also need to enter Y for yes when prompted. We also need to install a tool called osmctools that helps us work with and manipulate OSM data. We can install that with this command and also entering Y when prompted.

Listing 3.4: More installations

```
1   apt install osmctools
```

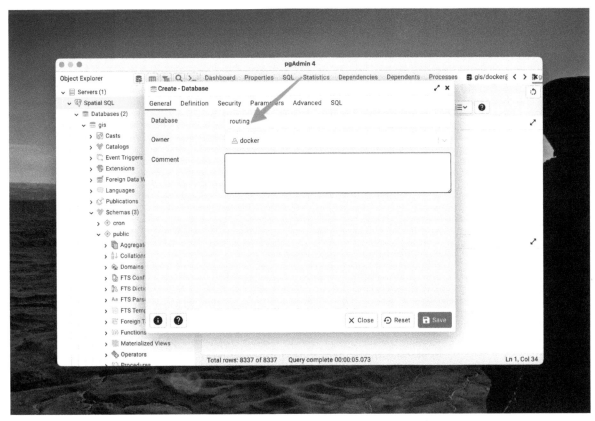

Figure 3.2: Naming our new database

Now that we have our tools installed, we need to get some data. Fortunately we can extract batches of OSM data using a tool named BBBike. You can open up this URL to open the interface where we can extract our data - `https://extract.bbbike.org/`.

Once you have opened the website you can see there are several options, including one to find areas to search for. While the data is also included in the book files, if you want to download the data for yourself with a more recent version of the data, you can select the option at the top of the page to show the lat/long options (Figure 3.4, on the next page):

Next enter the following values:

- Left lower corner
  - *Lng*: -74.459
  - *Lat*: 40.488
- Right top corner
  - *Lng*: -73.385
  - *Lat*: 41.055

Once all values are entered you should see a bounding box around the New York City area that looks like this (Figure 3.5, on page 413):

Next select the option for "*OSM XML gzip'd*" from the "*Format*" dropdown. Finally, enter your email address and a name for your dataset and hit "*extract*". Once you have downloaded your data you will need to extract it from the gzip file, which will open the enclosed *.osm* file. Our next step is to use

Figure 3.3: The comparable SQL command to create the database

Figure 3.4: Exporting OSM data

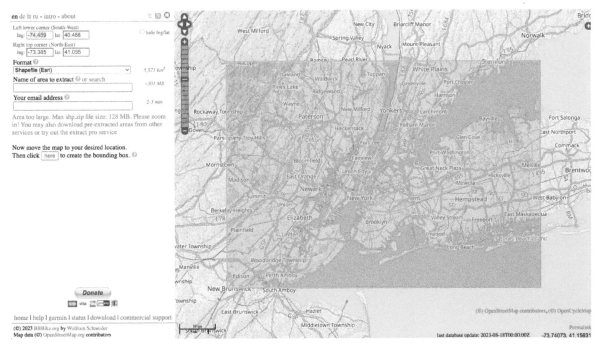

Figure 3.5: Our area of interest from OSM

`osmfilter` to filter out the data that we need. Below is the command we will use to do so:

Listing 3.5: Filtering our OSM data

```
1  osmfilter /mnt/mydata/planet_-74.459,40.488_-73.385,41.055.osm --keep="highway=" \
2  -o=/mnt/mydata/good_ways.osm
```

There are three positional commands. The first is the path to our data within our Docker container. Next is a filter starting with the `-keep` argument to keep only the data with the tag "`highway`". The last command starting with `-o` is the path and name for the filtered OSM data. For the tag structure in the `-keep` argument you can use a variety of combinations of OSM tags. Below are some examples from the `osmfilter` documentation on the OSM Wiki[127]:

```
./osmfilter norway.osm --keep="highway=primary =secondary waterway=river" >streets.osm

./osmfilter switzerland.o5m --keep="highway=cycleway and lit=yes" >litcycles.osm

./osmfilter europe.o5m --keep= --keep-relations="route=bus" --out-o5m >bus_lines.o5m

./osmfilter bayern.o5m --keep="admin_level=6 and name=NürnbergerLand" -o=nbg_boundaries.osm
```

Once the process has completed your terminal will look something like this (Figure 3.6, on the next page):

Next we will use `osm2pgrouting` into our new database. Below is the full command:

Listing 3.6: Loading the OSM data

```
1  osm2pgrouting \
2      -f "/mnt/mydata/good_ways.osm" \
3      -d routing \
```

---

[127]https://wiki.openstreetmap.org/wiki/Osmfilter

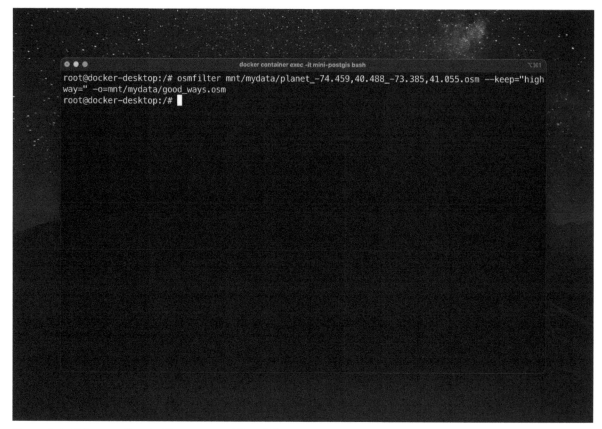

Figure 3.6: Using osmfilter inside our second PostGIS container

```
4       -p 25432 \
5       -U docker \
6       -W docker \
7       --clean
```

The arguments should look similar to some of our other commands that we use to import data via the command line:

1. The file to import

2. The database name

3. The port of the database

4. The database username

5. The database password

The *–clean* argument will drop any previously existing tables if they have already been created. This process will create several tables which we will look at after the import is completed. Go ahead and run the above command (note that this is a long-running process and could take upwards of 10 minutes), and once completed your terminal should look something like this (Figure 3.7, on the facing page):

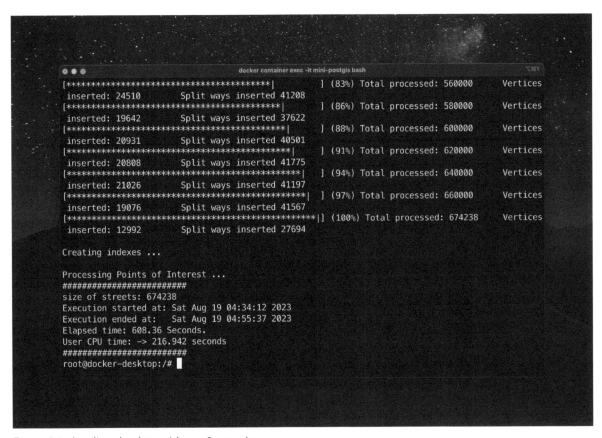

Figure 3.7: Loading the data with osm2pgrouting

Once the process is complete you will have all the data loaded into several tables that you will use with pgRouting. Below is the table structure that you should see when you open the list of tables in pgAdmin (Figure 3.8, on the next page):

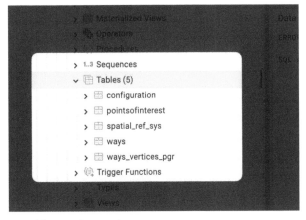

Figure 3.8: Our new tables created by osm2pgrouting

There should be a total of 5 tables. The *spatial_ref_sys* is the table that contains the spatial reference information or projection data that comes along with PostGIS and the *pointsofinterest* will be empty since we only chose to import the road data. The other three tables are:

- *'configuration'* This contains information about the path or "ways" such as the tag (i.e. highway, bike, etc.), max speed, and more
- **ways_vertices_pgr**: This contains the points where ways intersect
- *'ways'* These are the actual path segments that also contain information about the distance, speed, and more. They also contain columns that represent the cost and cost in seconds which will be used to decide how to choose which way to include or exclude in a route

3.2   Create a simple route in pgRouting

Now that we have our data imported to use in pgRouting we can create our first route. For this first query we will use the pure distance cost method which will find the most efficient route by distance only. This route will look very different that what you might expect coming from something like Google Maps or any other routing service. Following that query we will modify the configuration table to create a weighted cost that will emphasize or reward the algorithm for choosing routes that are more efficient for cars, focusing on using primary roads over side streets. First let's take a look at how we can construct a query to calculate a route.

The function we will be using is the pgr_dijkstra[128] function which will calculate the shortest path using Dijkstra's algorithm[129]. This is only one of many algorithms that you can use, but in general it is reliable and usually the one you will see in examples, so we will start here. This algorithm can also calculate one-to-one routes (which is what we are doing in this section), one-to-many, many-to-one, and many-to-many. The function signature looks like this:

```
pgr_dijkstra(Edges SQL, start_vid, end_vid [, directed])
```

Example:

Listing 3.7: Example pgRouting query

```
1  SELECT
2      *
3  FROM
4      pgr_dijkstra(
5          'SELECT id, source, target, cost, reverse_cost FROM edge_table',
6          2,
7          3
8      );
```

This may be a bit confusing for now but in short, you provide the function with:

- **Edges SQL** - The SQL (where the query is written as a string) that contains the data about the edges, or in our case data from the ways table
- **start_vid** - The starting way ID(s)
- **end_vid** - The starting way ID(s)
- **[, directed]** - If the path is directed, meaning that it is specifically going from the start point to the end point, which will take things like one way streets into consideration

Our first task is to find the way ID for our start and end points, which will be from the southernmost point in New York City (Ward's Point in Staten Island) and the northernmost point (at the College of Mount Saint Vincent in the Bronx). To find the closest way, or line, to each point, we can use our shorthand expression for ST_Distance, <->, and query for both locations in two separate subqueries:

Listing 3.8: Tying road segments to locations

---

[128]https://docs.pgrouting.org/3.1/en/pgr_dijkstra.html

[129]https://en.wikipedia.org/wiki/Dijkstra%27s_algorithm

```
1   with start AS (
2       SELECT
3           source
4       FROM
5           ways
6       ORDER BY
7           the_geom <-> ST_SetSRID(
8               ST_GeomFromText('POINT (-74.244391 40.498995)'),
9               4326
10          )
11      LIMIT
12          1
13  )
```

We select the `source` column from the ways table which contains the unique IDs for each road segment. Next, we order the results by the distance from the starting point and limit the results to 1. We can repeat the same process with our destination in a second subquery:

Listing 3.9: Doing the same for destinations

```
1   destination AS (
2       SELECT
3           source
4       FROM
5           ways
6       ORDER BY
7           the_geom <-> ST_SetSRID(
8               ST_GeomFromText('POINT (-73.902630 40.912329)'),
9               4326
10          )
11      LIMIT
12          1
13  )
```

Now we can construct our query to generate the route:

Listing 3.10: Building the rest of the route

```
1   select
2
3       -- This will union the geometry columns from the
4       -- pgr_dijkstra function
5       st_union(the_geom) as route
6   from
7       pgr_dijkstra(
8
9           -- The query is passed as a string into the pgr_dijkstra function
10          'select
11          gid as id,
12          source,
13          target,
14          cost,
15          reverse_cost,
16          st_length(st_transform(the_geom, 3857)) as cost
17          from ways',
18
19          -- This selects the start way id
20          (
21              select
22                  source
23              from
24                  start
25          ),
26
```

```
27        -- This selects the destination way id
28        (
29            select
30                source
31            from
32                destination
33        ),
34        true
35    ) as di
36    join ways as pt on di.edge = pt.gid;
```

The first thing you will notice is that we use the `pgr_dijkstra` function . This is followed by a query contained in single quotes as the query in pgRouting is passed as a string, which is our first argument in the function. The second and third select the source IDs from our start and destination table. The fourth argument tells the function that we want the route to be directed, meaning that it will utilize one way streets as if we are going from the southernmost point in Staten Island to the northernmost point in the Bronx.

On the outer parts of the query, you can see at the beginning that we are performing a union with `ST_Union` on the geometry column, `the_geom`, from the ways table since the query returns individual rows, each with a line segment ID. To get the geometry, we join the ways table using the `edge` column from the `pgr_dijkstra` query and the `gid` column from the ways table. With that you can go ahead and run the complete query:

Listing 3.11: The full routing query

```
1    -- Find the source ID closest to the starting point
2    with start as (
3        select
4            source
5        from
6            ways
7        order by
8            the_geom <-> st_setsrid(
9                st_geomfromtext('point (-74.244391 40.498995)'),
10               4326
11           )
12       limit
13           1
14   ),
15
16   -- Find the source ID closest to the end point
17   destination as (
18       select
19           source
20       from
21           ways
22       order by
23           the_geom <-> st_setsrid(
24               st_geomfromtext('point (-73.902630 40.912329)'),
25               4326
26           )
27       limit
28           1
29   )
30
31   -- Run our pgRouting query
32   select
33       st_union(the_geom) as route
34   from
35       pgr_dijkstra(
36           'select gid as id, source, target, cost,
```

```
37          reverse_cost, st_length(st_transform(the_geom, 3857))
38          as cost from ways',
39          (
40              select
41                  source
42              from
43                  start
44          ),
45          (
46              select
47                  source
48              from
49                  destination
50          ),
51          true
52      ) as di
53      join ways as pt on di.edge = pt.gid;
```

And you should see something like this (Figure 3.9):

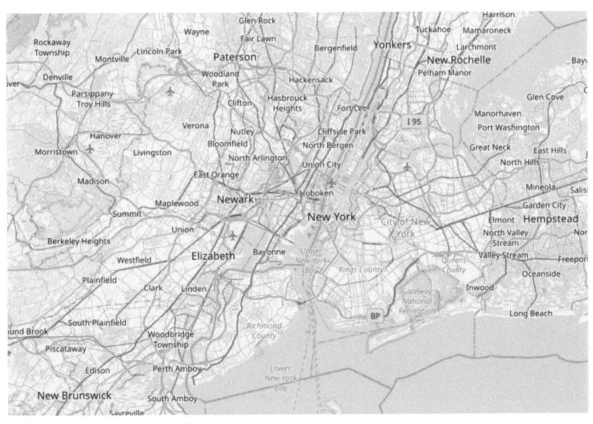

Figure 3.9: Our final route...or is it?

Congrats! You have created your first route in spatial SQL. The only problem is that no one could actually follow that route.

As stated above, the algorithm is only focused on finding the **shortest** route using all the ways within the dataset. This includes everything including highways, streets, side streets, alleys, bike paths, walking paths, and anything in between. For example, this part goes from the street on to a sidewalk (Figure 3.10, on the next page):

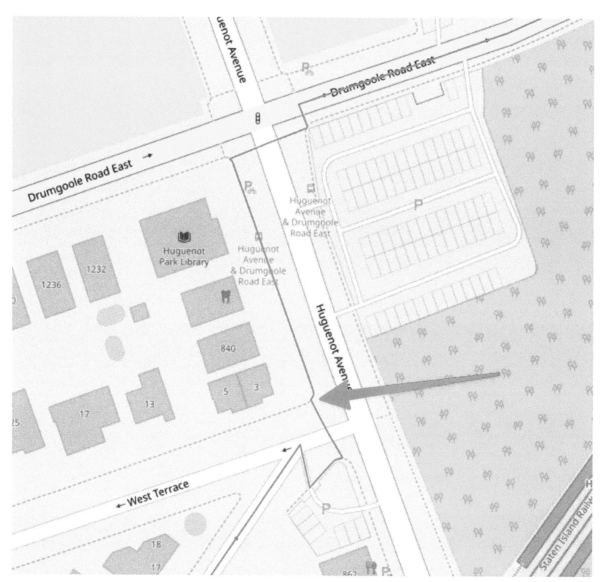

Figure 3.10: Using sidewalks and streets

Here we cut through two parking garages (Figure 3.11):

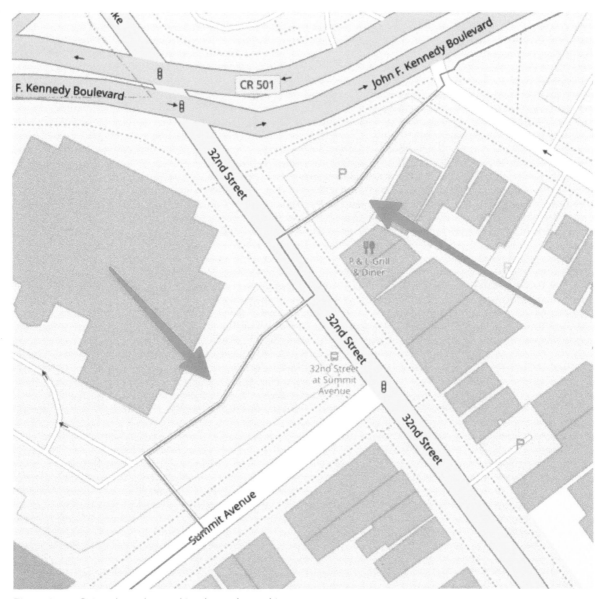

Figure 3.11: Going through a parking lot and a parking garage

Here we go through a walking path in a park (Figure 3.12, on the next page):

And finally we take the bike path over the George Washington Bridge and then get back on the West Side Highway (Figure 3.13, on page 423):

So what is the solution? This query only took the cost parameter into consideration which as of now is just the distances. The ways table also includes a column called cost_s which is the time it will take to traverse the route in seconds. Our import process produces this column for us using the distance and the speed along that route. However, to demonstrate how changes to the cost will impact the route, we will actually create a modified configuration table to exaggerate the costs for roads cars can travel on.

While this sounds like it could potentially be complicated, it is actually only a few steps. We will need

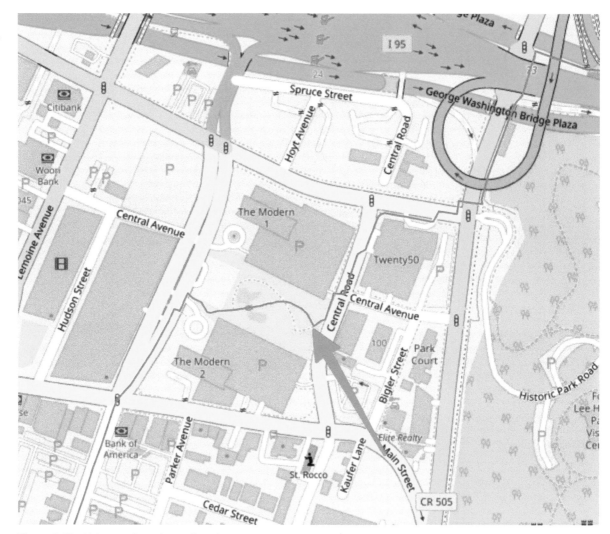

Figure 3.12: Using roads and a park path

to add a new column to our configuration table and then weight the different costs to incentivize the algorithm to use specific road types. Finally, we will pass those new values into the same query we just wrote and see the results.

Our first step is to take a look at the tags currently in the configuration table:

Listing 3.12: Querying the configuration table

```
1  select
2      tag_id,
3      tag_key,
4      tag_value
5  from
6      configuration
7  order by
8      tag_id;
```

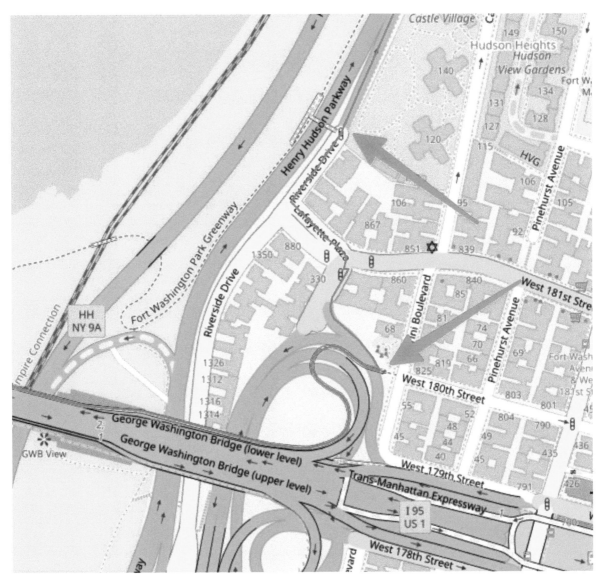

Figure 3.13: Bike path on the George Washington Bridge, back to a highway exit, then on to the West Side Highway

tag_id	tag_key	tag_value
100	highway	road
101	highway	motorway
102	highway	motorway_link
103	highway	motorway_junction
104	highway	trunk
105	highway	trunk_link
106	highway	primary
107	highway	primary_link
108	highway	secondary
109	highway	tertiary
110	highway	residential
111	highway	living_street
112	highway	service
113	highway	track
114	highway	pedestrian
115	highway	services
116	highway	bus_guideway
117	highway	path
118	highway	cycleway
119	highway	footway
120	highway	bridleway
121	highway	byway
122	highway	steps
123	highway	unclassified
124	highway	secondary_link
125	highway	tertiary_link
201	cycleway	lane
202	cycleway	track
203	cycleway	opposite_lane
204	cycleway	opposite
301	tracktype	grade1
302	tracktype	grade2
303	tracktype	grade3
304	tracktype	grade4
305	tracktype	grade5
401	junction	roundabout

As you can see there are road types that we would generally prioritize if you were driving a car and others that you would not want to use if you are driving. From here we can pick some of the tags we want to prioritize, but before that we can create a copy of the configuration table so we can keep the tables separate:

Listing 3.13: Create a new configuration table

```
1  create table car_config as
2  select
3      *
4  from
5      configuration
```

And then add a new column called *penalty*:

Listing 3.14: Adding a penalty column

```
1  alter table
2      car_config
3  add
4      column penalty float;
```

Finally, we will give every value in the new column a value of 1:

Listing 3.15: Setting the base to 1

```
1  update car_config set penalty=1
```

Next we want to update the penalty column which will be used to multiply the *cost* column when we run the routing query. You can take a look at all the different tags used in OSM for highways here[130]. The closer to 0 means that those roads will be more highly incentivized. First, we want to deincentivize roads we do not want cars driving on:

Listing 3.16: Updating the penalty columns

```
1  update
2      car_config
3  set
4      penalty = -1.0
5  where
6      tag_value in ('steps', 'footway', 'pedestrian');
7
8  update
9      car_config
10 set
11     penalty = 5
12 where
13     tag_value in ('unclassified');
```

This will make sure that the routing will not route on any paths that are steps, footways, or used by pedestrians and will make it very costly to go on unclassified roads.

Next we will incentivize different highway types that we want cars to travel on. These are extreme weightings for demonstration purposes, so keep that in mind:

Listing 3.17: More penalty updates

```
1  update
2      car_config
3  set
4      penalty = 0.5
5  where
6      tag_value in ('tertiary');
7
8  update
9      car_config
10 set
```

---

[130]https://wiki.openstreetmap.org/wiki/Key:highway

```
11        penalty = 0.3
12   where
13        tag_value in (
14            'primary',
15            'primary_link',
16            'trunk',
17            'trunk_link',
18            'motorway',
19            'motorway_junction',
20            'motorway_link',
21            'secondary'
22        );
```

Next we will re-run our query with a few modifications in the query we send to pgRouting:

Listing 3.18: Modified pgRouting query

```
1    select
2        gid as id,
3        source,
4        target,
5
6        -- multiply the cost in seconds by the new configuration file
7        cost_s * penalty as cost,
8        reverse_cost_s * penalty as reverse_cost,
9        st_length(st_transform(the_geom, 3857)) as length
10   from
11        ways
12        join car_config using (tag_id)
```

Here you can see that we are using the cost_s column which uses cost in seconds rather than distance.
Then we also multiply it by our penalty meaning that if a road has a travel time of 60 seconds and the
penalty is 0.5, then the weighted cost will be 30 seconds. The last step is we swap in our new *car_config*
table for the original configuration table:

Listing 3.19: Complete modified query

```
1    with start as (
2        select
3            source
4        from
5            ways
6        order by
7            the_geom <-> st_setsrid(
8                st_geomfromtext('point (-74.244391 40.498995)'),
9                4326
10           )
11       limit
12           1
13   ), destination as (
14       select
15           source
16       from
17           ways
18       order by
19           the_geom <-> st_setsrid(
20               st_geomfromtext('point (-73.902630 40.912329)'),
21               4326
22           )
23       limit
24           1
25   )
26   select
27       st_union(the_geom) as route
```

```
28   from
29       pgr_dijkstra(
30           'select
31               gid as id,
32               source,
33               target,
34               cost_s * penalty as cost,
35               reverse_cost_s * penalty as reverse_cost,
36               st_length(st_transform(the_geom, 3857)) as length
37           from
38               ways
39               join car_config using (tag_id)',
40           (
41               select
42                   source
43               from
44                   start
45           ),
46           (
47               select
48                   source
49               from
50                   destination
51           ),
52           true
53       ) as di
54   join ways as pt on di.edge = pt.gid;
```

And here are our results (Figures 3.15, on page 429 and 3.15, on page 429):

And here you can see this looks much closer to a route we would see when driving. You can do this weighting with any type of path to prioritize routing for walkers, cyclists, wheelchairs, or even any other metric you so choose.

3.3   Building an origin-destination matrix

An origin destination matrix is effectively a cross join between all the locations in one dataset to all the locations in another. This is a common input to problems such as the Vehicle Routing Problem (VRP) that finds the best solution for deliveries leaving a single distribution center with multiple vehicles. There are other versions of the VRP too, such as the VRP with capacity constraints, VRP with pickup and delivery constraints, VRP with time window constraints, and VRP with start and end locations. One of the most complicated VRP problems I have seen comes from Instacart. In this post on their public Medium page, they describe the the SCVRPTWMT - or **stochastic** (uncertainty of driver shifts, weather, etc.) **capacitated** (amount of space or capacity of the driver) **vehicle routing problem time window** (when an order must be fulfilled) **multiple trips** (multiple orders from one driver)[131].

While there are many methods to perform the analyses we described above (pgRouting even has experimental functions for the VRP) the one thing that all these tools depend on is data from an origin-destination matrix. This is another great example of using the right tool for the job. Certainly you can perform the analysis using straight line distances, but that does not account for the road network, and unless you are operating a fleet of drones, you will likely be using the road network to make deliveries.

Many tools in these languages have ways to calculate an origin destination matrix, yet when the scale increases this becomes challenging. APIs and routing tools like Google Maps are meant for one off API calls not large scale batch operations. Other tools exist such as the open source routing tools such as the Open Source Routing Machine or OSRM[132] which is a similar routing tool on top of Open Street Map.

---

[131]https://tech.instacart.com/space-time-and-groceries-a315925acf3a

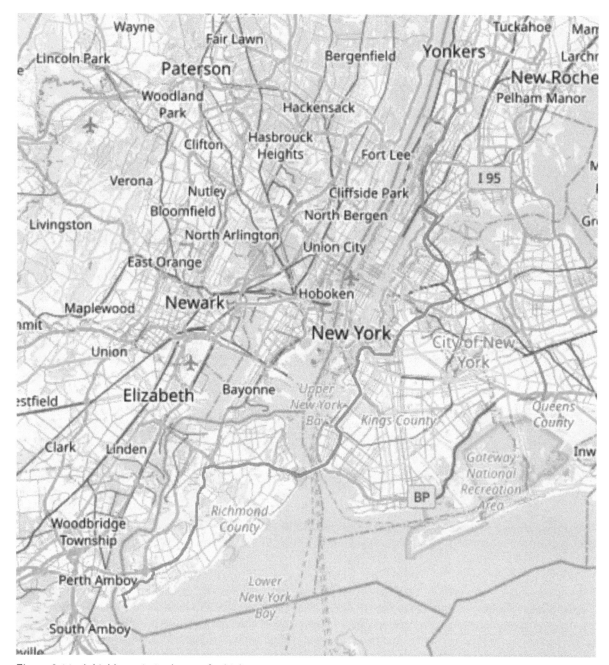

Figure 3.14: A highly optimized route for highways

Figure 3.15: Optimized route zoomed in

However, this requires that you stand up an additional backend service. pgRouting provides the same level of service and, if your data is already in a database, then this makes it a logical choice to use.

As we saw in the last section you can calculate cost in terms of distance or time, and for this example we will be using time. We will also be creating a new database and configuration to use for bicycles as many delivery services in New York City are delivered by cyclists. Finally, we will also re-import our pharmacy data into our new database.

As a first step we will need to create a new database. Once again right-click on the database connection, hover over, then click "Database". Then add *bike* as the new database name and click "Save" (Figures 3.16, on the next page 3.17, on page 431):

Next we want to reprocess our OSM data extract to include all bike specific routes. First, create another terminal session into our mini PostGIS Docker container:

```
docker container exec -it mini-postgis bash
```

Then run this command to process the OSM data:

---

[132]https://github.com/Project-OSRM/osrm-backend

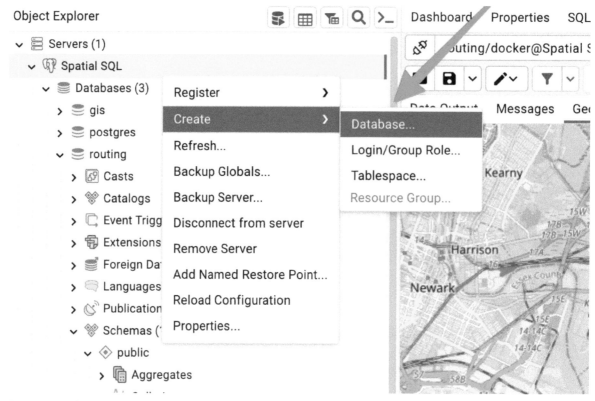

Figure 3.16: Creating a new database for our bikes data

Listing 3.20: Filtering bike route data

```
1   osmfilter mnt/mydata/planet_-74.459,40.488_-73.385,41.055.osm \
2   --keep="highway= route= cycleway= bicycle= segregated=" \
3   -o=mnt/mydata/bike_ways.osm
```

Finally, import that data into the new "*bike*" database:

Listing 3.21: Importing bike data

```
1   osm2pgrouting \
2   -f "mnt/mydata/bike_ways.osm" \
3   -d bike \
4   -p 25432 \
5   -U docker \
6   -W docker \
7   --clean
```

Next we need to reimport two datasets into our new database: the pharmacy locations and the NYC Building Footprints:

Listing 3.22: Importing new datasets

```
1   ogr2ogr \
2   -f PostgreSQL PG:"host=localhost user=docker password=docker dbname=bike port=25432" \
3   nyc_pharmacies.geojson \
4   -nln nyc_pharmacies -lco GEOMETRY_NAME=geom
5
6   ogr2ogr \
7   -f PostgreSQL PG:"host=localhost user=docker password=docker dbname=bike port=25432" \
```

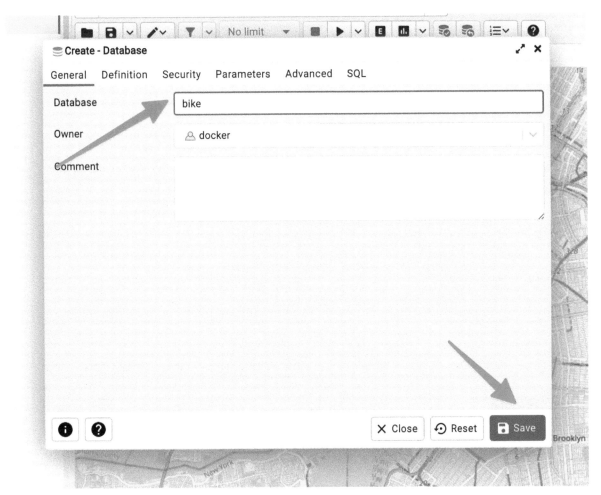

Figure 3.17: Naming our database

```
8  Building_Footprints.geojson \
9  -nln nyc_building_footprints -lco GEOMETRY_NAME=geom
```

Next, we need to modify our `configuration` table to favor bicycle routes. With this query below, we first favor routes that are meant for bicycles, then streets that are generally residential, set a negative penalty for highways, and slightly higher penalties for primary streets. First you need to add the penalty column to the `configuration` table:

Listing 3.23: Adding in a penalty column

```
1  alter table
2      configuration
3  add
4      column penalty float;
5
6  update
7      configuration
8  set
9      penalty = 1.0;
```

Then run the query below to update the table:

Listing 3.24: Updating the configuration table

```
1  update
2      configuration
3  set
4      penalty = 10.0
5  where
6      tag_value in ('steps', 'footway', 'pedestrian');
7
8  update
9      configuration
10 set
11     penalty = 0.3
12 where
13     tag_key in ('cycleway');
14
15 update
16     configuration
17 set
18     penalty = 0.3
19 where
20     tag_value in ('cycleway', 'bicycle');
21
22 update
23     configuration
24 set
25     penalty = 0.7
26 where
27     tag_value in ('tertiary', 'residential');
28
29 update
30     configuration
31 set
32     penalty = 1
33 where
34     tag_value in ('secondary');
35
36 update
37     configuration
38 set
39     penalty = 1.2
40 where
41     tag_value in ('primary', 'primary_link');
42
43 update
44     configuration
45 set
46     penalty = 2
47 where
48     tag_value in (
49         'trunk',
50         'trunk_link',
51         'motorway',
52         'motorway_junction',
53         'motorway_link'
54     );
```

Now that we have our data ready we can start to construct our query. First we need to select the locations we will use. To get started, we will get random 5 pharmacy locations and 20 random building locations in a constrained area in Brooklyn (3 kilometers around Grand Army Plaza) which will end up with 100 total routes. To do so we can create two CTEs:

Listing 3.25: Closest roads to buildings and pharmacies

```
1   with pharm as (
2
3       -- Find 5 random pharmacies within 3 kilometers of Grand Army Plaza
4       select
5           name,
6           st_centroid(geom) as geom,
7           id
8       from
9           nyc_pharmacies
10      where
11          st_dwithin(
12              st_centroid(geom) :: geography,
13              st_setsrid(st_makepoint(-73.9700743, 40.6738928), 4326) :: geography,
14              3000
15          )
16      order by
17          random()
18      limit
19          5
20  ),
21
22  -- Select 20 random buildings within within 3 kilometers of Grand Army Plaza
23  bldgs as (
24      select
25          st_centroid(geom) as bldg_geom,
26          bin
27      from
28          nyc_building_footprints
29      where
30          st_dwithin(
31              st_centroid(geom) :: geography,
32              st_setsrid(st_makepoint(-73.9700743, 40.6738928), 4326) :: geography,
33              3000
34          )
35      order by
36          random()
37      limit
38          20
39  )
```

Since the pgr_dijkstra function accepts "many-to-many" routes, we can actually just use the query we used previously with a few modifications. First we need to have two arrays of data with our start way IDs and end way IDs. Then we will also need to aggregate and group our results by the start and end IDs, which are named columns within the pgr_dijkstra query called start_vid and end_vid. The complete query looks like this:

Listing 3.26: Final query

```
1   with pharm as (
2       select
3           name,
4           st_centroid(geom) as geom,
5           id
6       from
7           nyc_pharmacies
8       where
9           st_dwithin(
10              st_centroid(geom) :: geography,
11              st_setsrid(st_makepoint(-73.9700743, 40.6738928), 4326) :: geography,
12              3000
13          )
14      order by
15          random()
16      limit
```

```
17              3
18  ), bldgs as (
19      select
20          st_centroid(geom) as bldg_geom,
21          bin
22      from
23          nyc_building_footprints
24      where
25          st_dwithin(
26              st_centroid(geom) :: geography,
27              st_setsrid(st_makepoint(-73.9700743, 40.6738928), 4326) :: geography,
28              3000
29          )
30      order by
31          random()
32      limit
33          10
34  ),
35
36  c as (
37
38      -- First we select all the columns from the pharm, bldgs, and wid CTEs and sub-queries
39      select
40          pharm.*,
41          bldgs.*,
42          wid.*
43      from
44
45          -- We perform a cross join to find all possible matches between
46          -- the 5 pharmacies and the 20 buildings
47          pharm,
48          bldgs
49          cross join lateral (
50
51              -- For each row find the start and end way IDs
52              with start as (
53                  select
54                      source
55                  from
56                      ways
57                  order by
58                      the_geom <-> pharm.geom
59                  limit
60                      1
61              ), destination as (
62                  select
63                      source
64                  from
65                      ways
66                  order by
67                      ways.the_geom <-> st_centroid(bldgs.bldg_geom)
68                  limit
69                      1
70              )
71              select
72                  start.source as start_id,
73                  destination.source as end_id
74              from
75                  start,
76                  destination
77          ) wid
78  )
79  select
80      -- For each combination we get the sum of the cost in distance, seconds, and route length
81      -- and we repeat this for every row, or possible combination
```

```
82      sum(di.cost) as cost,
83      sum(length) as length,
84      sum(pt.cost_s) as seconds,
85      st_union(st_transform(the_geom, 4326)) as route
86  from
87      pgr_dijkstra(
88          'select
89          gid as id,
90          source,
91          target,
92          cost_s * penalty as cost,
93          reverse_cost_s * penalty as reverse_cost,
94          st_length(st_transform(the_geom, 3857)) as length
95          from ways
96          join configuration using (tag_id)',
97          array(
98              select
99                  distinct start_id
100             from
101                 c
102         ),
103         array(
104             select
105                 distinct end_id
106             from
107                 c
108         ),
109         true
110     ) as di
111     join ways as pt on di.edge = pt.gid
112 group by
113     start_vid,
114     end_vid
```

Our final results look like this (Figure 3.18, on the next page):

As you can see the paths make use of bike routes in Prospect Park (the large park in the middle of the image) and other streets that are designated bike routes. It is optional to include the routes themselves as you generally only need the cost (be it distance or seconds), but for our purposes it makes sense to include them to see what the results look like. The nice part is that this scales quite well. The query above took about 8 seconds on my computer which is 100 total routes. When I run 1,000 routes took about 11 seconds, 10,000 took about 17 seconds, and 100,000 took about 48 seconds.

As you scale up there are some different methods you can use to constrain the query. First you can create batches of queries so you can process them individually, such as one query per depot. Second, for locations that need to be delivered to that are close together in compact groups, such as several houses in a row, you can use a clustering method like ST_DBSCAN to group locations together since they would likely be served by the same route. Finally, you can also limit the locations to each depot within a certain distance. For example, if our pharmacy in Brooklyn only delivers within 2 kilometers or won't deliver into Manhattan, you can add that spatial constraint.

3.4 Traveling salesman problem

One of the most common problems in logistics or network analysis is solving the traveling salesman[133] problem. This means finding the most efficient route between three or more locations on a network that need to be visited. It is classified as an NP-Hard problem in network science and is used in a wide range of fields and pgRouting has tools to address this specific problem.

---

[133]https://en.wikipedia.org/wiki/Travelling_salesman_problem

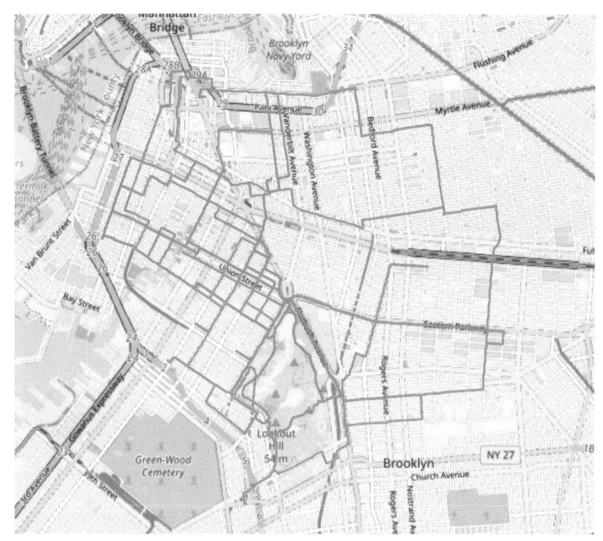

Figure 3.18: Origin destination matrix visualized

The function structure is a bit different from the other functions we have explored so far, but it uses a string query input as well:

Listing 3.27: pgr_TSP example

```
1   select
2       *
3   from
4       pgr_tsp(
5
6           -- We need to use the double $ string notation since
7           -- there is another string inside that string. Also,
8           -- note that the pgr_TSP function accepts the pgr_dijkstraCostMatrix
9           -- function as a string.
10          $$
11          select
12              *
13          from
14              pgr_dijkstracostmatrix(
15                  'select id, source, target, cost, reverse_cost from edge_table',
```

```
16                    (
17                        select
18                            array_agg(id)
19                        from
20                            edge_table_vertices_pgr
21                        where
22                            id < 14
23                    ),
24                    directed := false
25                ) $$,
26                randomize := false
27        );
```

This time it accepts one of its own functions, `pgr_dijkstraCostMatrix`, within the double dollar sign string notation since the `pgr_dijkstraCostMatrix` also accepts a string. So in reality we need to take a look at the function signature of `pgr_dijkstraCostMatrix` to see how we need to structure our data:

Listing 3.28: Example cost matrix

```
1    select
2        *
3    from
4        pgr_dijkstracostmatrix(
5            'select id, source, target, cost, reverse_cost from edges',
6            (
7                select
8                    array_agg(id)
9                from
10                   vertices
11               where
12                   id in (5, 6, 10, 15)
13           ),
14           false
15       );
```

What this will do is calculate all the possible distances and costs between all of these points, which is a bit different from our previous cost matrix analysis where we compared all the points in one table to another. First we can create a static table with a sample of ten delivery locations per Rite-Aid pharmacy in Brooklyn, with a total of 10 pharmacies we will ananlyze. I created the table using this query if you want to create it on your own:

Listing 3.29: Finding 10 buildings near each Rite Aid

```
1    -- Find 10 random Rite-Aid locations
2    with a as (
3        select
4            *
5        from
6            nyc_pharmacies
7        where
8            name ilike '%rite%'
9        limit
10           10
11   )
12   select
13
14       -- For each pharmacy we will find 10 random
15       -- buildings within 800 meters
16       a.name,
17       a.id as pharm_id,
18       a.geom as pharm_geom,
19       b.*
20   from
```

```
21      a
22      cross join lateral (
23          select
24              bin as building_id,
25              geom
26          from
27              nyc_building_footprints
28          where
29              st_dwithin(
30                  st_centroid(geom) :: geography,
31                  st_centroid(a.geom) :: geography,
32                  800
33              )
34          order by
35              random()
36          limit
37              10
38      ) b
```

However, if you want to use the exact same data as you will see in the example, you can import and transform the CSV from the book files using the commands below:

Listing 3.30: Import rite_aid_odm.csv

```
1  ogr2ogr \
2  -f PostgreSQL PG:"host=localhost user=docker password=docker dbname=bike port=25432" \
3  rite_aid_odm.csv \
4  -nln rite_aid_odm -lco GEOMETRY_NAME=geom -oo AUTODETECT_TYPE=true
```

Once we have that table set up we want to create a table that we can use with a specific structure which will have three columns:

1. Rite-Aid store ID

2. Way ID for each Rite-Aid store

3. Array of way IDs for the buildings

In our first two steps we need to find the way IDs for the stores and the buildings. Note that we find the distinct IDs for the Rite-Aid locations since each one is repeated ten times:

Listing 3.31: Finding the closest road segments

```
1  with a as (
2      select
3          distinct b.pharm_id as id,
4          b.geom,
5          s.source
6      from
7
8          -- For each pharmacy find the closest way ID
9          rite_aid_odm b
10         cross join lateral(
11             SELECT
12                 source
13             FROM
14                 ways
15             ORDER BY
16                 the_geom <-> b.pharm_geom
17             limit
18                 1
```

```
19          ) s
20  ), b as (
21      select
22          b.pharm_id as id,
23          s.source
24      from
25
26          -- For each building find the closest way ID
27          rite_aid_odm b
28          cross join lateral(
29              SELECT
30                  source
31              FROM
32                  ways
33              ORDER BY
34                  the_geom <-> b.geom
35              limit
36                  1
37          ) s
38  ),
```

Next we group the destinations into an array and append the array we are creating with the way ID of the store using the `array_prepend` function. Our final query will look like this with the added CREATE TABLE call to store the table to make our results easier:

Listing 3.32: Creating the data structure for each store

```
1   create table rite_aid_tsp as with a as (
2       select
3           distinct b.pharm_id as id,
4           b.geom,
5           s.source
6       from
7           rite_aid_odm b
8           cross join lateral(
9               SELECT
10                  source
11              FROM
12                  ways
13              ORDER BY
14                  the_geom <-> b.pharm_geom
15              limit
16                  1
17          ) s
18  ), b as (
19      select
20          b.pharm_id as id,
21          s.source
22      from
23          rite_aid_odm b
24          cross join lateral(
25              SELECT
26                  source
27              FROM
28                  ways
29              ORDER BY
30                  the_geom <-> b.geom
31              limit
32                  1
33          ) s
34  ), c as (
35      select
36          a.id,
37          a.source,
```

```
38
39          -- Constructs an array with the way ID of the pharmacy as the first item
40          array_prepend(a.source, array_agg(distinct b.source)) as destinations
41      from
42          a
43          join b using (id)
44
45      -- Will return one row per pharmacy ID
46      group by
47          a.id,
48          a.source
49  )
50  select
51      *
52  from
53      c
```

As another step, we will also create the cost matrix using `pgr_dijkstraCostMatrix` ahead of time using this query:

Listing 3.33: Creating the cost matrix ahead of time

```
1   create table rite_aid_tsp_odm as
2
3   -- Select all the values from the table created in the last step
4   select
5       a.*,
6       r.*
7   from
8       rite_aid_tsp a
9       cross join lateral (
10          select
11              *
12          from
13
14              -- This will create the cost matrix for each pharmacy
15              pgr_dijkstracostmatrix(
16                  'select
17                  gid as id,
18                  source,
19                  target,
20                  cost_s * penalty as cost,
21                  reverse_cost_s * penalty as reverse_cost
22                  from ways
23                  join configuration
24                  using (tag_id)',
25
26                  -- We can use the array to calculate the distances
27                  -- between all locations in the array
28                  (
29                      select
30                          destinations
31                      from
32                          rite_aid_tsp
33                      where
34                          id = a.id
35                  ),
36                  directed := false
37              )
38      ) r
```

As you can see we select all the values from the table we just created, and for each row in the table the query will return the costs between every point in the array using our weighted costs for bike routes.

Since we don't want to do this for every single point, we use a `CROSS JOIN LATERAL` to create just the cost matrix for each Rite-Aid location and the specific buildings it needs to deliver to.

Now we are able to construct our second query. This one has a few key components to it, so I will break it down step by step:

Listing 3.34: Creating the solved TSP

```
1   create table solved_tsp as
2   select
3       s.id,
4       s.source,
5
6       -- This will come from the CROSS JOIN LATERAL
7       -- in the next step
8       tsp.*,
9
10      -- LEAD lets us find the next row forward in our results
11      -- and 1 means that we look one row forward. We partition
12      -- the results by the pharmacy or "source" and order
13      -- the results by the sequence from our TSP solver
14      lead(tsp.node, 1) over (
15          partition by s.source
16          order by
17              tsp.seq
18      ) next_node
19  from
20      rite_aid_tsp s
```

In this first section we will be selecting columns that ultimately come from the table we just created with the alias s being used and from a `CROSS JOIN LATERAL` which we will create in the next step. We also add in a window function to find the next node (way) that the route will use, which we will use to build the actual route geometries. The `LEAD` function lets us look into the next row, and our partition limits it to the specific source ID, or Rite-Aid location. In the next part of the query we structure our `CROSS JOIN` for the `pgr_TSP` function:

Listing 3.35: Step 2

```
1   cross join lateral (
2           select
3               *
4           from
5
6               -- We call the pgr_TSP function for each row
7               -- and we can just call the table we created earlier
8               pgr_TSP(
9                   $$
10                  select
11                      *
12                  from
13                      rite_aid_tsp_odm
14                  where
15
16                      -- Since this is inside a $$ string we can pass
17                      -- the source, or pharmacy ID, into the query
18                      -- by effectively inserting the column that
19                      -- comes from the outer query and concatenating
20                      -- the strings together with the || shorthand
21                      source = $$ || s.source || $$
22                  $$
23              )
24      ) tsp
```

This one is a bit funky, but let me explain. As you can see we are creating a CROSS JOIN LATERAL as we discussed. Within that we create a subquery to actually call our pgr_TSP function, which of course accepts the data from the cost matrix we created. So instead of calling that function again we can simply query our table. But since this is a CROSS JOIN LATERAL we will want to ensure we do this for the source ID that matches each other source ID, or Rite-Aid location, for the outer table. Using a shorthand for concatenation we can actually join the column into the string by inserting the pharmacy way ID, or source after the "=" then adding the column using || on both sides which acts as a shorthand for CONCAT, and the finish the query with "$$" to close it out.

You can see what this looks like using this query:

Listing 3.36: Example string with double dollar signs

```
1   with a as (
2       select
3           1 as source
4   )
5   select
6       $$
7   select
8       *
9   from
10      rite_aid_tsp_odm
11  where
12      source = $$ || source || $$ $$
13  from
14      a
```

Which will return this string:

"select * from rite_aid_tsp_odm where source = 1"

You can run this using the full query:

Listing 3.37: Full solved TSP

```
1   create table solved_tsp as
2   select
3       s.id,
4       s.source,
5       tsp.*,
6       lead(tsp.node, 1) over (
7           partition by s.source
8           order by
9               tsp.seq
10      ) as next_node
11  from
12      rite_aid_tsp s
13      cross join lateral (
14          select
15              *
16          from
17              pgr_TSP(
18                  $$
19                  select
20                      *
21                  from
22                      rite_aid_tsp_odm
23                  where
24                      source = $$ || s.source || $$$$
25              )
26      ) tsp
```

Finally, since we want the cyclist to start and end at the store we pass the *s.source* column twice to have the route start and end at the same location. This is the data we will end up with:

way/249581424	74875	1	74875	0	0	456491
way/249581424	74875	2	456491	43.49399878451973	43.49399878451973	409078
way/249581424	74875	3	409078	23.918349293903137	67.41234807842287	729681
way/249581424	74875	4	729681	28.00037829391514	95.412726372338	4189
way/249581424	74875	5	4189	28.666557989874065	124.07928436221206	54272

In our last query we will create the routes. This query involves three tables: `solved_tsp`, `ways`, and the return values from `pgr_dijkstra`. First in our CTE we select several columns from our `solved_tsp` table: id, source, seq, node, next_node. Then we select all the return values from the `pgr_dijkstra` function. This will result in one optimized route between **each point in the route** meaning that if we have to visit 10 points, we will have ten rows of data, each containing a route. In the final step, we aggregate the data from the CTE to create a combined geometry and find the sum of the time in seconds the route will take (of course not accounting for stops, traffic lights, etc.), and the length of the route. FYI this is a long-running query, so I would recommend making a table from it.

Listing 3.38: Final TSP query

```
1   create table final_tsp_test as
2   with a as (
3       select
4           s.id,
5           s.source,
6           s.seq,
7           s.node,
8           s.next_node,
9           di.*,
10          ways.the_geom,
11          st_length(st_transform(ways.the_geom, 3857)) as length
12      from
13          solved_tsp s,
14
15          -- We cross join this to each row
16          pgr_dijkstra(
17              'select
18              gid as id,
19              source,
20              target,
21              cost_s,
22                      cost_s * penalty as cost,
23                      reverse_cost_s * penalty as reverse_cost
24          from ways
25          join configuration
26          using (tag_id)',
27
28              -- We create a route between the current node and the next node
29              s.node,
30              s.next_node,
31              true
32          ) as di
33          join ways on di.node = ways.source
34  )
35  select
36
37      -- Union the geometries and find the sum of the cost and length for each route
38      st_union(st_transform(the_geom, 4326)) as route,
39      source,
```

```
40      sum(cost) as cost,
41      sum(length) as length
42  from
43      a
44  group by
45      source
```

And here are our results (Figures 3.19 and 3.20, on the next page):

Figure 3.19: Output of the traveling salesman problem for bikes

3.5 Creating travel time polygons or isochones

In our last routing-specific exercise we will use pgRouting to create isochonre polygons. These area polygons that show what areas can be reached within a certain distance or time from a specific point. For example, you can create an isochrone around your home to see the areas you can reach within a ten-minute drive. With pgRouting you can create various network types, so you could apply this to cyclist, pedestrians, and more. Once again, isochrones are a common service provided by location data service providers via APIs, which are great for one time calls, but batch processes can take some time or not work at all. Even though the service speeds have greatly improved in recent years, having the flexibility to do this within the same location as your data can be highly beneficial.

Isochrones can be used for a wide range of analysis as they often provide a more accurate picture of a population that can reach a certain location. This can be used to analyze retail trade areas, identify how many people can reach a health care facility, accessibility to a government office, identify cannibalization and overlap between locations, and much more. The functions we will be using are pgr_drivingDistance, which, despite its name, uses any cost metric to find all the nodes that are less than

Figure 3.20: Output of the traveling salesman problem for bikes zoomed out

or equal to the cost we input into the function. From there we will construct a polygon around those nodes using ST_ConcaveHull.

Our first task will be to identify the way ID closest to our starting point, in this case the entry to Katz's Deli, a famous New York City restaurant. Similar to before we want to make sure to exclude sidewalks and match the location to the closest driveable road:

Listing 3.39: Finding closest road segments

```
1  with start as (
2      select
3          source
4      from
5          ways
6          join car_config using (tag_id)
7
8      -- Finding the closest road segment to Katz's
9      where
10         car_config.penalty != -1
11     order by
12         the_geom <-> st_setsrid(
13             st_geomfromtext('POINT (-73.987374 40.722349)'),
14             4326
15         )
16     limit
17         1
18 ),
```

Next we call the `pgr_drivingDistance` function to find all the nodes that are equal to or less than the cost of our third argument, in this case 600 seconds or 10 minutes. In this case we are using the column `cost_s` rather than using distance since we are creating isochrones based on time. We also only select the road tags that are driveable:

Listing 3.40: Using pgr_drivingDistance

```
1   b as (
2       SELECT
3           *
4       FROM
5           pgr_drivingDistance(
6               'SELECT
7               gid as id,
8               source,
9               target,
10              cost,
11              cost_s,
12              reverse_cost,
13              st_transform(the_geom, 3857) as the_geom
14              FROM ways',
15
16              -- This will find all the points that are within
17              -- a 600 second distance of the source location
18              (
19                  select
20                      source
21                  from
22                      start
23              ),
24              600
25          )
26  )
```

Using the query below we can see the results up to this point (Figure 3.21, on the facing page):

Listing 3.41: Query thus far

```
1   with start as (
2       select
3           source
4       from
5           ways
6           join car_config using (tag_id)
7       where
8           car_config.penalty != -1
9       order by
10          the_geom <-> st_setsrid(
11              st_geomfromtext('POINT (-73.987374 40.722349)'),
12              4326
13          )
14      limit
15          1
16  ), b as (
17      select
18          *
19      from
20          pgr_drivingdistance(
21              'select
22              gid as id,
23              source,
24              target,
25              cost_s * 2.5 as cost,
26              reverse_cost_s * 2.5 as reverse_cost
```

```
27            from ways
28            join car_config
29            using (tag_id)
30            where tag_id in (110, 100, 124, 115, 112, 125, 109, 101,
31            103, 102, 106, 107, 108, 104, 105)',
32            (
33                select
34                    source
35                from
36                    start
37            ),
38            600
39        )
40    )
41
42    -- Union the geometries into a single geometry
43    select
44            st_union(ways.the_geom)
45    from
46        ways
47    where
48            gid in (select edge from b)
```

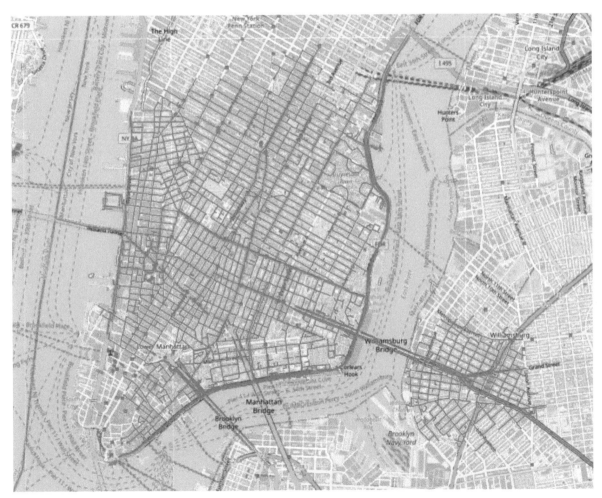

Figure 3.21: All the roads used for our isochrone

In our final step we create a concave hull around the combined geometries to create our drive time area

(Figure 3.22, on the next page):

Listing 3.42: Building isocrhone with a concave hull

```sql
1   with start as (
2       select
3           source
4       from
5           ways
6           join car_config using (tag_id)
7       where
8           car_config.penalty != -1
9       order by
10          the_geom <-> st_setsrid(
11              st_geomfromtext('POINT (-73.987374 40.722349)'),
12              4326
13          )
14      limit
15          1
16  ), b as (
17      select
18          *
19      from
20          pgr_drivingdistance(
21              'select
22              gid as id,
23              source,
24              target,
25              cost_s * 2.5 as cost,
26              reverse_cost_s * 2.5 as reverse_cost
27              from ways
28              join car_config
29              using (tag_id)
30              where tag_id in (110, 100, 124, 115, 112, 125,
31              109, 101, 103, 102, 106, 107, 108, 104, 105)',
32              (
33                  select
34                      source
35                  from
36                      start
37              ),
38              600
39          )
40  )
41  select
42      -- Creates a concave hull around the entire routes geometry
43      st_concavehull(
44          st_transform(
45              st_union(the_geom), 4326),
46          0.1) as geom
47  from
48      ways
49  where
50      gid in (
51          select
52              distinct edge
53          from
54              b
55      )
```

This method is great for intersecting with other data as it ultimately has fewer vertices but if you want a more "accurate" looking drive time you can substitute buffers for the concave hull. After we create the buffers, in this example using a 20 meter buffer, we then find the exterior ring using ST_ExteriorRing of the polygon to remove any holes, then turn it back to a polygon using ST_MakePolygon (Figure 3.23,

Figure 3.22: Isochrone using a concave hull

on page 451):

Listing 3.43: Isochones with buffers

```
1   with start as (
2       select
3           source
4       from
5           ways
6           join car_config using (tag_id)
7       where
8           car_config.penalty != -1
9       order by
10          the_geom <-> st_setsrid(
11              st_geomfromtext('POINT (-73.987374 40.722349)'),
12              4326
13          )
14      limit
15          1
16  ), b as (
17      select
18          *
19      from
20          pgr_drivingdistance(
21              'select gid as id,
```

```
22              source,
23              target,
24              cost_s * 2.5 as cost,
25              reverse_cost_s * 2.5 as reverse_cost
26              from ways
27              join car_config
28              using (tag_id)
29              where tag_id in (110, 100, 124, 115, 112,
30              125, 109, 101, 103, 102, 106, 107, 108, 104, 105)',
31              (
32                  select
33                      source
34                  from
35                      start
36              ),
37              600
38          )
39  )
40  select
41
42      -- Turn it all into a polygon
43      st_makepolygon(
44
45          -- Find the exterior ring which will eliminate islands
46          st_exteriorring(
47
48              -- Create a 20 meter buffer
49              st_buffer(
50                  st_transform(
51                      st_union(the_geom), 4326) :: geography,
52                  20
53              ) :: geometry
54          )
55      ) as geom
56  from
57      ways
58  where
59      gid in (
60          select
61              distinct edge
62          from
63              b
64      )
```

We can also do this for cycling using our *bike* database by changing out our configuration table name
and then selecting only roads that we don't penalize (Figure 3.24, on page 452):

Listing 3.44: Bike isochrones

```
1   with start as (
2       select
3           source
4       from
5           ways
6           join configuration using (tag_id)
7       where
8           configuration.penalty <= 1
9       order by
10          the_geom <-> st_setsrid(
11              st_geomfromtext('POINT (-73.987374 40.722349)'),
12              4326
13          )
14      limit
15          1
```

Figure 3.23: Isochrone using buffers

```
16   ), b as (
17       select
18           *
19       from
20           pgr_drivingdistance(
21               'select
22               gid as id,
23               source,
24               target,
25               cost_s * 2.5 as cost,
26               reverse_cost_s * 2.5 as reverse_cost
27               from ways
28               join configuration
29               using (tag_id)
30               where penalty <= 1',
31               (
32                   select
33                       source
34                   from
35                       start
36               ),
37               600
```

```
38            )
39    )
40    select
41        st_makepolygon(
42            st_exteriorring(
43                st_buffer(
44                    st_transform(st_union(the_geom), 4326) :: geography,
45                    20
46                ) :: geometry
47            )
48        ) as geom
49    from
50        ways
51    where
52        gid in (
53            select
54                distinct edge
55            from
56                b
57        )
```

3.6   Expert Voices: Aaron Fraint

Name: Aaron Fraint **Title**: Solutions Engineering Team Lead, North America @ CARTO

How/where did you learn spatial SQL?

The first time I encountered spatial SQL was on the job while working for Azavea. I was embedded within the Stormwater Billing unit of the Philadelphia Water Department, and I quickly learned how important SQL and Python were. The job required the ability to query a vast billing database and intersect it with a land coverage dataset to determine the stormwater charge for every account. The more impervious land cover on a property, the larger the bill. I also had to answer the phone and speak to people about potential issues with their bills, sometimes writing SQL queries in real time! Using photographic and other evidence, we were able to update our source data and fix any errors that may have resulted in customers being charged too much. When this happened, we'd also use spatial SQL to calculate the amount of the refund owed to the customer.

Why do you enjoy using spatial SQL?

I enjoy using spatial SQL as it allows me to express simple or complex data transformations in a straightforward manner. Instead of running numerous geoprocessing tools in a manual sequence, I can run an entire analysis end to end as a single query, organizing my logical steps into common table expressions. I find this to be an excellent environment that encourages experimentation and iteration.

Can you share an interesting way or use case that you are using spatial SQL for today?

While working as the Associate Manager of the Delaware Valley Regional Planning Commission's (DVRPC) Office of Mobility Analysis & Design, I leveraged spatial SQL within an API to solve end-to-end routing requests with the least-stressful path for bicyclists.

To do this, I performed an ELT process with the agency's Level of Traffic Stress dataset, where I ingested the raw data into Postgres, and then reformatted it to work with pgRouting, the routing engine for the project. I then used the FastAPI library in Python to write an API where requests with a start and endpoint are then passed into a query that leverages pgRouting functions against a network with a custom impedance variable that considers not just the length of the trip, but the stress levels as well.

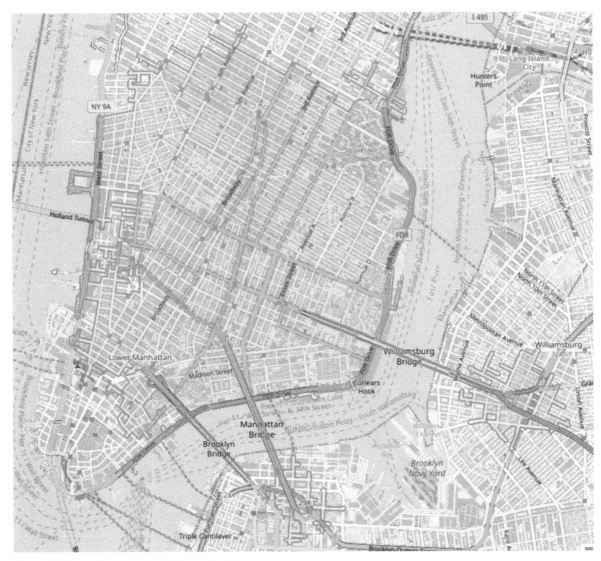

Figure 3.24: Isochrone using buffers with bikes

This API is currently being used in an app called Ruti, which is a trip planning tool for finding the least stressful bike routes developed by Corey Acri at AG Strategic in partnership with DVRPC. When you visit https://ruti.bike/go and plan a trip between two places, a spatial SQL query using pgRouting will return the least stressful path.

You can find the code for this on GitHub[134]

---

[134]https://github.com/dvrpc/low-stress-bike-routing

4. Spatial Autocorrelation and Optimization With Python and PySAL

Spatial data science is an area that has grown tremendously within the last several years. This took place alongside broader growth in roles and jobs in data science and has also expanded usage of open source GIS tools, specifically within the Python ecosystem. There are many types of analysis you can perform in this space, but these slides[135] from Luc Anselin, Ph. D. from the Center for Spatial Data Science at the University of Chicago (Figure 4.1):

Figure 4.1: Spatial analytics questions from the YouTube Video "Spatial Data Science Overview" by Dr. Luc Anselin

In this section we will work to answer some of these questions such as clustering using spatial autocorrelation, optimization by combining areas into regions or territories, and locating new facilities optimally using location allocation. The interesting part is that we will actually be using Python to accomplish this **within** our PostGIS database. I will explain why and with what tools in the next section so let's jump in!

---

[135]https://www.youtube.com/watch?v=lawWM6jQYEE&t=986s

457

4.1 Spatial autocorrelation

The tutorials in this section will feature tools and analyses from the Python Spatial Analysis Library or PySAL. In my opinion it is the best library for performing analysis that you might categorize as spatial data science, but can also be categorized as spatial econometrics or spatial statistics. The challenge for us is that this library, as its name implies, is written in Python.

Before we get into the examples I want to call out a few important points. First is that this is a book about spatial SQL not Python. So why are we talking about it here? As you have likely experienced, it is near impossible to grow your geospatial toolkit without encountering Python. Python is a critical language for modern GIS and one that I enjoy using for different problems and analyses as discussed earlier in the book. Specifically as it relates to PySAL, what I value most is that I can use tools developed by the best leaders, thinkers, and teachers in this field that have focused much of their time, research, and energy into building tools like PySAL. This in turn makes complex analysis accessible to a user like myself who does not have a background in these types of problems, but wants to solve them nonetheless.

The same goes for PostGIS and any other tool under the spatial SQL umbrella. I am not a database or C/C++/C# developer, and it would be a difficult task for me to implement a new function or even some basic fixes into something like PostGIS. But as a user I can benefit from all this amazing work to use PostGIS as a user to work with data in a flexible and scalable environment.

Now to answer the question about why we are using both spatial SQL and Python in one function. Both spatial SQL and Python have their strengths and weaknesses. SQL is fantastic at working with and manipulating data as we have seen throughout the course of this book. Python is great at creating complex functions and scripting analytical processes. While you can perform data manipulation with Python and libraries like Pandas and GeoPandas, at a certain point the speed at which you can manipulate data starts to decrease. Specific to PySAL, some of their internal functions such as creating spatial weights can also be slow and even fail at times with large data. As for SQL, while you can program to do analysis like those in PySAL, it isn't necessarily a straight forward process and Python is generally efficient to perform statistical analysis on data within a native Python data structure. But above all, the analysis we need is already built and maintained in PySAL, and if we don't use this library we would not be able to take advantage of all the work that already exists.

Our use cases that we will explore meet all of these conditions and by creating a solution that merges the best of Python and SQL, we will create the best possible outcome to address scale and efficiency. The solution we will explore will use PL/Python, or the Python Procedural Language which is a part of PostgreSQL. It allows us to create our own functions that use Python or Python libraries that we have installed on the server (in this case Docker container) where we are running PostgreSQL.

I do want to also state that this is not the only solution for performing this analysis. Certainly we can use the same query process to pull data into Python code using sqlalchemy or other Python libraries with similar functionality (most notably Pandas[136] and GeoPandas[137] to connect to your PostGIS instance.

The main problem we will be addressing is using SQL to quickly analyze our data using spatial relationships and to structure the data into the format the functions in PySAL need to use. How and where you choose to execute this is up to you, but we will focus on the methods within PostgreSQL here.

A final note is that many, but not all, databases and data warehouses will include functionality to support developing functions with other languages. Snowflake for example supports Python as a UDF like we will do in our example, or using its Snowpark product which allows you to scale the computational

---

[136]https://pandas.pydata.org/docs/reference/api/pandas.read_sql.html

[137]https://loc8.cc/sql/geopandas-geodataframe

support for that Python code. Amazon Web Services Redshift also allows you to create Python UDFs like we will see shortly, and BigQuery allows you to use JavaScript to create UDFs. The differentiating factor here is that these tools allow you to query data and run Python all in the same compute infrastructure, reducing data transfer and complexity. So with that we can get started.

Before we can create our function we need to run a few steps to set up our instance to work with the Python libraries we need. One of the first ones is the PL/Python extension which can be activated by running this command:

```
CREATE EXTENSION plpython3u;
```

This will allow us to query our database from inside the the SQL function using Python. In the next steps we are going to open a terminal connection into our Docker container to install the Python libraries we need. To do so, you will need to open a new terminal window to run these commands. Once this is done can start to enter the commands. To do so we can run this command:

```
docker container exec -it docker-postgis-db-1 bash
```

Once the command is run you should see this screen (Figure 4.2):

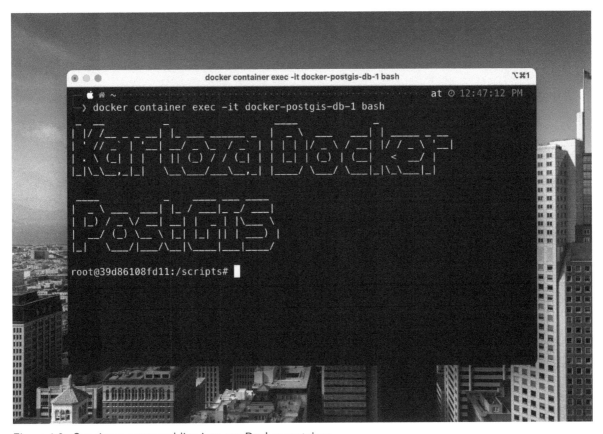

Figure 4.2: Opening a command line into our Docker container

Now we have opened a new terminal session in our Docker container via the terminal on your computer, so all commands from this point forward will be run on the Docker container. Our PostGIS container is based on Debian which means that we will be using the package manager apt, or Ubuntu's Advanced Packaging Tool (APT). Our first command will be to update APT (Figure 4.3):

```
apt update
```

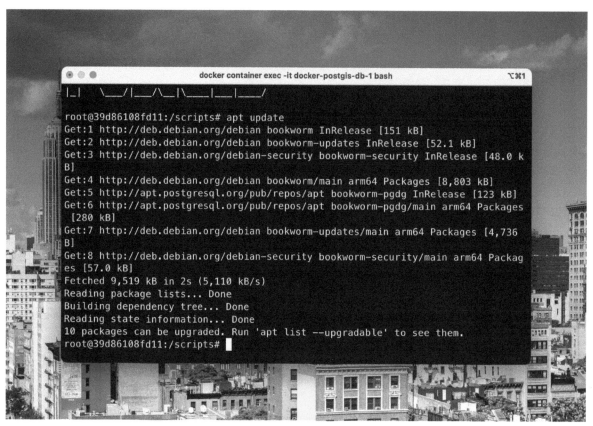

Figure 4.3: Updating apt

Next we need to install Python 3 and `pip3`, the Python package manger PyPI. Below is the output for installing Python (Figure 4.4, on the next page):

When you install `pip3` you will also need to enter "Y" for yes when prompted to complete the installation. First run this command and then enter "Y" when you are prompted (Figure 4.5, on page 460):

```
apt install python3-pip
```

We can check that the installations ran correctly by running the following commands (Figure 4.6, on page 461):

```
python3 --version
pip3 --version
```

Next we are going to install GDAL which requires two commands, the second of which will require the "Y" for yes prompt:

```
apt-get install gdal-bin
apt-get install libgdal-dev
```

Figure 4.4: Installing Python3

Now finally we can run our command to install our Python libraries using `pip3` (Figure 4.7, on page 462):

```
pip3 install esda matplotlib libpysal spopt geopandas scikit-learn --break-system-packages
```

Once you see this message you have successfully installed all the required packages. Before we start to build our function we should first take a look at the new tools we will use. For the most part the Python UDFs follow the same structure as the other UDFs we have created so far over the course of the book. The main difference is that the majority of the function is actually written in Python as the core language.

The second is that, to access data in our database, we use the procedural PL/Python language with a built-in library called `plpy`[138]. This allows us to write queries to our database and return the data in a dictionary format in Python. The queries are passed to the database as strings which means that they can be formatted the same way you would a normal Python string.

Let's take a look at a sample function to understand how this works. First is a simple function that will return the greater of two integers from the PostgreSQL documentation:

Listing 4.1: PL/Python function

```
1   CREATE FUNCTION pymax (a integer, b integer)
2   RETURNS integer
```

---

[138]https://www.postgresql.org/docs/current/plpython-database.html

Figure 4.5: Installing pip3

```
3   AS $$
4       if a > b:
5           return a
6       return b
7   $$
8   LANGUAGE plpython3u;
```

This function runs a simple if statement in Python to return the larger of two integers which you can test with this query:

Listing 4.2: Using our function

```
1   select
2       pymax(100, 1)
```

To see how the database calls with plpy will work we can run another test function:

Listing 4.3: Using plpy

```
1   create function python_limit_5 (tablename TEXT)
2   returns text
3   AS $$
4       data = plpy.execute(f'''select * from {tablename} limit 5''')
5       return data
6   $$
7   LANGUAGE plpython3u;
```

Figure 4.6: Checking the Python and pip installs

This function will return five rows of our data as text from within the function which will allow us to see the data structure that is returned from a query call to "plpy". To do this we can create a table without a geometry since that will show as a very long string:

```
1  create table nyc_neighborhoods_no_geom as
2  select
3      ogc_fid,
4      neighborhood,
5      boroughcode,
6      borough
7  from
8      nyc_neighborhoods
```

And now we can run our new function:

Listing 4.4: Returned data structure from plpy

```
1   <PLyResult status=5 nrows=5 rows=[{
2        'ogc_fid': 1,
3        'neighborhood': 'Allerton',
4        'boroughcode': '2',
5        'borough': 'Bronx'
6    },
7    {
8        'ogc_fid': 2,
9        'neighborhood': 'Alley Pond Park',
10       'boroughcode': '4',
11       'borough': 'Queens'
12   },
```

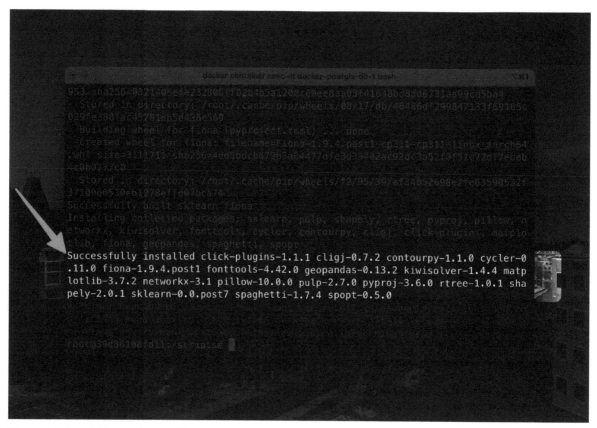

Figure 4.7: Installing our Python files

```
13      {
14          'ogc_fid': 3,
15          'neighborhood': 'Arden Heights',
16          'boroughcode': '5',
17          'borough': 'Staten Island'
18      },
19      {
20          'ogc_fid': 4,
21          'neighborhood': 'Arlington',
22          'boroughcode': '5',
23          'borough': 'Staten Island'
24      },
25      {
26          'ogc_fid': 5,
27          'neighborhood': 'Arrochar',
28          'boroughcode': '5',
29          'borough': 'Staten Island'
30      }]>
```

As you can see we have an object with our target data in a dictionary structure in Python. We can extract the data itself by accessing each row by accessing the data as an array such as below:

Listing 4.5: Returning one value

```
1   create or replace function python_limit_5 (tablename TEXT)
2   returns text
3   AS $$
4       data = plpy.execute(f'''select * from {tablename} limit 5''')
```

```
5      return data[0]
6  $$
7  LANGUAGE plpython3u;
```

Running this function will return the first row of data:

Listing 4.6: One row of data

```
1  {
2      'ogc_fid': 1,
3      'neighborhood': 'Allerton',
4      'boroughcode': '2',
5      'borough': 'Bronx'
6  }
```

To access a specific column in that row we can access it using the column name and dictionary notation:

Listing 4.7: Accessing specific values

```
1  create or replace function python_limit_5 (tablename TEXT)
2  returns text
3  AS $$
4      data = plpy.execute(f'''select * from {tablename} limit 5''')
5      return data[0]['neighborhood']
6  $$
7  LANGUAGE plpython3u;
```

Which will return 'Allerton'. So with that, we are ready to start developing our new function.

For our first step, we can build out the structure of our function along with commented steps of the code we will fill in with equivalent Python code:

As we go along we will simply return text for our development function so we can see the results of each step, and then we can copy the successful code and create a function that returns a table. In our first step, we need to import our libraries, create our dictionaries for our neighboring polygons data, and our spatial weights data. Below is the full code which we will break down step by step:

Listing 4.8: Using text return to test our function

```
1  create
2  or replace function pysal_esda_test(
3      tablename TEXT,
4      geom TEXT,
5      col TEXT,
6      id_col TEXT,
7      similarity FLOAT
8  )
9  returns text
10 AS $$
11     import esda
12     import libpysal as lps
13     from libpysal.weights import W
14     import json
15     import numpy as np
16     import pandas as pd
17
18     neighbors = plpy.execute(
19         f '''
20         select
21             json_object_agg(b.{ id_col }, a.neighbors) as neighbors
22         from
23             { tablename } b
24             cross join lateral (
```

```
25              select
26                  array_agg(z.{ id_col } :: text) as neighbors
27              from
28                  { tablename } z
29              where
30                  st_intersects(z.{ geom }, b.{ geom })
31                  and z.{ id_col } != b.{ id_col }
32          ) a
33      where
34          a.neighbors is not null
35      '''
36  )
37
38  weights = plpy.execute(
39      f '''
40      select
41          json_object_agg(b.{ id_col }, a.weights) as weights
42      from
43          { tablename } b
44          cross join lateral (
45              select
46                  array_agg(z.{ id_col }) as neighbors,
47                  array_fill(
48                      (
49                          case
50                              when count(z.{ id_col }) = 0 then 0
51                              else 1 / count(z.{ id_col }) :: numeric
52                          end
53                      ),
54                      array [count(z.{id_col})::int]
55                  ) as weights
56              from
57                  { tablename } z
58              where
59                  st_intersects(z.{ geom }, b.{ geom })
60                  and z.{ id_col } != b.{ id_col }
61          ) a
62      where
63          a.neighbors is not null
64      '''
65  )
66  return neighbors
67  $$
68  LANGUAGE 'plpython3u';
```

In the first part of the query you can see that we imported all of our various libraries we need using the Python `import` process:

Listing 4.9: Python imports

```
1  import esda
2  import libpysal as lps
3  from libpysal.weights import W
4  import json
5  import numpy as np
6  import pandas as pd
```

Next we calculate our neighbors and weights data that will be used to calculate our spatial weights in the next step using a call to our database:

Listing 4.10: Querying our neighbors data structure

```
1  # In this query we are using a cross join lateral
2
```

```
3   neighbors = plpy.execute(f'''
4   select
5
6       -- This will create a JSON object with the ID column and an
7       -- array of the neighbor IDs
8
9       json_object_agg(b.{ id_col }, a.neighbors) as neighbors
10  from
11      { tablename } b
12
13      -- To accomplish this we use a cross join lateral
14      -- to find all the neighboring IDs and aggreagate
15      -- them into an array to match the PySAL formatting
16
17      cross join lateral (
18          select
19              array_agg(z.{ id_col } :: text) as neighbors
20          from
21              { tablename } z
22          where
23
24              -- A neighbor is considered anything that intersects or
25              -- touches the target ID and that isn't the target polyogon
26
27              st_intersects(z.{ geom }, b.{ geom })
28              and z.{ id_col } != b.{ id_col }
29      ) a
30  where
31
32      -- This removes any islands or non-conencted polygons
33
34      a.neighbors is not null
35  ''')
36
37  weights = plpy.execute(f'''
38  select
39      json_object_agg(b.{ id_col }, a.weights) as weights
40  from
41      { tablename } b
42      cross join lateral (
43          select
44              array_agg(z.{ id_col }) as neighbors,
45              array_fill(
46                  (
47                      case
48                          when count(z.{ id_col }) = 0 then 0
49                          else 1 / count(z.{ id_col }) :: numeric
50                      end
51                  ),
52                  array [count(z.{id_col})::int]
53              ) as weights
54          from
55              { tablename } z
56          where
57              st_intersects(z.{ geom }, b.{ geom })
58              and z.{ id_col } != b.{ id_col }
59      ) a
60  where
61      a.neighbors is not null
62  ''')
```

As you can see we store our results in a variable for each. In each query you will notice that we have some values within braces, such as *{id_col}*. We are using f-string formatting in Python which means that those values will be replaced by the values from our function. So if our ID columns is added as *'my_id'* all instances of *{id_col}* will be replaced with that.

For now lets take a look at the individual queries. The goal of each is to create data that looks like this for the neighbors dataset:

{ "360050001001" : ["*360050001000*","*360810331000*","*360810929000*","*360810107010*"]}

The key of the object is the census block ID of the target block group, in this case *360050001001*, and the values in the array are the block groups that touch it with at least one point.

The weights are similar except that each value is will be replaced with the value of one over the number of items in the array. Meaning in our example since there are four neighbors, each ID will be replaced by ¼ or 0.25. These are the data structures that are required to calculate our spatial weights as defined in the PySAL documentation[139].

Let's take a look at our query and review it step by step, with the values filled in:

Listing 4.11: Spatial weights query

```
1    -- No. 1
2    select
3        json_object_agg(b.geoid, a.neighbors) as neighbors
4    from
5        nyc_2021_census_block_groups b
6
7    -- No. 2
8        cross join lateral (
9
10   -- No. 3
11           select
12               array_agg(z.geoid :: text) as neighbors
13           from
14               nyc_2021_census_block_groups z
15
16   -- No.4
17           where
18               st_intersects(z.geom, b.geom)
19               and z.geoid != b.geoid
20       ) a
21
22   -- No. 5
23   where
24       a.neighbors is not null
```

1. Our target output is a JSON object with a key and an array value which will be read as a dictionary within Python, so we create a JSON object using `json_object_agg`

2. Next we use a cross join lateral to find all the polygons that touch the source polygon

3. We take all the IDs of the polygons that touch the source polygon and put them into an array

4. We use `ST_Intersects` to find the matches that touch and then exclude the source polygon in the second part of the where clause

5. PySAL will give an error for empty relationships so we exclude those

---

[139]https://pysal.org/libpysal/generated/libpysal.weights.W.html#libpysal.weights.W

We do the same thing for the weights, but we add this instead of the neighbors array.

Listing 4.12: Using array_fill

```
1   -- This will allow you to fill the array
2
3   array_fill(
4
5       -- The first value is the value we will fill with which
6       -- will be 0 if the count is 0 or 1 divide by the count
7       (
8           case
9               when count(z.{ id_col }) = 0 then 0
10              else 1 / count(z.{ id_col }) :: numeric
11          end
12      ),
13
14      -- This determines the length of the array which is the
15      -- count of the values
16      array [count(z.{id_col})::int]
17  ) as weights
```

Here we use the ST_Intersects function that takes two arguments. The first is the number to fill the array with, which in the case of our previous example is 0.25 since we have 4 entries. We then have the second argument which created the empty array to fill with the length of the total number of entries.

Moving on to the next steps, we will create our spatial weights using the W function from the main PySAL library, libpysal[140]. We will also create a matching data structure for our variable data, in this case our income column. If you want to learn more about spatial weights I would recommend this chapter from the Geospatial Data Science Book[141].

Our spatial weights are created with these two lines of code:

Listing 4.13: Creating spatial weights

```
1   w = W(json.loads(
2
3       # First we add the values from our neighbors query
4       neighbors[0]['neighbors']),
5
6       # Then our spatial weights
7       json.loads(weights[0]['weights']), silence_warnings = True)
8
9   w.transform='r'
```

We can access the data we want from our neighbors and weights query results using the array notation we saw earlier and wrapping them in the JSON loads function which will turn our string data into proper Python dictionary data.

Listing 4.14: Using JSON to load our query data

```
1   json.loads(neighbors[0]['neighbors'])
```

Next we will grab our income data using a similar query structure to our first two queries. As you can see in the last line of the query we are only returning our values from the query since we only need those values in an ordered array in Python. This means that we have to turn them into an array and account for null values by turning them to 0. To accomplish this we will loop over the items returned from our query and put them into an empty array using a for loop with a conditional if/else inside it:

---

[140]https://pysal.org/libpysal/generated/libpysal.weights.W.html#libpysal.weights.W

[141]https://geographicdata.science/book/notebooks/04_spatial_weights.html

Listing 4.15: Turning our data into a list

```
1  var_list = []
2
3  for i in var_data:
4
5      # This loops over each item in "var_data"
6
7      # If it is empty we set it to 0
8      if i['data_col'] == None:
9          var_list.append(float(0.0))
10
11     # Otherwise we set it to the actual value
12     else:
13         var_list.append(float(i['data_col']))
```

This returns a list with all the correct values:

```
[2499.0, 2499.0, 6152.0, 9208.0, 9457.0...
```

We will put this all into a Pandas `DataFrame` to use in our next step which is to calculate the Moran's I values with our list data that is turned into a numpy array:

Listing 4.16: Creating our Moran's local values

```
1  li = esda.moran.Moran_Local(np.array(var_list), w)
```

And this is where our function is up to this point:

Listing 4.17: Function up to this point

```
1  create
2  or replace function pysal_esda_test(
3      tablename TEXT,
4      geom TEXT,
5      col TEXT,
6      id_col TEXT,
7      similarity FLOAT
8  )
9  returns text
10 AS $$
11     import esda
12     import libpysal as lps
13     from libpysal.weights import W
14     import json
15     import numpy as np
16     import pandas as pd
17
18     neighbors = plpy.execute(
19         f '''
20         select
21             json_object_agg(b.{ id_col }, a.neighbors) as neighbors
22         from
23             { tablename } b
24             cross join lateral (
25                 select
26                     array_agg(z.{ id_col } :: text) as neighbors
27                 from
28                     { tablename } z
29                 where
30                     st_intersects(z.{ geom }, b.{ geom })
31                     and z.{ id_col } != b.{ id_col }
32             ) a
33         where
```

```
34              a.neighbors is not null
35          '''
36      )
37
38      weights = plpy.execute(
39          f '''
40          select
41              json_object_agg(b.{ id_col }, a.weights) as weights
42          from
43              { tablename } b
44              cross join lateral (
45                  select
46                      array_agg(z.{ id_col }) as neighbors,
47                      array_fill(
48                          (
49                              case
50                                  when count(z.{ id_col }) = 0 then 0
51                                  else 1 / count(z.{ id_col }) :: numeric
52                              end
53                          ),
54                          array [count(z.{id_col})::int]
55                      ) as weights
56                  from
57                      { tablename } z
58                  where
59                      st_intersects(z.{ geom }, b.{ geom })
60                      and z.{ id_col } != b.{ id_col }
61              ) a
62          where
63              a.neighbors is not null
64          '''
65      )
66
67      w = W(json.loads(neighbors [0] ['neighbors']), json.loads(weights [0] ['weights']), silence_warnings = True)
68      w.transform = 'r'
69
70      var_data = plpy.execute(
71          f '''
72          with a as (
73              select
74                  distinct b.{ col },
75                  b.{ id_col }
76              from
77                  { tablename } b
78                  cross join lateral (
79                      select
80                          array_agg(z.{ id_col }) as neighbors
81                      from
82                          { tablename } z
83                      where
84                          st_intersects(z.{ geom }, b.{ geom })
85                          and z.{ id_col } != b.{ id_col }
86                  ) a
87              where
88                  a.neighbors is not null
89          )
90          select
91              { col } as data_col
92          from
93              a
94          ''')
95
96      var_list = []
97      for i in var_data:
98          if i ['data_col'] == None:
```

```
99                 var_list.append(float(0.0))
100           else:
101                 var_list.append(float(i ['data_col']))
102
103      li = esda.moran.Moran_Local(np.array(var_list), w)
104
105      return var_list
106  $$
107  LANGUAGE 'plpython3u';
```

In our last set of steps we will query our data to find the original data which includes the geometry, create two lists of data which we can use to structure the final data output, and join our Pandas `DataFrame` and structure the data.

The first step is to create a query to retrieve the original data column (in our case income), id column, and geometry:

Listing 4.18: Querying our original daa

```
1   # This mirrors our original queries but
2   # retrieves the column, id column, and geometry
3   # and returns it as a normal tabular format
4
5   original = plpy.execute(f'''
6   with a as (
7      select
8         distinct b.{ col },
9         b.{ id_col },
10        b.{ geom }
11     from
12        { tablename } b
13        cross join lateral (
14           select
15              array_agg(z.{ id_col }) as neighbors
16           from
17              { tablename } z
18           where
19              st_intersects(z.{ geom }, b.{ geom })
20              and z.{ id_col } != b.{ id_col }
21        ) a
22     where
23        a.neighbors is not null
24   )
25   select
26      { id_col },
27      { col },
28      { geom }
29   from
30      a
31   ''')
```

Next we will loop over that data to create two new lists. One will be turned into a `DataFrame` to use to join to the other `DataFrame` we created in the earlier steps. The other will be a list to lookup the index position of a specific Census Block Group ID to extract values. The index position is a number that represents the position on a list starting at 0, so if I wanted to get the first position in a list called `my_list` I would use this code to access it:

```
my_list[0]
```

We will need the index to extract values from the results of our Moran's I results. We do that by finding the specific data point we want (you can see all the return results in the documentation[142]) along with the index position. So with that you can see how we create those lists using the following code:

Listing 4.19: Preparing our original data

```
1   original_data = []
2
3   lookup_table = []
4
5   # This allows us to create lists of just the values rather
6   # than the entire return structure to use going forward     .
7
8   for i in original:
9       original_data.append(i)
10      lookup_table.append(i[f'{id_col}'])
11
12  df = pd.DataFrame.from_dict(original_data)
```

Next we format our data using a similar process, and it is here where we extract the data from the Moran's I results, including the Moran's I values, p-value, and quadrant.

Listing 4.20: Final data preparation

```
1   formatted_data = []
2
3   for i in original_data:
4
5       # This will loop over each dictionary entry in the original data
6
7       dict = i
8
9       # Then we add the results of the Local Moran's I to the dictionary
10      res = lookup_table.index(i[f'{id_col}'])
11      dict['local_morani_values'] = li.Is[res]
12      dict['p_values'] = li.p_sim[res]
13      dict['quadrant'] = li.q[res]
14
15      # Then append that new dictionary to the new list
16
17      formatted_data.append(dict)
```

The last steps include:

1. Turning our formatted data we just created into a DataFrame

2. Merging our original data with the original data

3. Dropping duplicate columns

4. Renaming the columns

5. Turing the merged and renamed DataFrame into a dictionary which PostgreSQL will return as a table

Listing 4.21: Final steps

```
1   # Turn the data into a DataFrame
2
3   original_data_df = pd.DataFrame.from_dict(formatted_data)
```

---

[142]https://pysal.org/esda/generated/esda.Moran_Local.html#esda.Moran_Local

```
4
5    # Merge or join it with the original data
6
7    final = df.merge(original_data_df, how='inner', on=f'{id_col}')
8
9    # Drop duplicate columns
10
11   final_df = final.drop([f'{col}_x', f'{geom}_x'], axis=1)
12
13   # Rename the outputs
14
15   final_df = final_df.rename(columns={f'{col}_y': 'col', f'{geom}_y': f'{geom}', f'{id_col}': 'id' })
16
17   # Return the final formatted DataFrame as a dictionary using the .to_dict() function from Pandas
18
19   return final_df.to_dict(orient='records')
```

And that is it! You can see the complete code here:

Listing 4.22: Final spatial autocorrelation function

```
1    create or replace function pysal_esda (
2        tablename TEXT,
3        geom TEXT,
4        col TEXT,
5        id_col TEXT,
6        similarity FLOAT
7    )
8    returns table (
9        id TEXT,
10       col FLOAT,
11       local_morani_values FLOAT,
12       p_values FLOAT,
13       quadrant TEXT,
14       geom GEOMETRY
15   )
16   AS $$
17       import esda
18       import libpysal as lps
19       from libpysal.weights import W
20       import json
21       import numpy as np
22       import pandas as pd
23
24       neighbors = plpy.execute(
25           f'''
26           select
27               json_object_agg(b.{id_col}, a.neighbors) as neighbors
28           from
29               {tablename} b
30               cross join lateral (
31                   select
32                       array_agg(z.{id_col} :: text) as neighbors
33                   from
34                       {tablename} z
35                   where
36                       st_intersects(z.{geom}, b.{geom})
37                       and z.{id_col} != b.{id_col}
38               ) a
39           where
40               a.neighbors is not null
41           '''
42       )
43
44       weights = plpy.execute(
```

```
45          f'''
46          select
47              json_object_agg(b.{id_col}, a.weights) as weights
48          from
49              {tablename} b
50              cross join lateral (
51                  select
52                      array_agg(z.{id_col}) as neighbors,
53                      array_fill(
54                          (
55                              case
56                                  when count(z.{id_col}) = 0 then 0
57                                  else 1 / count(z.{id_col}) :: numeric
58                              end
59                          ),
60                          array [count(z.{id_col})::int]
61                      ) as weights
62                  from
63                      {tablename} z
64                  where
65                      st_intersects(z.{geom}, b.{geom})
66                      and z.{id_col} != b.{id_col}
67              ) a
68          where
69              a.neighbors is not null
70          '''
71      )
72
73      w = W(json.loads(neighbors[0]['neighbors']), json.loads(weights[0]['weights']), silence_warnings = True)
74      w.transform = 'r'
75
76      var_data = plpy.execute(
77          f'''
78          with a as (
79              select
80                  distinct b.{col},
81                  b.{id_col}
82              from
83                  {tablename} b
84                  cross join lateral (
85                      select
86                          array_agg(z.{id_col}) as neighbors
87                      from
88                          {tablename} z
89                      where
90                          st_intersects(z.{geom}, b.{geom})
91                          and z.{id_col} != b.{id_col}
92                  ) a
93              where
94                  a.neighbors is not null
95          )
96          select
97              {col} as data_col
98          from
99              a
100         ''')
101
102     var_list = []
103     for i in var_data:
104         if i['data_col'] == None:
105             var_list.append(float(0.0))
106         else:
107             var_list.append(float(i['data_col']))
108
109     li = esda.moran.Moran_Local(np.array(var_list), w)
```

```
110
111     original = plpy.execute(f'''
112     with a as (
113         select
114             distinct b.{col},
115             b.{id_col},
116             b.{geom}
117         from
118             {tablename} b
119             cross join lateral (
120                 select
121                     array_agg(z.{id_col}) as neighbors
122                 from
123                     {tablename} z
124                 where
125                     st_intersects(z.{geom}, b.{geom})
126                     and z.{id_col} != b.{id_col}
127             ) a
128         where
129             a.neighbors is not null
130     )
131     select
132         {id_col},
133         {col},
134         {geom}
135     from
136         a'''
137     )
138
139     original_data = []
140     lookup_table = []
141
142     for i in original:
143         original_data.append(i)
144         lookup_table.append(i[f'{id_col}'])
145
146     df = pd.DataFrame.from_dict(original_data)
147
148     formatted_data = []
149
150     for i in original_data:
151         dict = i
152         res = lookup_table.index(i[f'{id_col}'])
153         dict['local_morani_values'] = li.Is[res]
154         dict['p_values'] = li.p_sim[res]
155         dict['quadrant'] = li.q[res]
156         formatted_data.append(dict)
157
158     original_data_df = pd.DataFrame.from_dict(formatted_data)
159     final = df.merge(original_data_df, how='inner', on=f'{id_col}')
160     final_df = final.drop([f'{col}_x', f'{geom}_x'], axis=1)
161     final_df = final_df.rename(columns = {f'{col}_y': 'col', f'{geom}_y': f'{geom}', f'{id_col}': 'id'})
162
163     return final_df.to_dict(orient = 'records')
164 $$
165 LANGUAGE 'plpython3u';
```

Next, run the complete function code to create our function. First we will create a table of Census Block Groups that have a population greater than 0:

Listing 4.23: Block groups with at least 1 person living there

```
1   create table nyc_2021_census_block_groups_morans_i as
2   select
```

```
3        *
4    from
5        nys_2021_census_block_groups
6    where
7        left(geoid, 5) in ('36061', '36005', '36047', '36081', '36085')
8        and population > 0
```

Then we will call the function and create a new table so we can see our results in QGIS:

Listing 4.24: Using the new function

```
1    create table nyc_bgs_esda as
2    select
3        *
4    from
5        pysal_esda(
6            'nyc_2021_census_block_groups_morans_i',
7            'geom',
8            'income',
9            'geoid',
10           0.05
11       )
```

After loading the data in QGIS we will want to style the map categorically using the quadrant feature. While you can certainly use the statistics in the map to filter to find the most statistically significant areas, the quadrants will tell you how the data is clustered on the map. The column will have 5 different numbers ranging from 1 to 5. 5 means that there is no data, or it is not significant. The other four numbers represent different labeled clusters that tell you if the cluster falls in a high or low correlation (in this case of income) and a second label telling you if that block group is within a high or low cluster. The labels map to this schema:

- High near High or HH - 1
- Low near High or LH - 2
- Low near Low or LL - 3
- High near Low - 4

You can read more about local autocorrelation here in the Geospatial Data Science Book[143]. Once you have opened your data in QGIS, you can double-click on the layer in the bottom left-hand layer list to open the dialog to change the styling. First, click on the left-hand menu item called *"Symbology"*, then click the top menu dropdown and select *"Categorized"* (Figures 4.8, on the next page and 4.9, on page 477):

Once the menu opens click the dropdown next to the word *"Value"* then select quadrant from the list. After that click *"Classify"* near the bottom followed by *"OK"* which will return you to the map (Figures 4.10, on page 477 and 4.11, on page 478).

Once you do this you should see your final map, and we can see that there are many block groups in the HH and LL categories and how they are spatially distributed (Figure 4.12, on page 479) :

And for this section that is it! We implemented a complete function for performing spatial autocorrelation using PySAL all within PostGIS.

---

[143]https://geographicdata.science/book/notebooks/07_local_autocorrelation.html

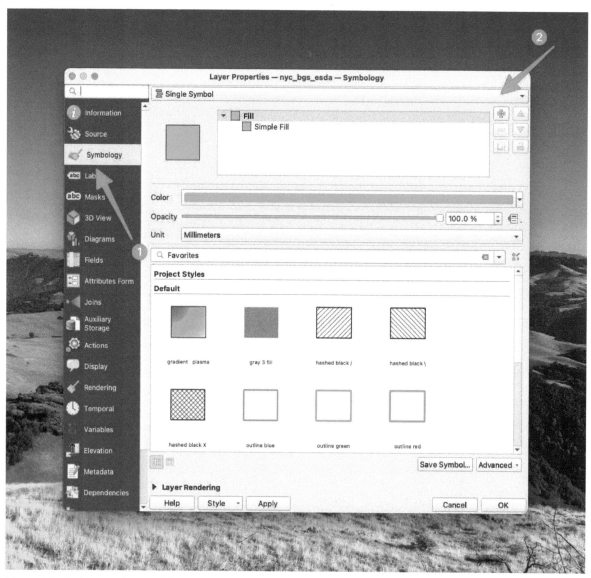

Figure 4.8: Stying our data in QGIS

Figure 4.9: Selecting categorized values

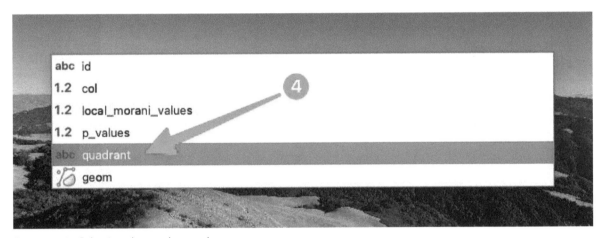

Figure 4.10: Selecting the quadrant value

4.2 Location allocation

Location allocation is the process of finding the most suitable location (facility) for a set of points (demand points) to serve various clients, with specific constraints in place. In more real world terms, an example of this is finding the best location for a new fire station. This would take into consideration the current fire stations and constraints, such as the service area cannot expand beyond 7 minutes driving time, or maximum service time. The same optimizations can be made for distance, coverage of demand points, facility capacity, accounting for backup coverage, distance between facilities, and more.

You need to have sites in mind before you run the analysis, but when combined with a suitability analysis, this can be a final step in the process for validating a location choice. This is another example of using the best tool for the job, meaning that again we will be using Python for one part of the analysis and SQL for the other.

The network analysis component of the process relies on a network, typically a road network optimized for a specific type of travel such as car, bike, etc. As we know this is a perfect fit for using pgRouting to calculate our routes efficiently and then structure the results that are required from Python. For the Python side, PySAL has an incredibly robust package named spopt that performs spatial optimization

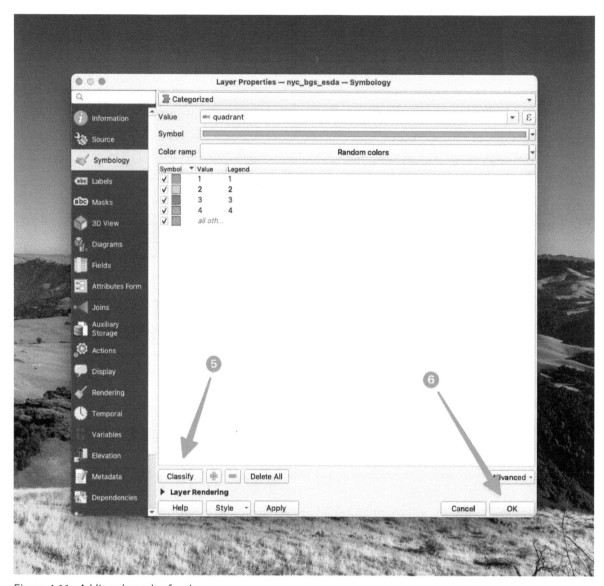

Figure 4.11: Adding the styles for the map

Figure 4.12: Our final spatial autocorrelation in QGIS

for location allocation problems and regionalization (more commonly known as building territories) which we will use in the next section. As of the writing of this book spopt supports the following analyses:

- **Location Set Covering Problem (LSCP)**
  - ...the LSCP model was proposed whereby the minimum number of facilities determined and located so that every demand area is covered within a predefined maximal service distance or time (Church and Murray, 2018)[144]

- **Capacitated Location Set Covering Problem–System Optimal (CLSCP-SO)**
  - "Locate just enough facilities and associated capacity such that all demand is served within the capacity limits of each facility, given the coverage capabilities of each facility." Church L. & Murray, A. (2018)

- **The Backup Coverage Location Problem (LSCP-B)**
  - "Find the minimum number of facilities and their locations such that each demand is covered, while maximizing the number of backup coverage instances among demand areas."[145]

- **Maximal Coverage Location Problem**

---

[144]https://pysal.org/spopt/notebooks/lscp.html

[145]https://pysal.org/spopt/notebooks/lscpb.html

- "Maximize the amount of demand covered within a maximal service distance or time standard by locating a fixed number of facilities."[146]

- **P-Center Problem**

  - "Hakimi (1964) introduced the absolute center problem to locate a police station or a hospital such that the maximum distance of the station to a set of communities connected by a highway system is minimized."[147]

- **P-Median Problem**

  - "Here the objective is to locate a fixed number of facilities such that the resulting sum of travel distances is minimized."[148]

- **P-Dispersion (max-min-min) Problem**

  - "...Kuby (1987) described the following problem: Locate p facilities so that the minimum distance between any pair of facilities is maximized."[149]

For this example we will use the P-Median problem. This is one that is fairly easy to approach conceptually because it looks to have N facilities that serve the greatest area where the total distance traveled between facilities is the lowest. In short, if you provide the model with 10 facilities, and you need 6, it will pick the best 6 to maximize coverage. Since we already installed spopt in our original Python installs we can go ahead and build out our function, but first let's import the NYC Fire Stations data to our routing database, so we can use it with pgRouting:

Listing 4.25: Importing fire station data

```
1  ogr2ogr \
2  -f PostgreSQL PG:"host=localhost user=docker password=docker dbname=routing port=25432" \
3  FDNY_Firehouse_Listing.csv \
4  -dialect sqlite -sql \
5  "select *, makepoint(cast(Longitude as float), cast(Latitude as float), 4326) as geom from FDNY_Firehouse_Listing" \
6  -nln nyc_fire_stations -lco GEOMETRY_NAME=geom
```

As well as our buildings dataset:

Listing 4.26: Importing buildings dataset

```
1  ogr2ogr \
2  -f PostgreSQL PG:"host=localhost user=docker password=docker \
3  dbname=routing port=25432" nyc_mappluto_22v3_shp/MapPLUTO.shp \
4  -nln building_footprints -lco GEOMETRY_NAME=geom \
5  -nlt MULTIPOLYGON -mapFieldType Real=String
```

And out neighborhoods dataset:

Listing 4.27: Import neighborhoods

```
1  ogr2ogr \
2  -f PostgreSQL PG:"host=localhost user=docker password=docker \
3  dbname=routing port=25432" \
4  -dialect SQLite -sql "SELECT neighborhood, boroughcode, borough, \
5  ST_Area(st_collect(st_transform(geometry, 3857))) AS area, \
6  st_collect(geometry) as geom FROM nyc_hoods \
7  group by neighborhood, boroughcode, borough" \
```

---

[146]https://pysal.org/spopt/notebooks/mclp.html

[147]https://pysal.org/spopt/notebooks/p-center.html

[148]https://pysal.org/spopt/notebooks/p-median.html

[149]https://pysal.org/spopt/notebooks/p-dispersion.html

```
8   nyc_hoods.geojson \
9   -nln nyc_neighborhoods -lco GEOMETRY_NAME=geom -nlt PROMOTE_TO_MULTI
```

For this analysis we are going to find the best location for a new fire station in the Willamsburg, Greenpoint, and East Williamsburg neighborhoods by combining the existing fire stations with three new locations. To do this we want to create a single table of inputs for all the locations. For our new locations we will need to create a new table:

Listing 4.28: Creating a new table

```
1   create table new_stations (name text, geom geometry)
```

And then fill it with these values:

Listing 4.29: Adding potential new stations

```
1    insert into
2        new_stations (name, geom)
3    values
4        (
5            'Withers and Woodpoint',
6            st_setsrid(st_makepoint(-73.941455, 40.717628), 4326)
7        ),
8        (
9            'Grand and Graham',
10           st_setsrid(st_makepoint(-73.943791, 40.711584), 4326)
11       ),
12       (
13           'Berry and N 11th',
14           st_setsrid(st_makepoint(-73.9566498, 40.7207395), 4326)
15       )
```

And create a table with all the stations in it:

Listing 4.30: Creating a table for potential fire station sites

```
1    create table all_stations as
2    select
3        facilityname as name,
4        geom
5    from
6        nyc_fire_stations
7    where
8
9        -- Finding all the stations in our three target neighborhoods
10       st_intersects(
11           geom,
12           (
13               select
14                   st_union(st_transform(geom, 4326))
15               from
16                   nyc_neighborhoods
17               where
18                   neighborhood in (
19                       'Williamsburg',
20                       'East Williamsburg',
21                       'Greenpoint'
22                   )
23           )
24       )
25   union
26   select
27       *
28   from
```

```
29      new_stations
```

Before we calculate our origin destination matrix, we also want to create a table of only the buildings we will evaluate to cut down on how much we need to calculate (Figure 4.13, on page 483):

Listing 4.31: Querying building in our target area

```
1   create table bk_blgds as
2   select
3       *
4   from
5       building_footprints
6   where
7       st_intersects(
8           st_transform(geom, 4326),
9
10          -- Find all the buildings that are in the three neighborhoods
11          -- and within 100 meters
12          (
13              select
14                  st_buffer(st_union(geom) :: geography, 100) :: geometry
15              from
16                  nyc_neighborhoods
17              where
18                  neighborhood in (
19                      'Williamsburg',
20                      'East Williamsburg',
21                      'Greenpoint'
22                  )
23          )
24      )
```

Now that we have the stations we need to create an origin destination matrix to use in the function. Since we only need the costs we can actually use a different pgRouting function named pgr_bdDijkstraCost which calculates only the cost between two points:

Listing 4.32: Building our cost or origin destination matrix

```
1   create table fire_odm as
2   with starts as (
3
4       -- Aggregate the source way ID into an array for
5       -- the closest way ID to each station
6       select
7           array_agg(z.source)
8       from
9           all_stations
10          cross join lateral (
11              select
12                  source
13              from
14                  ways
15                  join car_config c using (tag_id)
16              where
17
18                  -- Here we are picking all the way tags that
19                  -- are not in this list
20                  c.tag_value not in (
21                      'track',
22                      'bridleway',
23                      'bus_guideway',
24                      'byway',
25                      'cycleway',
26                      'path',
```

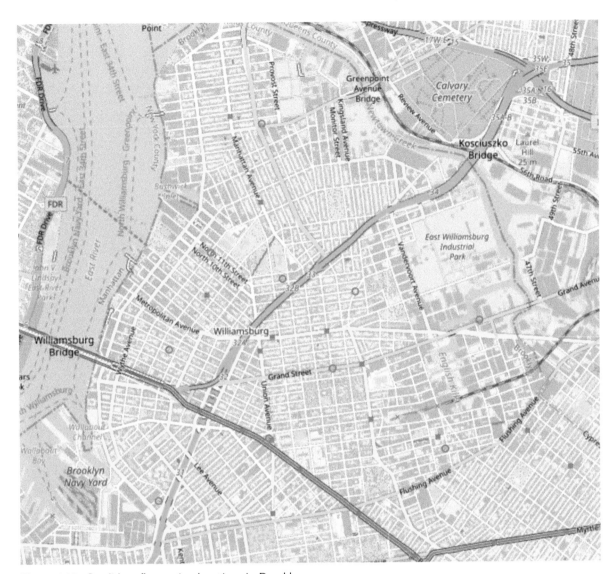

Figure 4.13: Candidate fire station locations in Brooklyn

```
27                    'track',
28                    'grade1',
29                    'grade2',
30                    'grade3',
31                    'grade4',
32                    'grade5',
33                    'unclassified',
34                    'footway',
35                    'pedestrian',
36                    'steps'
37                )
38           order by
39                the_geom <-> all_stations.geom
40           limit
41                1
42        ) z
43   ),
44
```

```
45    -- Here we do the same with the destinations for the buildings
46    destinations as (
47        select
48            array_agg(z.source)
49        from
50            bk_blgds
51            cross join lateral (
52                select
53                    source
54                from
55                    ways
56                    join car_config c using (tag_id)
57                where
58                    c.tag_value not in (
59                        'track',
60                        'bridleway',
61                        'bus_guideway',
62                        'byway',
63                        'cycleway',
64                        'path',
65                        'track',
66                        'grade1',
67                        'grade2',
68                        'grade3',
69                        'grade4',
70                        'grade5',
71                        'unclassified',
72                        'footway',
73                        'pedestrian',
74                        'steps'
75                    )
76                order by
77                    ways.the_geom <-> st_transform(st_centroid(bk_blgds.geom), 4326)
78                limit
79                    1
80            ) z
81
82        -- We only select the buildings in the neighborhood boundaries
83        where
84            st_intersects(
85                st_transform(geom, 4326),
86                (
87                    select
88                        st_buffer(st_union(geom) :: geography, 100) :: geometry
89                    from
90                        nyc_neighborhoods
91                    where
92                        neighborhood in (
93                            'williamsburg',
94                            'east williamsburg',
95                            'greenpoint'
96                        )
97                )
98            )
99    )
100   select
101       *
102   from
103
104       -- Here we pass these arguments to the pgr_bdDijkstraCost function
105       pgr_bddijkstracost(
106           $$
107           select
108               id,
109               source,
```

```
110        target,
111        cost_s as cost,
112        reverse_cost_s as reverse_cost
113    from
114        ways
115        join car_config using (tag_id)
116    where
117        st_intersects(
118            st_transform(the_geom, 4326),
119            (
120                select
121                    st_buffer(st_union(geom) :: geography, 100) :: geometry
122                from
123                    nyc_neighborhoods
124                where
125                    neighborhood in (
126                        'williamsburg',
127                        'east williamsburg',
128                        'greenpoint'
129                    )
130            )
131    ) $$,
132
133    -- We pass the arrays from above as the two arguments
134    (
135        select
136            *
137        from
138            starts
139    ),
140    (
141        select
142            *
143        from
144            destinations
145    ),
146    true
147    );
```

A few notes about the above query:

- You can see that we are creating two arrays of data, one with the way ID for our stations and all the buildings that fall within the boundaries of the three neighborhoods, or within a 100 meter buffer of those three neighborhoods to find any edge cases
- Next we are also joining the ways table to the configuration table in the CTEs, and finding all the values that are not in a set of tag_values. This is because most of the closest ways are actually sidewalks and since fire trucks can't drive on sidewalks or any other non-street path, we can exclude those

Once we run this query and create our origin destination matrix table, we will start to build our function using PL/Python language. As we have already installed the libraries that we will need we are ready to start building our function. The first step will be to create the inputs of the function:

Listing 4.33: Opening line of our function

```
1  create
2  or replace function spopt_pmedian(
3      odm_table TEXT,
4      optimal_facilities INT,
5      clients_table TEXT,
6      facilities_table TEXT
7  )
```

The inputs for this function are:

- The table name of the origin destination matrix we just created
- The optimal number of facilities we want to include
- The table with the clients (in this case it is our buildings in the three neighborhoods under consideration)
- The table with the facilities we will evaluate

Next we will set up our return value, which is a table with the facility ID, the end road segment or end_vid, the ogc_fid which is the ID of the building, and the geometry. In the example here these outputs are built to accommodate our specific data structure, so they would need to be generalized to accommodate a wider set of inputs and outputs.

Listing 4.34: Function return structure

```
1   returns table (
2       facility TEXT,
3       end_vid INT,
4       ogc_fid INT,
5       geom GEOMETRY
6   ) AS $$
```

Next we will import our libraries that we will be using and also call our origin destination matrix table using the `plpy` built in library:

Listing 4.35: Python imports

```
1   import spopt
2   from spopt.locate import PMedian
3   import numpy
4   import pulp
5   import pandas as pd
6
7   odm = plpy.execute(f''' select * from {odm_table} ''')
```

Here we iterate over the return values by querying our origin destination matrix table, and using a loop in Python, we add those values to an empty list named odm_new:

Listing 4.36: Structuring data from our ODM

```
1   odm_new = []
2
3   # This restructures the data for the rest of our function
4
5   for i in odm:
6       odm_new.append({'start_vid': i['start_vid'], 'end_vid': i['end_vid'], 'agg_cost': i['agg_cost']})
```

This next step sets up our solver from the `pulp` library, which contains many optimization solver tools for linear programming problems. The library is installed with `spopt` as a dependency, so there is no need to install it separately.

Listing 4.37: Pulp solver

```
1   solver = pulp.PULP_CBC_CMD(keepFiles=True)
```

From here we will do some data prep to set up our data in the required formats to run the optimization. In this case we will need to create a new Pandas `DataFrame` from our list which we created in the previous step. The required data structure for the optimization is a true matrix, meaning that instead of the data structure in our DataFrame, which has a start and end ID for each row and the associated cost, we need to create a matrix that has all the start IDs as columns and end IDs as rows. Pandas has a built-in function that operates on a DataFrame named *pivot_table* that allows us to do this. We have four positional arguments:

- index: The value we will use as the rows, in this case the end ID
- columns: Values we will use as the columns, in this case the start ID
- values: These are the values we will use which is our aggregate cost value or agg_cost
- fill_values: The functions we are going to use need data with no empty values, and in this case we will fill those with a very large value so that the cost will be too high to use that value

We will run this query twice. First in the data variable we will add the .values operator on the end to get the values as a pure Python list, which is required for the P-Median functions. The second we will leave as a DataFrame to use to map the individual buildings to the road segments they have been assigned to.

Listing 4.38: Creating our pivot tables

```
1  df = pd.DataFrame.from_dict(odm_new)
2  data = df.pivot_table(index='end_vid', columns='start_vid', values='agg_cost', fill_value=1000000).values
3  vals = df.pivot_table(index='end_vid', columns='start_vid', values='agg_cost', fill_value=1000000)
```

In this step we will assign weights for each of the ending street segment IDs. In this case we will keep them all equal at 1, but you could weight these by the number of buildings on the road segment or something similar depending on your needs (more on this in the example notebook[150]). This will create a list with each item being "1" that is the same length as the total number of ending road segments.

Listing 4.39: Creating equal weights

```
1  clients = data.shape[0]
2  weights = [1] * clients
```

Now we are ready to run our P-Median calculation. The first step is to use the function we imported from the spopt library, and we will use the from_cost_matrix option with the following positional arguments:

- **numpy.array(data)** - Our origin destination matrix as a numpy array
- **numpy.array(weights)** - The weights list as a numpy array
- **p_facilities=int(optimal_facilities)** - The ideal number of facilities using the argument from our original SQL function arguments. We make sure that it is an integer by wrapping it inside the *int* function in Python
- **name="p-median-network-distance"** - The name of the analysis we want to run as specified in the example notebook[151]

If you so choose you can add an argument for predefined facilities which is also a numpy array of the facility ids (in our case the road start IDs) that must be in the solution. This would account for cases where you want to evaluate adding in new locations without removing any of the existing locations. This would follow the p_facilities argument.

The last step is to run the solver using the pulp solver we established earlier. We take the variable pmedian_from_cm that stored our data in the previous step and run the .solve() function on that variable, passing the solver variable as the only argument. This will reassign the results to the pmedian_from_cm variable.

Listing 4.40: Solving the P-Median problem

---

[150]https://pysal.org/spopt/notebooks/p-median.html#Simulate-points-in-a-network

[151]https://pysal.org/spopt/notebooks/p-median.html#Calculating-the-(network-distance)-cost-matrix

```
1  pmedian_from_cm = PMedian.from_cost_matrix(
2      numpy.array(data),
3      numpy.array(weights),
4      p_facilities=int(optimal_facilities),
5      name="p-median-network-distance" )
6
7  pmedian_from_cm = pmedian_from_cm.solve(solver)
```

Now that we have our results we need to create a data structure that contains the assigned facility, or fire station, for each end road ID. To do this we can access a data structure from our `pmedian_from_cm` value using the `pmedian_from_cm.fac2cli` operator which will return a data structure that contains a dictionary with the ID of the starting point (in this case the starting road segment ID or `start_vid`) and a list of the clients it serves (there will be one `end_vid` for multiple buildings). Our goal is to create a data structure that we can turn into a `DataFrame` to later join to our original data. Before we do this, we first need to create a table that contains the end segment ID for each of our stations being evaluated. First we will create our query that will find the nearest road segment to each station then turn that into a `DataFrame` we can use later on.

Listing 4.41: Reintroducing the station names

```
1   # This is the same query we used before but just allows us to tie
2   # the way ID to the stations
3
4   station_ids = plpy.execute(f'''
5   select
6       z.source as end_vid,
7       { facilities_table }.name
8   from
9       { facilities_table }
10      cross join lateral (
11          SELECT
12              source
13          FROM
14              ways
15              join configuration c using (tag_id)
16          where
17              c.tag_value not in (
18                  'track',
19                  'bridleway',
20                  'bus_guideway',
21                  'byway',
22                  'cycleway',
23                  'path',
24                  'track',
25                  'grade1',
26                  'grade2',
27                  'grade3',
28                  'grade4',
29                  'grade5',
30                  'unclassified',
31                  'footway',
32                  'pedestrian',
33                  'steps'
34              )
35          ORDER BY
36              ways.the_geom <-> st_transform(st_centroid({ facilities_table }.geom), 4326)
37          limit
38              1
39      ) z
40  ''')
41
42  stations = []
43
```

```
44   for i in station_ids:
45       stations.append(i)
46
47   stations_df = pd.DataFrame.from_dict(stations)
```

After this, our first step is to create a new empty list:

```
cleaned_points = []
```

Next we will create two for loops. The first will go through each item in the `pmedian_from_cm.fac2cli` object and if it has more than 0 values (meaning that facility is included in the solution) then it goes to the next step. In the next step it goes through each client, or end road segment ID (`end_vid`), and adds it to the dictionary. This has two values: The first the facility name from our table of locations under evaluation which is represented by this line of code:

Listing 4.42: Getting station names and region IDs from the list

```
1    # First we filter the DataFrame to find
2    # the end way ID we are evaluating
3    z = stations_df[stations_df['end_vid']
4
5    ## Then we look in the columns in the vals pivot table
6    == vals.columns[
7
8        # Here we use the index position from the pmedian_from_cm.fac2cli
9        # object to find the value by row index, or i
10       pmedian_from_cm.fac2cli.index(i)]
11
12       # Finally from that list we access the name attribute and get
13       # the value from index position 0 which represents our facility
14       # assignment for each building
15       ]['name'].values[0]
```

Here we are filtering our `stations_df` DataFrame to find the `end_vid` that is at the index position of the `pmedian_from_cm.fac2cli` values. More plainly, we have a DataFrame that has the name of each station and the `end_vid` for that station. We know that in the `pmedian_from_cm.fac2cli` values have an index position instead of the `end_vid`. That index position, for example 0, represents the first column of the `vals` DataFrame or pivot table. To get that actual value, we use this code:

```
vals.columns[pmedian_from_cm.fac2cli.index(i)]
```

`vals.columns` returns a list of the end road segment IDs. To get the right one we get the index value of 0 from* pmedian_from_cm.fac2cli.index(i). .index()* allows us to find the index by the row value, in this case represented by "i".

Next we will get the actual value for the end ID, the only issue being that the data structure contains the index location of that value within the original dataset. This means that if the end road segment ID "12345" was assigned, we would only get the index which could be "0" if this were the first value in the dataset. To find the actual ID value, we can use the index location of that value represented by "j" in our for loop, and find the exact value from the DataFrame we created called `vals`. We can retrieve the index values from that DataFrame (remember that this is a pivot table, so the index values are actually our end IDs), then find the exact value by accessing that specific value using "j". Then we append this to our empty list, and we are ready to move on.

Listing 4.43: Full code to map names and region IDs

```
1   for i in pmedian_from_cm.fac2cli:
2       if len(i) > 0:
3           z = stations_df[stations_df['end_vid'] == vals.columns[pmedian_from_cm.fac2cli.index(i)]]['name'].values[0]
4           for j in i:
5
6               # Here we can find the end ID by using the index value in the array to
7               # find the end ID, here represented by "j"
8               struct = {'facility': z, 'end_vid': list(vals.index)[j]}
9               cleaned_points.append(struct)
```

Finally, we create a new DataFrame from this dictionary we created for use later on.

```
df_startids = pd.DataFrame.from_dict(cleaned_points)
```

Our next few steps will include recreating our original origin-destination matrix table and turning it into a DataFrame that contains each original building ID and the end road segment ID it is closest to. This will allow us to assign the facility or fire station for each individual building. It is important to note that this code is built for this specific example, meaning that it has the road tag IDs that we want to exclude hard coded into the query. If you want to make this function fully repeatable you will have to either limit your pgRouting ways data to only those values or provide another argument in your function to pass those to the query.

With that said, the below query selects the source as the end road segment ID, the ID of the building, and the centroid of the building to use as the geometry. It then performs a cross lateral join to find the nearest road ID from the data in pgRouting. Once that is complete we use another for loop to format the data into a dictionary which can then be turned into a Pandas DataFrame.

Listing 4.44: Structure original data

```
1   # This structures the final data using the same query we have been using
2
3   orig_data = plpy.execute(f'''
4   select
5       z.source as end_vid,
6       { clients_table }.ogc_fid,
7       st_transform(st_centroid({ clients_table }.geom), 4326) as geom
8   from
9       { clients_table }
10      cross join lateral (
11          SELECT
12              source
13          FROM
14              ways
15              join car_config c using (tag_id)
16          where
17              c.tag_value not in (
18                  'track',
19                  'bridleway',
20                  'bus_guideway',
21                  'byway',
22                  'cycleway',
23                  'path',
24                  'track',
25                  'grade1',
26                  'grade2',
27                  'grade3',
28                  'grade4',
29                  'grade5',
30                  'unclassified',
31                  'footway',
```

```
32                'pedestrian',
33                'steps'
34             )
35         ORDER BY
36             ways.the_geom <-> st_transform(st_centroid(building_footprints.geom), 4326)
37         limit
38             1
39     ) z
40 ''')
41
42 orig_formatted = []
43 for i in orig_data:
44     orig_formatted.append(i)
45
46 orig_df = pd.DataFrame.from_dict(orig_formatted)
```

And in our last steps we do the following:

- Merge our original data `DataFrame` with the results from the P-Median analysis that have been turned into a `DataFrame`
- We replace any `NULL` values in numpy with the *None* value in Python
- Return the new `DataFrame` as the return value after turning it into a dictionary.

Listing 4.45: Final steps

```
1 final_df = orig_df.merge(df_startids, how='left', on='end_vid')
2 final_df = final_df.replace(numpy.nan, None)
3
4 return final_df.to_dict(orient='records')
```

With that we can create and run our complete function to create our new function in our database:

Listing 4.46: Creating the new function on our database

```
1  create
2  or replace function spopt_pmedian(
3      odm_table TEXT,
4      optimal_facilities INT,
5      clients_table TEXT,
6      facilities_table TEXT
7  )
8  returns table (
9      facility TEXT,
10     end_vid INT,
11     ogc_fid INT,
12     geom GEOMETRY
13 ) AS $$
14     import spopt
15     from spopt.locate import PMedian
16     import numpy
17     import pulp
18     import pandas as pd
19
20     odm = plpy.execute(f''' select * from {odm_table} ''')
21     odm_new = []
22
23     for i in odm:
24         odm_new.append({'start_vid': i['start_vid'], 'end_vid': i['end_vid'], 'agg_cost': i['agg_cost']})
25
26     solver = pulp.PULP_CBC_CMD(keepFiles=True)
27
28     df = pd.DataFrame.from_dict(odm_new)
29     data = df.pivot_table(index='end_vid', columns='start_vid', values='agg_cost', fill_value=1000000).values
30     vals = df.pivot_table(index='end_vid', columns='start_vid', values='agg_cost', fill_value=1000000)
```

```
31
32      clients = data.shape[0]
33      weights = [1] * clients
34
35      pmedian_from_cm = PMedian.from_cost_matrix(
36          numpy.array(data),
37          numpy.array(weights),
38          p_facilities=int(optimal_facilities),
39          name="p-median-network-distance" )
40
41      pmedian_from_cm = pmedian_from_cm.solve(solver)
42
43      station_ids = plpy.execute(f'''
44      select
45          z.source as end_vid,
46          {facilities_table}.name
47      from
48          {facilities_table}
49          cross join lateral (
50              SELECT
51                  source
52              FROM
53                  ways
54                  join configuration c using (tag_id)
55              where
56                  c.tag_value not in (
57                      'track',
58                      'bridleway',
59                      'bus_guideway',
60                      'byway',
61                      'cycleway',
62                      'path',
63                      'track',
64                      'grade1',
65                      'grade2',
66                      'grade3',
67                      'grade4',
68                      'grade5',
69                      'unclassified',
70                      'footway',
71                      'pedestrian',
72                      'steps'
73                  )
74              ORDER BY
75                  ways.the_geom <-> st_transform(st_centroid({facilities_table}.geom), 4326)
76              limit
77                  1
78          ) z
79      ''')
80
81      stations = []
82
83      for i in station_ids:
84          stations.append(i)
85
86      stations_df = pd.DataFrame.from_dict(stations)
87
88      cleaned_points = []
89
90      for i in pmedian_from_cm.fac2cli:
91        if len(i) > 0:
92          z = stations_df[stations_df['end_vid'] == vals.columns[pmedian_from_cm.fac2cli.index(i)]]['name'].values[0]
93          for j in i:
94              struct = {'facility': z, 'end_vid': list(vals.index)[j]}
95              cleaned_points.append(struct)
```

```
96
97      df_startids = pd.DataFrame.from_dict(cleaned_points)
98
99      orig_data = plpy.execute(f'''
100     select
101         z.source as end_vid,
102         {clients_table}.ogc_fid,
103         st_transform(st_centroid({clients_table}.geom), 4326) as geom
104     from
105         {clients_table}
106         cross join lateral (
107             SELECT
108                 source
109             FROM
110                 ways
111                 join car_config c using (tag_id)
112             where
113                 c.tag_value not in (
114                     'track',
115                     'bridleway',
116                     'bus_guideway',
117                     'byway',
118                     'cycleway',
119                     'path',
120                     'track',
121                     'grade1',
122                     'grade2',
123                     'grade3',
124                     'grade4',
125                     'grade5',
126                     'unclassified',
127                     'footway',
128                     'pedestrian',
129                     'steps'
130                 )
131             ORDER BY
132                 ways.the_geom <-> st_transform(st_centroid({clients_table}.geom), 4326)
133             limit
134                 1
135         ) z
136     ''')
137
138     orig_formatted = []
139     for i in orig_data:
140         orig_formatted.append(i)
141
142     orig_df = pd.DataFrame.from_dict(orig_formatted)
143
144     final_df = orig_df.merge(df_startids, how='left', on='end_vid')
145     final_df = final_df.replace(numpy.nan, None)
146
147     return final_df.to_dict(orient='records')
148 $$
149 LANGUAGE 'plpython3u';
```

Listing 4.47: Running the new function

```
1   create table bk_final as
2   select
3       *
4   from
5       spopt_pmedian('fire_odm', 5, 'bk_blgds', 'all_stations');
```

And also create a table of the final selected sites:

Listing 4.48: Building a table for QGIS

```
1   create table final_stations as
2   select
3       *
4   from
5       all_stations
6   where
7       name in (
8           select
9               distinct facility
10          from
11              bk_final
12      )
```

We can then load this into QGIS to see what the results look like (Figure 4.14):

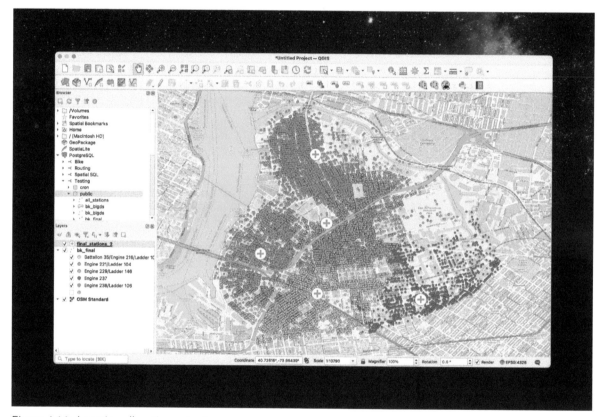

Figure 4.14: Location allocation output

As you can see there are a few odd results, likely due to the specific road types we selected but overall we see that most all the buildings are covered and all using existing locations!

4.3   Build balanced territories

In our final optimization exercise, we will be creating balanced territories from polygon data that contains some sort of numeric data with the goal of creating a target number of territories with equally balanced values between each territory. In a real world example, this is a similar process to creating balanced sales territories based on customer locations or balanced political districts based on constituents. This problem is also known as regionalization and, once again, the spopt library from PySAL has tools for us to do this.

There are several methods that are available to use to create balanced territories:

- **Max-P Regionalization**: "The max-p problem involves the clustering of a set of geographic areas into the maximum number of homogeneous regions such that the value of a spatially extensive regional attribute is above a predefined threshold value"[152]

- **Automatic Zoning Procedure (AZP) algorithm**: "AZP can work with different types of objective functions, which are very sensitive to aggregating data from a large number of zones into a pre-designated smaller number of regions."[153]

- **SKATER**: "SKATER (Assunção et al. 2006) is a constrained spatial regionalization algorithm based on spanning tree pruning. The number of edges is pre-specified to be cut in a continuous tree to group spatial units into contiguous regions. The first step of SKATER is to create a connectivity graph that captures the neighbourhood relationship between the spatial objects. The cost of each edge in the graph is inversely proportional to the similarity between the regions it joins. The neighbourhood is structured by a minimum spanning tree (MST), which is a connected tree with no circuits. The next step is to partition the MST by successive removal of edges that link dissimilar regions. The final result is the division of the spatial objects into connected regions that have maximum internal homogeneity."[154]

- **Ward**: "This algorithm is an agglomerative clustering using ward linkage with a spatial connectivity constraint. Specifically, it is a "bottom-up" approach: each zone starts as its own cluster, and pairs of clusters are chosen to merge at each step in order to minimally increase a given linkage distance. Ward linkage refers to the variance of the clusters being merged."[155]

- **Regional-k-means**: "Regional-k-means is K-means with the constraint that each cluster forms a spatially connected component."[156]

In this example we will be using the SKATER algorithm since it has some controls for the number of clusters, minimum number of features in each cluster, and handling islands, or areas that are not connected. For these functions almost all of them require a *GeoDataFrame* from GeoPandas to actually perform the operations, so they may not be as efficient as if we used the raw data outputs directly from our PostGIS queries. With that said they can still be efficient for creating the data structures for the neighbor relationships and weights just as we did with our spatial autocorrelation example. With that let's begin by constructing our function.

First as before we will create the structure of our function:

Listing 4.49: Creating the function

```
1  create
2  or replace function pysal_skater(
3      tablename TEXT,
4      geometry TEXT,
5      col TEXT,
6      id_col TEXT,
7      n_clusters INT,
8      floor INT
9  )
```

---

[152]https://pysal.org/spopt/notebooks/maxp.html

[153]https://pysal.org/spopt/notebooks/azp.html

[154]https://pysal.org/spopt/notebooks/skater.html

[155]https://pysal.org/spopt/notebooks/ward.html

[156]https://pysal.org/spopt/notebooks/reg-k-means.html

The arguments here are:

- **tablename**: The name of the table we will analyze
- **geometry**: Name of the geometry column in the table
- **col**: Name of the column containing the numeric data that the analysis will use to balance regions
- **id_col**: ID column of the table
- **n_clusters**: Target number of clusters for the regions
- **floor**: Minimum number of features a region can contain

And then of course we will create our return table structure:

Listing 4.50: Function return structure

```
1   returns table (id TEXT, col FLOAT, regions INT, geometry TEXT) AS $$
```

This table will have an ID, the data column from the original table, an integer that will identify the region the polygon is a part of, and the geometry.

Next we perform our imports of our Python libraries:

Listing 4.51: Python imports

```
1   import spopt
2   import libpysal as lps
3   import json
4   import numpy as np
5   import pandas as pd
6   import geopandas as gpd
7   from sklearn.metrics import pairwise as skm
8   import numpy
9   from shapely import wkt
```

Here you will notice that we will be using GeoPandas to create a *GeoDataFrame*, Shapely to manage Well Known Text data, and SciKitLearn to use the pairwise function to calculate distances. Our next step will be to calculate data structures for the neighbors and weights. The only difference here is that we want to ensure that we have contiguous territories, meaning that we want to ensure that two polygons that only share one point are not considered neighbors and not considered eligible to be a part of the same territory. You can modify this if you want to include those but in most cases this will lead to odd connections in your territories.

The good news is that we can reuse the code that we wrote to find polygons that share more than one point in common in this situation:

Listing 4.52: Neighbors query

```
1   # This query follows the same structure as our spatial autocorrelation
2   # query apart from the code on line 17 which finds the
3   # polygons that have more than one point touching
4
5   neighbors = plpy.execute(f'''
6   select
7       json_object_agg(b.{ id_col }, a.neighbors) as neighbors
8   from
9       { tablename } b
10      cross join lateral (
11          select
12              array_agg(z.{ id_col } :: text) as neighbors
13          from
14              { tablename } z
15          where
16              st_intersects(z.{ geometry }, b.{ geometry })
```

```
17              and st_npoints(st_intersection(b.{ geometry }, z.{ geometry })) > 1
18              and z.{ id_col } != b.{ id_col }
19        ) a
20    where
21        a.neighbors is not null
22    ''')
```

As you can see we are creating a JSON object containing the ID column and neighboring polygon IDs. We retrieve those from a CROSS JOIN LATERAL and within that query we use the WHERE clause to exclude those polygons that only have 1 point in common. We repeat the same process for the weights as well:

Listing 4.53: Calculating spatial weights

```
1   weights = plpy.execute(f'''
2   select
3       json_object_agg(b.{ id_col }, a.weights) as weights
4   from
5       { tablename } b
6       cross join lateral (
7           select
8               array_agg(z.{ id_col }) as neighbors,
9               array_fill(
10                  (
11                      case
12                          when count(z.{ id_col }) = 0 then 0
13                          else 1 / count(z.{ id_col }) :: numeric
14                      end
15                  ),
16                  array [count(z.{id_col})::int]
17              ) as weights
18          from
19              { tablename } z
20          where
21              st_intersects(z.{ geometry }, b.{ geometry })
22              and st_npoints(st_intersection(b.{ geometry }, z.{ geometry })) > 1
23              and z.{ id_col } != b.{ id_col }
24      ) a
25  where
26      a.neighbors is not null
27  ''')
```

Once again, just like our spatial autocorrelation analysis, we will compute the spatial weights object using the *libpysal* library. However, we will use an additional argument named *id_order* which takes a list of IDs that shows the order of the IDs that are provided from the neighbors and weights objects. To do this we can create a new list and then add the IDs for each entry to that list:

Listing 4.54: Calculating spatial weights

```
1   ids = []
2
3   for i in json.loads(weights[0]['weights']):
4       ids.append(i)
5
6   w = lps.weights.W(
7       json.loads(neighbors[0]['neighbors']),
8       json.loads(weights[0]['weights']),
9       silence_warnings = True,
10      id_order=ids)
11
12  w.transform='r'
```

Next we will set up our *GeoDataFrame* to pass into the SKATER function. First we will run a query that matches the same conditions as our previous query to ensure our data matches given our WHERE clauses. While this is likely unnecessary it will cover any edge cases that may cause errors. We only need the geometry column as WKT, the ID column, and the numeric value.

Listing 4.55: Setting up data for the GeoDataFrame

```
1   # We have to turn the geometry into text for the GeoDataFrame on line 6
2   # and use the same array_fill function for our weights on line 14
3
4   to_gdf = plpy.execute(f'''
5   select
6       st_astext(st_transform({ geometry }, 4326)) as geometry,
7       { col } :: numeric as col,
8       { id_col } as id
9   from
10      { tablename } b
11      cross join lateral (
12          select
13              array_agg(z.{ id_col }) as neighbors,
14              array_fill(
15                  (
16                      case
17                          when count(z.{ id_col }) = 0 then 0
18                          else 1 / count(z.{ id_col }) :: numeric
19                      end
20                  ),
21                  array [count(z.{id_col})::int]
22              ) as weights
23          from
24              { tablename } z
25          where
26              st_intersects(z.{ geometry }, b.{ geometry })
27              and st_npoints(st_intersection(b.{ geometry }, z.{ geometry })) > 1
28              and z.{ id_col } != b.{ id_col }
29      ) a
30  where
31      a.neighbors is not null
32  ''')
```

Once that is complete we will set up an empty list to add our values to that will allow us to create a *GeoDataFrame* from the new dictionary:

Listing 4.56: Building our GeoDataFrame

```
1   gdf_data = []
2
3   for i in to_gdf:
4       gdf_data.append(i)
5
6   gdf = gpd.GeoDataFrame(gdf_data)
```

And we will create a true geometry from our WKT geometry using the *.apply()* method in Pandas to run the *wkt.loads* function on each entry.

```
gdf['geometry'] = gdf['geometry'].apply(wkt.loads)
```

And finally set the geometry on the *GeoDataFrame* and assign it the EPSG of 4326:

```
gdf = gdf.set_geometry('geometry', crs = 'epsg:4326')
```

Next we need to create a new variable that contains information about our minimum spanning tree. This is effectively a dictionary that contains several arguments, which are described below using the definitions from the PySAL SKATER notebook[157].

- **dissimilarity**
    - A callable distance metric, with the default as `sklearn.metrics.pairwise.manhattan_distances`[158].

- **affinity**
    - A callable affinity metric between 0 and 1, which is inverted to provide a dissimilarity metric. No metric is provided as a default (None). If affinity is desired, dissimilarity must explicitly be set to None.

- **reduction**
    - The reduction applied over all clusters to provide the map score, with the default as `numpy.sum()`[159].

- **center**
    - The method for computing the center of each region in attribute space with the default as `numpy.mean()`[160].

- **verbose**
    - A flag for how much output to provide to the user in terms of print statements and progress bars. Set to 1 for minimal output and 2 for full output. The default is False, which provides no output

Listing 4.57: Creating the spanning tree

```
1   spanning_forest_kwds = dict(
2       dissimilarity=skm.manhattan_distances,
3       affinity=None,
4       reduction=numpy.sum,
5       center=numpy.mean,
6       verbose=False
7       )
```

Next we will create a model using the SKATER function from the `spopt` package. This function has the following options for arguments:

- **gdf**: The GeoDataFrame containing our polygon data which was created earlier
- **w**: The spatial weights object created earlier
- **['col']**: This is the numeric value that we will be balancing our regions on which we have renamed to *col* in our SQL query to build out the GeoDataFram
- **n_clusters**: The number of clusters or regions we want to create which is defined from the input argument of the function
- **floor**: The minimum number of polygons any region can have which is defined from the input argument of the function
- **trace**: "trace is a bool denoting whether to store intermediate labelings as the tree gets pruned."[161]

---

[157]https://pysal.org/spopt/notebooks/skater.html

[158]https://loc8.cc/sql/scitkit-learn

[159]https://numpy.org/doc/stable/reference/generated/numpy.sum.html

[160]https://numpy.org/doc/stable/reference/generated/numpy.mean.html

[161]https://pysal.org/spopt/notebooks/skater.html

- **islands**: "The islands keyword argument describes what is to be done with islands. It can be set to either 'ignore', which will treat each island as its own region when solving for n_clusters regions, or 'increase', which will consider each island as its own region and add to n_clusters regions."[162]

- **spanning_forest_kwds**: The object containing the spanning tree which we just created

Listing 4.58: Creating the model

```
1   model = spopt.region.Skater(
2       gdf,
3       w,
4       ['col'],
5       n_clusters=n_clusters,
6       floor=floor,
7       trace=False,
8       islands='increase',
9       spanning_forest_kwds=spanning_forest_kwds
10      )
```

And to complete the process we can solve our model using this line of code.

```
model.solve()
```

Once the model has run it is actually a simple process. We can add a new column to our *GeoDataFrame* that contains the labels of the territories using this code:

```
gdf['regions'] = model.labels_
```

The *model.labels_* object contains the labels for our territories and by assigning it to *gdf['regions']* we can add this as a new column. Finally, we transform our data to a dictionary so that it can be rendered as a table in SQL:

```
return gdf.to_dict(orient='records')
```

Below is the complete function which you can add to your database:

Listing 4.59: The complete SKATER function

```
1   create
2   or replace function pysal_skater(
3       tablename TEXT,
4       geometry TEXT,
5       col TEXT,
6       id_col TEXT,
7       n_clusters INT,
8       floor INT
9   ) returns table (id TEXT, col FLOAT, regions INT, geometry TEXT)
10  AS $$
11      import spopt
12      import libpysal as lps
13      import json
14      import numpy as np
15      import pandas as pd
16      import geopandas as gpd
```

---

[162]https://pysal.org/spopt/notebooks/skater.html

```
17    from sklearn.metrics import pairwise as skm
18    import numpy
19    from shapely import wkt
20
21    neighbors = plpy.execute(f'''
22    select
23        json_object_agg(b.{ id_col }, a.neighbors) as neighbors
24    from
25        { tablename } b
26        cross join lateral (
27            select
28                array_agg(z.{ id_col } :: text) as neighbors
29            from
30                { tablename } z
31            where
32                st_intersects(z.{ geometry }, b.{ geometry })
33                and st_npoints(st_intersection(b.{ geometry }, z.{ geometry })) > 1
34                and z.{ id_col } != b.{ id_col }
35        ) a
36    where
37        a.neighbors is not null
38    ''')
39
40    weights = plpy.execute(f'''
41    select
42        json_object_agg(b.{ id_col }, a.weights) as weights
43    from
44        { tablename } b
45        cross join lateral (
46            select
47                array_agg(z.{ id_col }) as neighbors,
48                array_fill(
49                    (
50                        case
51                            when count(z.{ id_col }) = 0 then 0
52                            else 1 / count(z.{ id_col }) :: numeric
53                        end
54                    ),
55                    array [count(z.{id_col})::int]
56                ) as weights
57            from
58                { tablename } z
59            where
60                st_intersects(z.{ geometry }, b.{ geometry })
61                and st_npoints(st_intersection(b.{ geometry }, z.{ geometry })) > 1
62                and z.{ id_col } != b.{ id_col }
63        ) a
64    where
65        a.neighbors is not null
66    ''')
67
68    ids = []
69
70    for i in json.loads(weights[0]['weights']):
71        ids.append(i)
72
73    w = lps.weights.W(json.loads(neighbors[0]['neighbors']), json.loads(weights[0]['weights']),
74        silence_warnings = True, id_order=ids)
75    w.transform='r'
76
77    to_gdf = plpy.execute(f'''
78    select
79        st_astext(st_transform({ geometry }, 4326)) as geometry,
80        { col } :: numeric as col,
81        { id_col } as id
```

```
82      from
83          { tablename } b
84          cross join lateral (
85              select
86                  array_agg(z.{ id_col }) as neighbors,
87                  array_fill(
88                      (
89                          case
90                              when count(z.{ id_col }) = 0 then 0
91                              else 1 / count(z.{ id_col }) :: numeric
92                          end
93                      ),
94                      array [count(z.{id_col})::int]
95                  ) as weights
96              from
97                  { tablename } z
98              where
99                  st_intersects(z.{ geometry }, b.{ geometry })
100                 and st_npoints(st_intersection(b.{ geometry }, z.{ geometry })) > 1
101                 and z.{ id_col } != b.{ id_col }
102         ) a
103     where
104         a.neighbors is not null
105     ''')
106
107     gdf_data = []
108
109     for i in to_gdf:
110         gdf_data.append(i)
111
112     gdf = gpd.GeoDataFrame(gdf_data)
113
114     spanning_forest_kwds = dict(
115         dissimilarity=skm.manhattan_distances,
116         affinity=None,
117         reduction=numpy.sum,
118         center=numpy.mean,
119         verbose=False
120     )
121
122     model = spopt.region.Skater(
123         gdf,
124         w,
125         ['col'],
126         n_clusters=n_clusters,
127         floor=floor,
128         trace=False,
129         islands='increase',
130         spanning_forest_kwds=spanning_forest_kwds
131     )
132
133     model.solve()
134
135     gdf['regions'] = model.labels_
136
137     return gdf.to_dict(orient = 'records')
138 $$
139 LANGUAGE 'plpython3u';
```

To test our new function we will create 9 territories with equally balanced population in Brooklyn. To create the table of block groups in Brooklyn we can first run this query which finds the county code from the *geoid* column by removing the first two digits from the Census Block Group ID which match to the state ID of New York State, then discarding the next seven digits to get the three we want to use which are "047" which is the county code for Brooklyn

Listing 4.60: All block groups in Brooklyn

```
1   create table bklyn_bgs as
2   select
3       *
4   from
5       nyc_2021_census_block_groups
6   where
7       left(right(geoid, 10), 3) = '047'
```

From here we can run our function and create a new table. The arguments are as follows:

- **'bklyn_bgs'**: The table we just created
- **'geom'**: Our geometry column
- **'population'**: The column we want to balance on
- **'geoid'**: The unique identifier in our dataset
- **9**: The total number of regions we want to create
- **150**: The minimum number of geometries in any given region, or the floor

As you will see since we are returning the geometry as Well Known Text we will also create a new geometry column by using ST_GeomFromText.

Listing 4.61: Running the SKATER function

```
1   create table brklyn_bgs_skater as
2   select
3       *,
4       st_geomfromtext(geometry) as geom
5   from
6       pysal_skater('bklyn_bgs', 'geom', 'population', 'geoid', 8, 250)
```

And once that is complete we can see our newly created regions in QGIS (Figure 4.15, on the following page):

It is important to test some different options for the number of regions and floor values to see the results that come back. You can see some of the options in the example notebooks on the PySAL website. In addition, you can also include multiple variables, although it will require that you modify the code of the function.

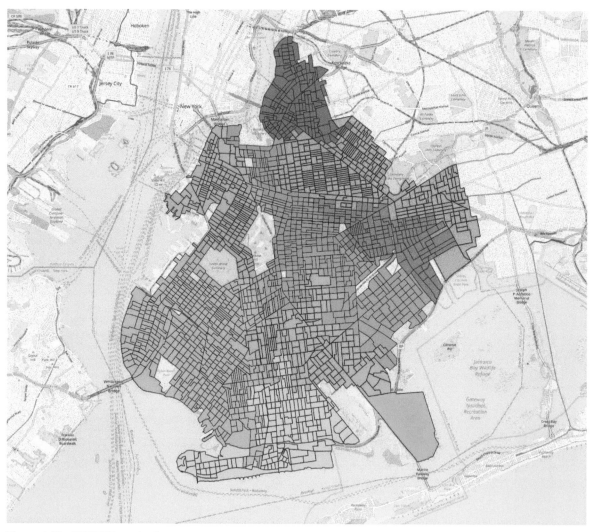

Figure 4.15: SKATER territories

5. Conclusion

Before going further, I first want to thank you, the reader. Without you this book would not be possible and my only hope that you found this useful for your work, career, research, or however you are using spatial SQL. I believe that SQL is a critical skill in modern GIS and within data science and analytics in general and can help you not only grow your skills and find new opportunities in your career.

SQL continues to be the third or fourth most popular language in Stack Overflow's annual Developer Survey. While this doesn't pertain directly to spatial SQL, the fact that it remains near the top annually shows the staying power of SQL (Figure 5.1).

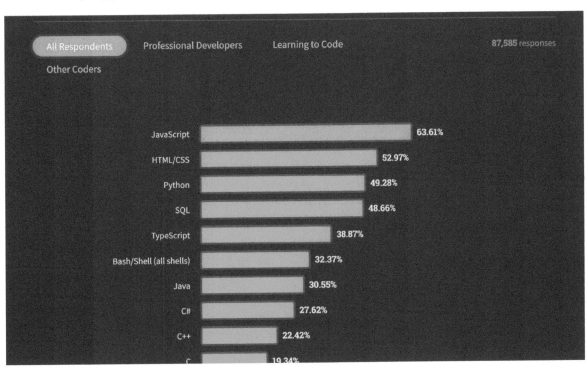

Figure 5.1: Top languages from Stack Overflow's 2023 Developers Survey

I also found that SQL is a critical skill for careers in geospatial and GIS. Using data collected from Google Jobs focused on "GIS" and "Geospatial" as keywords and data from the wider data space for roles such as data scientist, data analyst, data engineer, etc. that contain the keyword "geospatial" or "GIS" in the description, it was clear that SQL is a top skill for these positions (note that these are only postings in the United States).

SQL is the second top skill across the entire dataset, but for salary positions it is actually the top skill as seen below (Figure 5.2, on the following page):

Additionally, it is the second most important skill in both the GIS specific roles and the roles in the wider "data" role category (Figures 5.3, on the next page and 5.4, on page 507):

Spatial SQL has the ability not only to help you accelerate your analysis, and potentially your career

All Salaries and Hourly

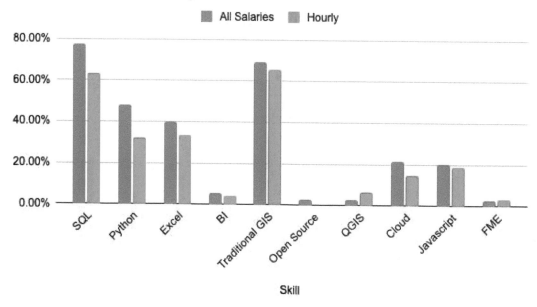

Figure 5.2: Skills listed in hourly and salaried positions

GIS Only Data

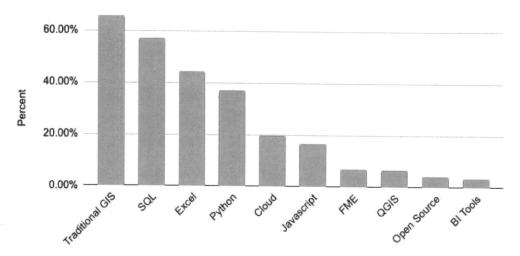

Figure 5.3: Top skills for GIS positions

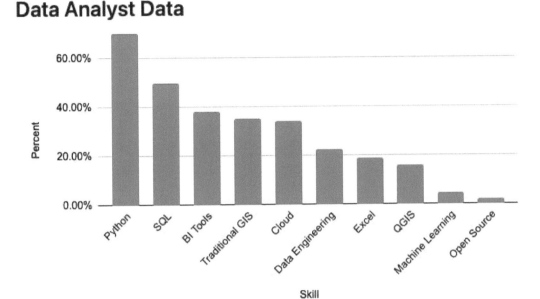

Figure 5.4: Top skills for data analyst positions with a geospatial focus

prospects in the current job market. Keep in mind that this is for the current job market as of 2023, and as spatial SQL continues to grow in adoption and usage, this may very well continue to change and grow. The question becomes where is spatial SQL going to go in the future? While any prediction like this can be difficult, I would like to offer my opinions based on the current trends taking place.

5.1 SQL beyond the database

We only explored using spatial SQL in one other tool outside a database in this book, which in this case is GDAL. However, SQL is showing up in more locations as a general purpose language for data outside a traditional database. Two great examples of this are dbt or Data Build Tool and DuckDB with WebAssembly or WASM.

dbt is a toll that allows you to create data transformation pipelines using SQL. It follows an ELT or extract load transform, transformation process which means that raw data is loaded into the database or data warehouse of choice, and is then transformed once it has landed in the destination. This differs from ETL or extract transform load, where data is transformed before it is loaded into the destination. The definition from the dbt website adds more detail:

dbt™ is a SQL-first transformation workflow that lets teams quickly and collaboratively deploy analytics code following software engineering best practices like modularity, portability, CI/CD, and documentation. Now anyone on the data team can safely contribute to production-grade data pipelines.[163]

This allows you to use the same SQL you do in your database, but with dbt you can create complex pipelines to transform raw data into reports, aggregated views, clean data, turn latitude and longitude points to geometries, and much more. This gives you far more control and predictability around your data and allows you to orchestrate common and regular tasks in a much cleaner way (Figure 5.5, on the next page).

---

[163]https://www.getdbt.com/product/what-is-dbt

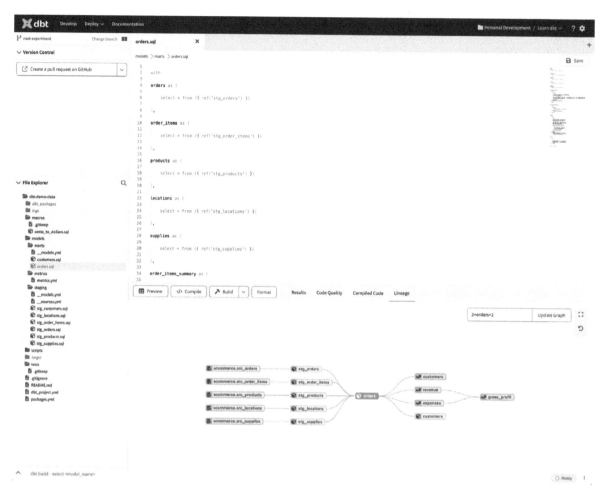

Figure 5.5: Example of dbt cloud

The second tool is DuckDB, which we mentioned earlier in this book, but in this case it is DuckDB with WebAssembly. WebAssembly or WASM is more or less a virtual environment inside your browser. Here is the definition from the WebAssembly website:

WebAssembly (abbreviated Wasm) is a binary instruction format for a stack-based virtual machine. Wasm is designed as a portable compilation target for programming languages, enabling deployment on the web for client and server applications.[164]

For our purposes, this means that you can run DuckDB inside a JavaScript application, meaning that your backend or database is bundled and runs right inside your client side application. Every time someone opens your application they are running the database which means that there is no database you have to maintain, build, connect to, or read from.

The best example of this is an application developed by Youssef Harby that allows you to query data from Overture Maps that is stored in GeoParquet files and show it on the map.[165] The app also converts the data to GeoJSON and allows you to export the results. The impressive part is that there is no database, server, or any backend infrastructure. Just files that are hosted on the web and queried via DuckDB in the browser. This removes a major obstacle for many developers that allows them much

---

[164]https://webassembly.org/

more flexibility to build fully interactive applications (Figure 5.6).

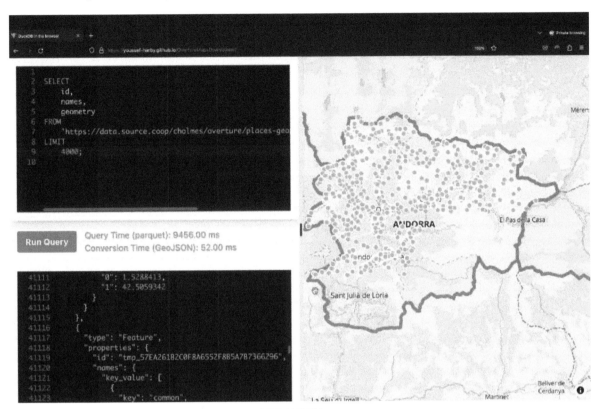

Figure 5.6: Youssef Harby's application using DuckDB WASM

5.2   Spatial SQL made easy

Another major hurdle has been the maintenance, set up, and development of spatial databases has been historically difficult and required skills in programming beyond just spatial SQL. While some steps in this book required knowledge about Docker, basic shell commands, and other languages, this process is overall far easier due to the help and hard work of developers that create and maintain Docker containers that abstract away much of this difficult work and makes it easy to run a container on any computer or cloud service that can run a container.

Even more so DuckDB makes it incredibly simple to start a SQL environment and read data directly from files without importing them into a database like we did throughout this book. I believe that DuckDB will be a core technology for geospatial in the coming years and will make spatial SQL far more accessible to new and current users. Dr. Qiusheng Wu, Associate Professor in the Department of Geography & Sustainability at the University of Tennessee, Knoxville has already started teaching DuckDB for geospatial in his courses which are also published on YouTube. One of his first videos he states the following:

"... personally, now I use it every day."[166]

---

[165]https://github.com/Youssef-Harby/OvertureMapsDownloader/

[166]https://youtu.be/LM3mp97E84Q?si=xihFPvjzJTms_1zV&t=56

5.3   Spatial SQL as a central hub

Another trend is that more core geospatial services are starting to integrate with spatial SQL or will actually run inside the infrastructure dedicated to spatial SQL. There are two practical examples of this. The first is map tiling, or the creation of web map tiles for use in spatial applications and geoportals. PostGIS already supports the creation of tiles from tables or queries with functions such as ST_AsMVT, and Crunchy Data, a company that supports and creates cloud solutions and tools for PostGIS and PostgreSQL, also maintains a library called pg_tileserv which provides an API to request and retrieve tiles from your database. This means that not only can your data and analysis live in PostGIS, but your visualization engine can as well.

The other is the CARTO Analytics Toolbox which provides tools and functions that run within the data warehouse or database infrastructure for PostGIS and data warehouses such as Snowflake, BigQuery, Redshift, and Databricks. These functions act as stored procedures within the data warehouse that allows the user to leverage the same computing infrastructure as the data warehouse to perform different spatial functionality. This includes using spatial indexes like H3, creating tiles, connecting to services like geocoding and routing, and more complex spatial analysis similar to those that we developed, and more (Figure 5.7).

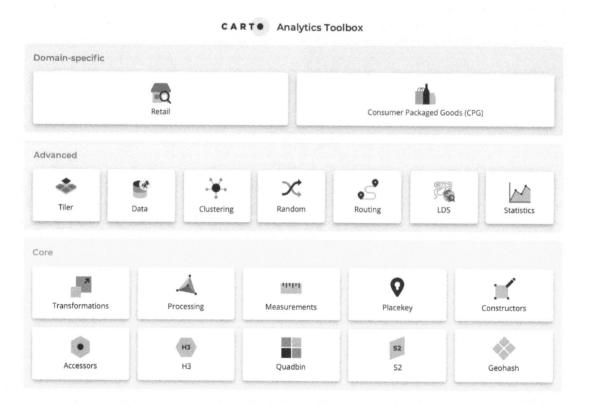

Figure 5.7: The CARTO Analytics Toolbox (via CARTO)

These trends indicate that more spatial functionality can actually move into a database or a data warehouse. This is advantageous because the more work you can move closer to your data, the faster the analysis will be.

5.4 Big data, no problem

The final area of growth is around data. While I believe the term big data will start to fade as tools are increasingly supporting larger data as evidenced by this post from Jordan Tigani, Founder and CEO of MotherDuck, this has still been a challenge in geospatial due to the complex nature of the geometry column.[167]

I do believe that this is changing. Within PostGIS there are methods to architect your data to perform and scale to be quite performant with millions of records, see this post from Paul Ramsey, Executive Geospatial Engineer at Crunchy Data and core member of the PostGIS development team.[168] And tools like DuckDB allow you to take this further into hundreds of millions, potentially billions of records.

Data warehouses like those mentioned above allow you to do even more by allocating processing power at scale to the queries and can take this even further, and spatial SQL is at the core of each of these solutions.

5.5 Spatial SQL in the field

The final question to explore is what this will look like in the field and in the day-to-day work for a GIS or geospatial professional and within the academic programs training the next generation of professionals. First let's explore what this might look like in the field.

In my opinion, there are a few areas that will see much change in the years to come from a technology shift:

- We stop thinking about layers and start thinking about tables
- Adding the layer of Geospatial Data Engineer and Analytics Engineer
- Spatial SQL as an analytical engine within a larger GIS

The concept of layers is so embedded within the core understanding of GIS, all the way back to the beginning when GIS meant literally overlaying layers of printed data. Thinking in this way is limiting. It limits the understanding of how data can be transformed, joined, and manipulated to show more in depth analysis. Layers also implies that the analysis should be visual, in that the reader should interpret the map layer to make the analysis, and the data is only there to be put on the map.

When we start to think of data as a more fluid concept that can open up the thinking around spatial analysis, but one has to experience this first to see how data can be use more effectively together rather than in separate layers.

I also anticipate that new terms will start to be a part of geospatial teams, namely Geospatial Data Engineer and Geospatial Analytics Engineer. Some of these are already starting to show up in job listings and I anticipate that will grow over time. These roles are focused on making data usable and useful within the organization, and as the name implies, with a specialty on spatial data. The Data Engineer focuses working with raw data and bringing it into a usable environment. Think of reading recurring location pings from a ship or ingesting a new batch of census data. The Analytics Engineer takes that data to create data products such as reports, usable tables, or data ready for upstream analysis. For example the Analytics Engineer might take the pings and create a report of distance traveled in the last 12 hours that runs every hour. With more data, the teams around this data will naturally need to grow.

Finally, I believe that spatial SQL will become a more integral analytics engine for geospatial and GIS teams. I don't think spatial SQL will replace desktop GIS, data science notebooks, web maps, or data

---

[167]https://motherduck.com/blog/big-data-is-dead/

[168]https://www.crunchydata.com/blog/performance-and-spatial-joins

visualization. I do however believe that much of the analysis and data prep that takes place in these tools today will move into the database and spatial SQL world. This means that users of the tools aforementioned can still continue to use them, but they will use spatial SQL to retrieve prepared data or create queries on data in the database or data warehouse to bring into those tools. Then they can use those tools to create more analysis or an end product from that data. This means that spatial SQL becomes the core of data capture, manipulation, transformation, and analysis, which in turns allows those same users to use much larger scales of data with superior performance.

In short, I would expect that professional teams will move more of the data intensive work into tool supported by spatial SQL, new roles will begin to emerge to support that work, and users of data will be able to interact with those new tables or query data as need be.

5.6   Spatial SQL in education

If we are to reach that point, we also need to ensure that the next generation of GIS and geospatial professionals have the opportunity to learn these skills in addition to those already in the field. In short, spatial SQL is generally taught as a database language today, one that allows users to manage, store, and update data in a database system. It is that exact concept that is the first that needs to change. As you have seen spatial SQL can support a range of analytical use cases that allow you to scale your analysis and ultimately move faster, so providing more courses and resources that focus on this is the first step.

Second is that the courses that do teach this trend to be at a higher course level, either in a postgraduate program or post-graduate/professional certificate program. Sometimes this is appropriate of course, but teaching spatial SQL and either creating courses or bringing spatial SQL elements into courses at an undergraduate level will be important in helping it reach a larger audience.

The last is creating more resources to help the wider geospatial community use and understand the power of spatial SQL. That could mean anything from talks, projects, blog posts, seminars, webinars, documentation, etc. Once you can see how something is done in a real world use case, it generally makes it easier for others to see how it can apply to them. Right now we are only scratching the surface, but great events like PostGIS Day, the Spatial Data Science Conference, the FOSS4G event series, and others are a great starting point for this.

I think that spatial SQL has a bright future ahead, and I am honored that this book could be a part of that journey for you. My hope is that it helps you apply these ideas and concepts to your geospatial work and career, and that you carry it forward as well. If that is helping other colleagues, sharing your work, speaking at events, or any other way you see fit, I hope that you continue to be a part of that bright future.

Books from Locate Press

Be sure to visit http://locatepress.com for information on new and upcoming titles.

Discover QGIS 3.x

SECOND EDITION: EXPLORE THE LATEST LONG TERM RELEASE (LTR) OF QGIS WITH DISCOVER QGIS 3.X!

Discover QGIS 3.x is a comprehensive up-to-date workbook built for both the classroom and professionals looking to build their skills.

Designed to take advantage of the latest QGIS features, this book will guide you in improving your maps and analysis.

You will find clear learning objectives and a task list at the beginning of each chapter. Of the 31 exercises in this workbook, 7 are new and 8 have seen considerable updates. All exercises are updated to support QGIS 3.26.

The book is a complete resource and includes: lab exercises, challenge exercises, all data, discussion questions, and solutions.

QGIS for Hydrological Applications

SECOND EDITION: RECIPES FOR CATCHMENT HYDROLOGY AND WATER MANAGEMENT.

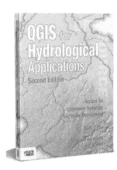

Now updated - learn even more GIS skills for catchment hydrology and water management with QGIS!

This second edition workbook introduces hydrological topics to professionals in the water sector using state of the art functionality in QGIS. The book is also useful as a beginner's course in GIS concepts, using a problem-based learning approach

Designed to take advantage of the latest QGIS features, this book will guide you in improving your maps and analysis.

Introduction to QGIS

GET STARTED WITH QGIS WITH THIS INTRODUCTION COVERING EVERYTHING NEEDED TO GET YOU GOING USING FREE AND OPEN SOURCE GIS SOFTWARE.

This QGIS tutorial, based on the 3.16 LTR version, introduces you to major concepts and techniques to get you started with viewing data, analysis, and creating maps and reports.

Building on the first edition, the authors take you step-by-step through the process of using the latest map design tools and techniques in QGIS 3. With numerous new map designs and completely overhauled workflows, this second edition brings you up to speed with current cartographic technology and trends.

With this book you'll learn about the QGIS interface, creating, analyzing, and editing vector data, working with raster (image) data, using plugins and the processing toolbox, and more.

Resources for further help and study and all the data you'll need to follow along with each chapter are included.

QGIS Map Design - 2nd Edition

LEARN HOW TO USE QGIS 3 TO TAKE YOUR CARTOGRAPHIC PRODUCTS TO THE HIGH-EST LEVEL.

QGIS 3.4 opens up exciting new possibilities for creating beautiful and compelling maps!

Building on the first edition, the authors take you step-by-step through the process of using the latest map design tools and techniques in QGIS 3. With numerous new map designs and completely overhauled workflows, this second edition brings you up to speed with current cartographic technology and trends.

See how QGIS continues to surpass the cartographic capabilities of other geoware available today with its data-driven overrides, flexible expression functions, multitudinous color tools, blend modes, and atlasing capabilities. A prior familiarity with basic QGIS capabilities is assumed. All example data and project files are included.

Get ready to launch into the next generation of map design!

Leaflet Cookbook

COOK UP DYNAMIC WEB MAPS USING THE RECIPES IN THE LEAFLET COOKBOOK.

Leaflet Cookbook will guide you in getting started with Leaflet, the leading open-source JavaScript library for creating interactive maps. You'll move swiftly along from the basics to creating interesting and dynamic web maps.

Even if you aren't an HTML/CSS wizard, this book will get you up to speed in creating dynamic and sophisticated web maps. With sample code and complete examples, you'll find it easy to create your own maps in no time.

A download package containing all the code and data used in the book is available so you can follow along as well as use the code as a starting point for your own web maps.

The PyQGIS Programmer's Guide

WELCOME TO THE WORLD OF PYQGIS, THE BLENDING OF QGIS AND PYTHON TO EXTEND AND ENHANCE YOUR OPEN SOURCE GIS TOOLBOX.

With PyQGIS you can write scripts and plugins to implement new features and perform automated tasks.

This book is updated to work with the next generation of QGIS—version 3.x. After a brief introduction to Python 3, you'll learn how to understand the QGIS Application Programmer Interface (API), write scripts, and build a plugin.

The book is designed to allow you to work through the examples as you go along. At the end of each chapter you will find a set of exercises you can do to enhance your learning experience.

The PyQGIS Programmer's Guide is compatible with the version 3.0 API released with QGIS 3.x and will work for the entire 3.x series of releases.

---

pgRouting: A Practical Guide

WHAT IS PGROUTING?

It's a PostgreSQL extension for developing network routing applications and doing graph analysis.

Interested in pgRouting? If so, chances are you already use PostGIS, the spatial extender for the PostgreSQL database management system.

So when you've got PostGIS, why do you need pgRouting? PostGIS is a great tool for molding geometries and doing proximity analysis, however it falls short when your proximity analysis involves constrained paths such as driving along a road or biking along defined paths.

This book will both get you started with pgRouting and guide you into routing, data fixing and costs, as well as using with QGIS and web applications.

Geospatial Power Tools

EVERYONE LOVES POWER TOOLS!

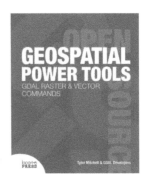

The GDAL and OGR apps are the power tools of the GIS world—best of all, they're free.

The utilities include tools for examining, converting, transforming, building, and analysing data. This book is a collection of the GDAL and OGR documentation, but also includes new content designed to help guide you in using the utilities to solve your current data problems.

Inside you'll find a quick reference for looking up the right syntax and example usage quickly. The book is divided into three parts: *Workflows and examples*, *GDAL raster utilities*, and *OGR vector utilities*.

Once you get a taste of the power the GDAL/OGR suite provides, you'll wonder how you ever got along without them.

See these books and more at http://locatepress.com